THE CALIFORNIANS:
WRITINGS OF THEIR PAST
AND PRESENT

The Californians:

WRITINGS OF THEIR PAST AND PRESENT

Edited by
URSULA SPIER ERICKSON
AND ROBERT PEARSALL

VOLUME II: ECONOMIC INTERPRETATIONS
∼ THE ADJUSTMENT OF IMAGES ∼
∼ THE SCENE ∼

SAN FRANCISCO

HESPERIAN HOUSE

Contents of Volume Two

Part VI

ECONOMIC INTERPRETATIONS

[v]

Part VII

THE ADJUSTMENT OF IMAGES

Part VIII

THE SCENE

[ix]

Acknowledgments

The Editors gratefully acknowledge the kindness and cooperation of authors and publishers in giving permission to reproduce material in *The Californians*. Much valuable assistance has also been given by librarians and the publisher's editorial staff in securing proper documentation for some of the pieces included in these two volumes.

VOLUME I
"Up and Down California" by William Brewer
From *Up and Down California in 1860–64* by William Brewer
Copyright 1930 by Yale University Press
Copyright 1949 by the University of California Press
Reprinted by permission of the University of California Press
"The Celebrated Jumping Frog of Calaveras County" by Samuel Clemens
Reprinted by permission of Harper & Brothers and by arrangement with the trustees of the estate of Samuel L. Clemens

"Chinatown and Women's Country" by Henry Sienkiewicz
From *Portrait of America: Letters of Henry Sienkiweicz*
by Charles Morley
Copyright 1959 by Columbia University Press
Reprinted by permission of the Columbia University Press
"The Third Circle" by Frank Norris
From *The Third Circle* by Frank Norris
Copyright 1909 by J. Lane and Company
Reprinted by arrangement with Frank C. Preston, Jr. and
Doubleday & Company
"The Golden Whales of California" by Vachel Lindsay
From *Collected Poems* by Vachel Lindsay
Copyright 1920, 1948 by The Macmillan Company
Reprinted by permission of The Macmillan Company

VOLUME II
"The Drama of the Reclamation" by Franklin Walker
From *A Literary History of Southern California* by
Franklin Walker
Copyright 1950 by Franklin Walker
Reprinted by permission of the University of California
Press
"Dead Man" by James M. Cain
Copyright 1936 by James M. Cain
Reprinted by permission of Harold Ober Associates, Inc.
"I Horn Into Hollywood" by Will Rogers
From the *Autobiography* by Will Rogers
Copyright 1949 by Houghton Mifflin Company
Reprinted by permission of Houghton Mifflin Company
"The Blond Dog" by Louis Clyde Stoumen
From *Story No. 1*
Copyright 1951 by Whit Burnett and Hallie Burnett
Reprinted by permission of Whit Burnett and Story, Inc.
"Concerning a Woman of Sin" by Ben Hecht

From *The Collected Stories of Ben Hecht*
Copyright 1945 by Ben Hecht
Reprinted by permission of Crown Publishers, Inc.
"Crazy Sunday" by F. Scott Fitzgerald
From *Taps at Reveille* by F. Scott Fitzgerald
Copyright 1932 by American Mercury, Inc.
Copyright 1960 by Frances Scott Fitzgerald Lanahan
Reprinted by permission of Charles Scribner's Sons
"The Girl" by Meridel Le Sueur
Reprinted by permission of Meridel Le Sueur
"Johnny Bear" by John Steinbeck
From *The Long Valley* by John Steinbeck
Copyright 1938 by John Steinbeck
Reprinted by permission of The Viking Press, Inc.
"Helen, Thy Beauty is to Me" by John Fante
Copyright 1941 by John Fante
Reprinted by permission of John Fante
"No More Sad Thoughts" by George Mardikian
From *Dinner at Omar Khayyam's* by George Mardikian
Copyright 1949 by George Mardikian
Reprinted by permission of George Mardikian
"Clouds of Evening" by Robinson Jeffers
Copyright 1924 and renewed 1951 by Robinson Jeffers
Reprinted from *Roan Stallion, Tamar, And Other Poems*,
by Robinson Jeffers, by permission of Random House, Inc.
"Continent's End" by Robinson Jeffers
Copyright 1924 and renewed 1951 by Robinson Jeffers
Reprinted from *The Selected Poetry of Robinson Jeffers*
by permission of Random House, Inc.
"Shine, Perishing Republic"
"Post Mortem" by Robinson Jeffers
Reprinted from *The Selected Poetry of Robinson Jeffers*
by permission of Random House, Inc.
"Hurt Hawks" by Robinson Jeffers

"29 March, 10:20 p.m."
"4 April, 1:45 a.m."
"5 June, 10 a.m." by Gil Orlovitz
   From *The Diary of Alexander Patience* by Gil Orlovitz
   Copyright 1958 by Inferno Press
   Reprinted by permission of Gil Orlovitz
"On Casting D. H. Lawrence" by Herbert Feinstein
   Copyright 1960 by Herbert Feinstein
"Lenore and the Boys" by Hamilton Wright
   From *Story No. 2*
   Copyright 1952 by Whit Burnett and Hallie Burnett
   Reprinted by permission of Whit Burnett and Story, Inc.
"The Fisherman from Chihauhua" by Evan S. Connell, Jr.
   From *The Anatomy Lesson and Other Stories* by Evan S.
   Connell, Jr.
   Copyright 1957 by Evan S. Connell, Jr.
   Reprinted by permission of The Viking Press, Inc.
"Eagle Day" by Esther R. B. Wagner
   Copyright 1959 by Harper's Magazine
   Reprinted by permission of Esther R. B. Wagner
"Don Giovanni to the Very Nice New Virgin"
"The Clever Troubadour of Amoret County"
"Looney Tom's Song" by James Broughton
   From *True and False Unicorns* by James Broughton
   Copyright 1957 by Grove Press
   Reprinted by permission of James Broughton
"The Shepherd's Urban Daughter" by James Broughton
   From *Musical Chairs* by James Broughton
   Copyright 1950 by Centaur Press
   Reprinted by permission of James Broughton
"Five Poems" by Muriel Loran
   Copyright 1960 by Muriel Loran
"Annul in Me My Manhood"
"The South Coast"

ACKNOWLEDGMENTS

"Out of the Ash" by Brother Antoninus, O. P.
  From *The Crooked Lines of God* by Brother Antoninus
  Copyright 1960 by the University of Detroit Press
  Reprinted by permission of the University of Detroit Press
"Was Peter Not Brought Up on Kascha?" by Irena Parker
  Copyright 1960 by Irena Parker
"Mother Lode, 1960" by Joseph McMahon
  Copyright 1960 by Joseph McMahon
"The Desert" by Michael Rumaker
  From *Short Story 2, Exit 3* by Michael Rumaker
  Copyright 1957 by Michael Rumaker
  Reprinted by permission of Charles Scribner's Sons
"Quite the Largest Thing the World Has Seen" by Bruce Dexter
  From *With Multitudes Bent* by Bruce Dexter
  Copyright 1960 by Bruce Dexter
  Reprinted by permission of Bruce Dexter
"The Slide Area" by Gavin Lambert
  From *The Slide Area* by Gavin Lambert
  Copyright 1959 by Gavin Lambert
  Reprinted by permission of The Viking Press, Inc.
"The Dancing Ape"
"Berkeley in Time of Plague"
"Psychoanalysis: An Elegy" by Jack Spicer
  Copyright 1957 by Jack Spicer
  Reprinted by permission of Jack Spicer and arrangement
  with *Evergreen Review*
"Dog"
"They Were Putting Up the Statue" by Lawrence Ferlinghetti
  From *A Coney Island of the Mind* by Lawrence Ferlinghetti
  Copyright 1958 by Lawrence Ferlinghetti; Copyright
  1955 by Lawrence Ferlinghetti

[xvii]

ACKNOWLEDGMENTS

Reprinted by permission of New Directions
Endpaper Map
From *California in Our Time* by Robert Glass Cleland
Copyright 1947 by Alfred A. Knopf, Inc.
Reprinted by permission of Alfred A. Knopf, Inc.

THE CALIFORNIANS:
WRITINGS OF THEIR PAST
AND PRESENT

PART VI

Economic Interpretations

PART VI

Economic Integration

Economic Interpretations

IN SPITE OF OCCASIONAL SETBACKS arising from legislative or social change, the enormous turn-of-the-century combinations have retained their basic shapes right down to the present day. But as the present century budded and bloomed there was a sort of regrouping or clubbing up of the various machines. By the late teens of the century, the California man in the street was likely to think of each separate integer as belonging either to the club of Capital (which, given the industrial-style ranching in California, also took in Agriculture), or to an opposing club loosely designated Labor. From around 1910 to around 1937 it was this simpler arrangement of forces which haunted the imagination of Californians, and to some extent guided their deeds. After 1937, when the world took to struggling in bloodier and more dubious battles, they thought generally of other things.

But the thematic history of the state during that approximate third of a century must still be written in terms of collision between capital (whether industrial or rural) and the laboring masses. Consider the new seaborne immigrations. As the employing class, capital exerted itself to bring in wave

[3]

after wave of cheap foreign labor. The Japanese make the best illustration; by 1920 72,000 of them were present in the state, all working too hard but somehow thriving; and it became the task of organized labor and organized one-family farming interests to get the flow stopped and its goods expropriated. Then it was Filipinoes, then Hindus, then Mexicans, each new recruitment by the employing classes being responded to by such resident classes as depended on wages for their bread. In each case it was capital which took the initiative. The response of labor was always tardy, and the necessary anti-immigration legislation usually took years to create and put into effect. California ethnography has been greatly enriched by these long delays between opening and closing of the western gates.

Fortunately for the employing groups, perhaps, there was no way to stop the ingress of working men from California's sister states. Encouraged by employment bureaus, Chambers of Commerce, and the big advertising agencies which took over agricultural recruitment, these people swarmed in more steadily than their foreign rivals. In depression and farm-surplus years they were driven in by hunger; in good years they were attracted by larger promises and an increased flow of advertising materials. The spread of this wave across the peculiar landscape of California became the significant cause of other social changes. For these newer and poorer immigrants usually entered California through the southern rather than the northern Sierra passes; and consequently depressed the price of labor in the Los Angeles area before working north into the great ranches of the central valley. In their less fortunate position off to the side of this regular route, the employers of the Bay Area had no comparable supply of poor, often desperate recruits. Supporting this geographical oddity with a militantly anti-union Merchants and Manufacturers Association, Los Angeles industrialists could maintain what workers called a fink-style, open-shop, coolie-pay system, and quickly transform their quiet city into a great industrial center. Industry in turn attracted more cheap workers, snowballing the city up and up. Meanwhile the streams of immigrants who bypassed the area, or whose services were rejected by it,moved into the agricultural valleys where still lower pay and sterner Associations awaited them. Even in the cropping seasons there were usually too many of them. In off seasons there was no work at all, and they wandered disconsolately up and down.

Against this grey and unlovely background there were a large number of hot and ugly incidents. In 1910, for example, the apparently insane leadership of the Structural Ironworkers union attempted to weaken the Merchants and Manufacturers Association by blowing up the Los Angeles *Times* and various other Gibraltars of the open shop. In subsequent years the attempts of workers to organize themselves were met with violence throughout the South and the valleys, notably in Fresno, Sacramento, and San Diego, where the "vigilante" pattern of labor control first reached maturity. This pattern involved such indefensible processes as denial of free-speech privileges by local ordinances, recruitment of armed, often deputized "vigilante" or "goon" squads, wholesale arrests and kidnappings, and a wide variety of beatings-up, castrations, camp-burnings, and other kinds of night-time violence. In gentle San Diego was first established the long gantlet of thugs armed with clubs and bullwhips through which naked men were to run, if they could. Meanwhile the practice of over-recruiting and subsequent pay-cutting went on, and the small human amenities which even a crop-worker now takes for granted were systematically denied. Durst, the Wheatland rancher who overhired, cut pay, gouged with a company store, denied water in order to promote the sale of company lemonade, encamped 2800 men, women, and children on what the official report called "a treeless hill . . . in topless squares of sacking or with piles of straw," providing "no organization for sanitation, no garbage disposal," and who at the first sign of protest whistled up a gang of lawmen—this Durst is known to California history because of the massacre which followed, not for adopting what the reporter called "these common practices." These practices are best written up by John Steinbeck in *The Grapes of Wrath* (1939), a novel which, like Mrs. Jackson's *Ramona* and Frank Norris's *The Octopus*, protests with great eloquence against a whole series of great injustices.

Although it was this sort of activity which made Californians alternately self-righteous and conscience-stricken during the period, they had other things to keep them busy. The cities grew; industries went from bust to boom to bust again; engineers coped as best they could with the antique problems of too much or too little water, or water inconveniently placed. It got so that everybody had a car and a radio. Sexual psychology took its place among the comforable themes of literature, the poets, especially Robinson Jeffers, being the notable exploiters of it. Almost overnight the dusty working-class suburb called Hollywood became the manufacturing center for all the world's day-dreams; it also became a challenge for writers. The strange insecurities of Southern California gave rise to bizarre new religions and panaceas and Plans, some of which might have worked had they been tried. But the grim, disturbing problem of the time was that of the distribution of wealth. Economic injustice, fear of hunger, and the threat of violence pressed with great heaviness upon a people too familiar with such pressures, and wanting now a little rest.

ALEXANDER J. CODY, S.J.

Father Cody was born in Auburn in 1886, and grew up in the Gold Country foothills. He took vows at Santa Clara in 1906, and devoted his long working-life to teaching, notably at Santa Clara, Loyola in Los Angeles, and the University of San Francisco. Among his volumes of poetry are *God's Looking Glass* (1927), *Peddler of Beauty* (1935), and *Hill Country* (1944). He died at San Francisco in 1957.

God's Harlequin

The buccaneers with frothy lips
Drank to the glory of their ships.
"We are the Heroes of the main,
The Almirantes of New Spain."
But Serra said: "The fame I win
Is fame as Christ's poor harlequin.
Blue is the bay of Monterey
And on your galleons sail away.
But I will follow poppy trails
And pitch Christ's tent in all the vales,
And find in lowly poor I know
My Lord in His incognito."

They laughed in swaggering seamen's glee:
What foolish folk these Friars be!"

II

The earthquake and the winter's moan
Have wrought weird silhouettes of stone.
Now sweet Castilian roses blow
Where roving herds of cattle go;
Now broken portals arch the sky

[7]

And pallid seafogs mustering by
Now point with lean, accusing hands
Where robbery plows the Mission lands;
A silver bell on barren hill
Finds one lone Indian praying still;
Fra Serra's work was built in vain,
The spoil of robbers, wreck and rain.

A gust of laughter from the sea
Is loud in pirate ribaldry.

III

Through poppied fields where Serra trod
Majestic, comes the Son of God.
He passes crescent Monterey
To Carmel on wee Carmel bay:
Where Santa Barbara fronts the sea
He rests in gardens wearily;
Where San Juan's campanile calls
He consecrates the crumbling walls.
A host of chosen souls await
Beside each ruined convent gate;
But none may dare to enter in
Till first He greets his harlequin.

A whisper faint from Channel pools:
"You are the wise and we were fools."

At Monterey

At Monterey the sea gulls fly
In silhouette against the sky;
   The taverns of Life's yesteryear
   Are weather-beaten, gray and drear;
How shabbily romances die!

Here dreaming Stevenson went by;
Here Sherman breathed a lover's sigh;
   The Gringoes gave a knowing leer
      At Monterey.

The cypresses with croon and cry
To moaning ocean make reply;
   The ghost of Jenny Lind steals near
   To pay song's tribute of a tear;
The trysting roses withered lie
      At Monterey.

The Drama of Reclamation

By FRANKLIN WALKER

This selection constitutes Chapter Eight of Walker's entertaining *Literary History of Southern California* (1950), a book setting forth to "study the development of Southern California by examining the literature dealing with that region." Dr. Walker teaches at Mills College, Oakland.

"The struggle of men with men is at best a sick and squalid affair for one of the parties; but men contriving against the gods for possession of the earth is your true epic," wrote Mary Austin in *The Lands of the Sun*. In doing so, she put her finger on the most promising subject for literary treatment in the arid countries of the Pacific Southwest, man's reclamation of the land. The literary output on this subject ranges from Kate Sanborn's aphorism, "irrigate, cultivate, and exaggerate," in her *A Truthful Woman in Southern California*, to William E. Smythe's imaginative and stirring plea for a new social order in *The Conquest of Arid America*. It varies from the bathos of the line in a local poem which reads "He walks with God who walks the flume" to the influential histrionics, meretricious and flamboyant though they be, of Harold Bell Wright's *The Winning of Barbara Worth*. It marches from such inadequate verse as A. J. Burdick's:

Where now but lurks grim, ghastly, burning death,
The violet may shed its fragrant breath.

to the vision and descriptive force that Mary Austin achieves in *The Ford*. Unfortunately, however, the subject has not to date produced the epic, either in poetry or prose, which it merits.

Irrigation, of course, had long been used in California; it

had been introduced by the Spanish padres, who showed great ingenuity in using the limited and irregular flow of the local streams to water their gardens. But in the disorganized period after secularization of the missions, irrigation nearly disappeared, except for the *zanja* which watered the gardens in Los Angeles; and after the conquest, in the decades when cattle and wheat ranching flourished, there was no need for systematic water control. By the late 'fifties, however, the German colonists at Anaheim were using the old Spanish irrigation methods to make their communal vineyards successful; and when in the 'seventies and 'eighties the settlers poured in from Indiana and Missouri and other Middle Western states, they quickly showed their ingenuity in obtaining water in a land where rainfall was not enough for their purposes, as it had been in their former homes. This was the era of individual engineering: on his property the farmer built small dams to check the runoff; bored artesian wells to release the liquid gold from a high water table where the pressure was intense; and, when the pressure slackened, installed first windmills and later engines or motors to pump the water. Such purely individual efforts in time gave way to efforts of nonprofit organizations such as the mutual water companies, and eventually whole communities entered the picture. These undertook more extensive projects and built storage dams in the mountains to catch the runoff, dams from which long flumes ran many miles through the hill country. Or they drove tunnels into the hills to tap underground currents and found that the old Spanish adage that "the rivers of California run bottom upward" was true.

Among the successful cooperative ventures of this early period, that of Riverside was the most prominent, earning an almost magic name. Under the leadership of J. W. North, the Riverside Colony turned the old Jurupa rancho into one of the wealthiest properties in the state. True, the introduction of the navel orange from Brazil and the discovery that the hill slopes were less subject to frosts than the bottom lands were both essential in this development, but so also was irrigation. The venture would not have been possible had not North and his companions been able to bring an ample water supply to the orange groves by building a $50,000 distribution canal which tapped the mountains back of the community.

Another such project was the work of George Chaffey, the most farsighted and ingenious of the early irrigators, who led the waters from beneath Mount San Antonio ("Old Baldy") to Etiwanda, to be divided equitably among the settlers whose membership in a mutual water company meant relief from the frustration created by the legal recognition of riparian water rights, a recognition which seemed to a time to doom anything like a democratic development of irrigation sources. George Chaffey carried on to create Ontario, with its utilization of hydroelectric power and its lavish display of gushing water in the fountain in front of the railway station, which for many years stood as a symbol of abundant water in a thirsty land.

George Chaffey played an important early role in the reclamation of the Imperial Valley also, and had all the men later connected with it been as capable and social-minded as he, the valley might never have faced the famous diasters of 1905-1907, when the entire area nearly reverted to the Salton Sea. It was a comparatively simple matter to tap the Colorado River, with its natural high dikes, to obtain water to irrigate the formidable desert in southeastern California, which had once been a neck of the Gulf of California and lay below sea level where the water could reach it by means of gravity. But the California Development Company found it easier to make the cut in the artery than to stem the flow when the need arose for strong controls. Its shabby, ill-considered improvisations of a dry year were washed out in a flood year, and, had not the

Southern Pacific Railroad put all its resources into closing the gap, most of Imperial Valley would have been irretrievably ruined. As it was, many a new house and many a green acre had been swallowed up and the New River had cut a trench hundreds of feet wide through the heart of the land before the river was returned to its original course. The nearly disastrous results of the venture showed that the time had certainly come when the state and federal governments were better fitted than the individual or company to make the desert bloom.

The drama of man against nature, in which man was inept and shortsighted, was not repeated when Los Angeles made its first long reach for water by building the Owens River aqueduct. Here it was careful and thorough and, many insist, sinister and secret, planning which supplied the drama. When, in 1908, the 250-mile aqueduct which was to bring water from the lower Owens Valley was started, plans had been drawn up and costs had been estimated that proved to be accurate right up to the date in November, 1913, when the water from the highest part of the Sierra began flowing into the San Fernando Valley. The engineering was worked out beautifully, and the achievement was the fit subject for nation-wide praise. The social consequences, resulting in the apparently permanent ruin of the farming lands of Owens Valley, were less fortunate. The results, which reached at times the proportion of a sectional civil war, are felt to this day.

The Owens River aqueduct was but the first of several major ventures to bring water from the outside to feed the thirsty soil south of the Tehachapis. More water brought more settlers and more farms; these in turn demanded more water. And so the problem was created which is still unsolved today, in spite of the building of Hoover Dam and the Colorado River aqueduct. Now the talk is of bringing water from the Columbia River or of distilling it from the ocean by means

[13]

of huge solar evaporating systems.

The subject of the finding and use of water has been a recurrent theme in fiction dealing with Southern California, although it has by no means received the treatment it deserves. American novelists, long skillful at describing the social situation in America, have not as yet, with a few exceptions like Frank Norris and George R. Stewart, succeeded effectively in utilizing the rich imaginative drama provided by American technological skills. And in the treatment of the reclamation theme in Southern California, the conquest of the desert has usually been subordinated to the portrayal of social or domestic problems. Thus, Beatrice Harraden, in *Hilda Strafford*, treating the period when irrigating was an individual effort, tells of the futile and agonizing efforts of a lemon rancher to build a reservoir to meet the demands of the dry years, only to have it washed out during the floods; but the main interest of the story is the bad effect of farming on the domestic life of Hilda Strafford. The short tales of Margaret Collier Graham are motivated primarily by the moral problems faced by local settlers, although the search for water enters into many of them. For instance, it furnishes a plot for "The Wizard's Daughter," in which a deaf "professor" confounds an engineer by finding water with an electric divining machine; and it provides a theme for "The Withrow Water Right," in which a desperate farmer protects with a gun the headwaters of his irrigation ditch, which is about to be taken over by a development company.

A more ambitious attempt to utilize the reclamation theme in this early era is found in Frank Lewis Nason's *The Vision of Elijah Berl* (1905). This is the story of the moral struggles that come to a New England Calvinist in Southern California in an area in the Redlands region saltily described by one of the characters as follows: "Lucky thing the Lord didn't start in makin' man in this section . . . he wouldn't have had water enough to have pasted him together with.' " Elijah Berl, almost singlehanded, tries to set up an entire irrigation system in order to get rich quick on an orange-ranch development scheme. His aim he states magniloquently:

When these great, barren red hillsides are all covered with orchards; with beautiful houses and thousands of happy, prosperous people; when the snows and rains of the San Bernardinos, instead of running to waste, will flow through tunnels and canals and make the desert bloom as a rose; then they will say that this is the work of one great man, of me, Elijah Berl!

The trouble is that he can't go it alone. He has to borrow money, an act that leads him to moral turpitude; and he has to hire a pretty secretary, a circumstance which, of course, arouses erotic complications, hard for a strict Yankee to handle. But he does build his dam and his flume, and he lives almost long enough to see an end to his bit of desert. Thinking he has been mistreated by his creditors and his engineer, however, poor Elijah tries to destroy his own dam; naturally, he learns his mistake at the last moment and sacrifices his life in saving the dam. This noble act makes his widow feel that her marriage was worth while after all. And the scene closes with Uncle Sid trotting the baby and planning for the next generation, which will presumably not have so many moral problems.

Of the novels dealing with reclamation, *The Winning of Barbara Worth* (1911), by Harold Bell Wright, was the most popular, attaining a sale of more than a million and a half copies. As a youth, Wright had determined to be a painter, but later he had turned to the ministry and in time had come to Southern California as pastor of the Redlands Christian Church. His heart was not entirely in the ministry, however, for he had already reached a larger public than his congregation through his two novels, *The Shepherd of the Hills* and *The Calling of Dan Matthews*. Accordingly, he resigned his pulpit and moved to the Imperial Valley, which he had decided

[15]

to use as the setting for this third sermon in fiction, *The Winning of Barbara Worth*. While working on this novel he lived near the town of Imperial on the Tecolote Ranch, where, while attempting to build up his frail health by outdoor living and the construction of an "arrow-reed house" with his own hands, he acquainted himself with the local scene and the people connected with the irrigation project. In his declaration at the beginning of the book he thanked various well-known engineers for their aid, and he dedicated the book to the promoter, W. F. Holt, the founder of Holtville and presumably the prototype for Jefferson Worth.

The themes which Wright used included some of the most timeworn stereotypes in popular fiction, as well as a few ideas which were just beginning to become a part of American folklore. there was, of course, the rescue of the child from the desert, quite properly a girl child who grew into a woman whose eyes revealed "the wholesome, challenging lure of an unmarred womanhood." Inevitably the child's presence brought reformation and kindness to the heart of the austere Jefferson Worth, her guardian, who had had hardly a friend before he found her in the desert. She grew up to be a true desert child, never as happy as when she was riding the open country in the sunset, mounted on her faithful horse. All sorts of people fell in love with her, including Abe Lee, himself a foundling of the desert, and Willard Holmes, an engineer of good family from back East. Abe, who is Natty Bumppo in still another disguise, learned that his role was to be the brother rather than the lover. But fortunately he had a desert to turn to; silhouetted against the sky at the end of the novel, he was granted a happiness "greater, it may be, than the joy of possession." Barbara Worth's eventual choice of Willard Holmes to be her mate and the father of her children came as the logical result of Wright's desire to reform the East to meet Western terms. Holmes had the best of blood and education—

[16]

all he needed to find himself was contact with a truly moral environment. He had considerably difficulty at first adjusting himself to "the mighty expanse of desert that lay as it was fashioned by the creative forces that formed the world." In a moment of crisis, he confessed to Barbara Worth: " 'I am out of place in the big desert. I should have stayed at home. I wish—I wish you had never wakened me to the possibilities of life—real life.' " But he came around all right in the end.

This theme of the superiority of the West over the East permeates the novel. The reader is assured that the West was ages old before the East was discovered, and that if Columbus had come first to the western coast New England would still be "an uninhabitable, howling wilderness." Moreover, as one character from the West puts it, "the only difference between the East and the West seems to be that you *have* ancestors and we are *going to be* ancestors."

Somehow mixed up with this juxtaposition of not entirely consistent ideas is the contrast drawn between the evils of absentee capital and the virtues of local investment—or at least local participation in the acts made possible by the investment. Quite ignoring the fact that it was local mismanagement that caused the mess in the Imperial Valley, and eastern capital—eventually paid back by the federal government— that came to the rescue, Wright made the villains of his novel the absentee stockholders in the development company (the time-honored mortgage holders and bankers in a new role), and the heroes the engineers and promoters that were on the spot, ready to do or die. "Face to face with the unconquered forces of nature, nothing remained but the real strength or weakness of the individual himself," he wrote. All is to be won by "the methods of a man laboring with his brother men, sharing their hardships, sharing their returns, a man using money as a workman uses his tools to fashion and build and develop, adding thus to the welfare of human kind." Wright apparently

[17]

was too close to the scene in both time and space to see that many of his hero promoters of the Imperial Valley had been irresponsible and shortsighted and had, as a consequence, nearly destroyed it. He did not have sufficient perspective to see that the development could have been done safely only by the federal government, which would have secured treaty rights, made surveys covering the entire western watershed, and built a dam upstream to prevent disaster. These conclusions came only later, after shoddy financing and promoting had done much damage.

As for the drama of the book, it concerns the fight of man against nature (and against other men), with the surveyors, engineers, and real-estate promoters as the Christian soldiers of the conflict. Their world-embracing goal is "the progress and the future of the great Reclamation work, of its value not only to our own nation but to the over-crowded nations beyond the seas, and of its place in the great forward march of the race." Unfortunately, however, Wright failed to make the best use of the climax of his novel, the truly remarkable fight the Southern Pacific made to stop the Colorado River in its apparently inexorable flow into the valley. The many attempts to divert the river, the intricate organization necessary to move materials to the site, the alarming collapse of whole farms and even towns, and the eventual victory are treated in rapid summary with little telling dramatic effect. Instead, Wright makes the climax of his book the ridiculous ride of his hero on a buckskin pony from San Diego to Mexicali to bring in much-needed money to pay back wages. That, and the desert, were all that he had to offer.

Ednah Aiken in her *The River*, which appeared three years after *The Winning of Barbara Worth*, did a better job in describing the fight to divert the river into its old channel, but did not do as good a job as she should have done, for she allowed her interest in a tedious domestic triangle to dull her

[18]

novel beyond repair. The humors of engineers and their bitchy wives and understanding sisters, sweating out their emotions in the tents and ramshackle huts of the Imperial Valley construction settlements while the river is undercutting the main street, fail to impress the reader. Not even the assurance that the engineers were the soldiers of the desert is convincing, for the introduction of the camp retainers vitiates the results on the battlefield. The most interesting feature of this novel is the presentation of a minor character named Brandon, a "lunger" turned newspaperman, who expresses many of the more important concepts that have arisen from the reclamation movement.

Whether the benefits obtained by the draining of Owens Valley to obtain water for the Los Angeles area ethically outbalanced the dubious methods utilized in effecting the plan is a matter for the historians to decide. But the fiction based upon the project reflects a philosophy current at the time, which had its seamy side, to say the least. In no place is this better seen than in Peter B. Kyne's *The Long Chance*, which appeared in 1914. Although much of this story deals with the fate of yet another desert orphan—female of course— who lived down in the heart of the Mojave, and with the kindheartedness of a saloonkeeper named Hennage (a reincarnation of Harte's Oakhurst) who treasured a pressed rose petal right up to his sacrificial end, the significant action concerns the efforts of a red-headed wanderer named Bob McGraw to improve nature with the aid of his wits and his six gun. McGraw goes into "the great, hot, panting hungry heart of Inyo," where, by exploring a bit, he discovers and lays claim to hidden sites for dam and reservoir, which, together with the tunnel he plans to build for $50,000, add up to a reclamation project. Without a cent he sets out on his devious way. He obtains capital by blackmailing the villain, a promoter who represents unscrupulous absentee investment, and by tricking the government by filing false claims, the shady legality of which is expounded at length throughout an entire chapter. But McGraw's aims in all this are above reproach. He dreams of creating a model farming land for the poverty-stricken of the eastern slums—a wonderland fully equipped with free electricity, gas, and water. " 'I'm going to convert an Eden out of an abandoned Hell,' " he boasts, adding that he is going to accomplish this reform through the aid of the "God of the Square Deal." He hopes some day to look down from the slope of Kearsage and say: " 'That is mine. I helped to create it, and I did it for love, I finished what the Almighty commenced, and the job was worthwhile.' " Needless to say, he succeeds in bilking the government, unmasking the wicked promoter, and winning the orphan girl. The model community is not in sight at the end of the novel, however. Southern Californians who eventually learned that a former mayor of Los Angeles had posed as the employee of the United States Reclamation Service in order to buy up lands in Owens Valley surreptitiously, that a leading representative of the same service had resigned to work for the Los Angeles Water Board, taking his notes and maps with him, and that the Secretary of the Interior had declared a wilderness of sagebrush and cactus a forest reserve in order to keep it out of the hands of homesteaders, might well ponder upon the ethics of exploitation as exemplified by Kyne's Bob McGraw.

Mary Austin, who suffered through the days when it became clear that Owens Valley was to be sacrificed, also pondered those values. At the time that the first moves in the gambit became apparent, she was living in Independence, where her husband, the register of the Land Office, was protesting to Washington against the machinations of Fred Eaton and J. B. Lippincott. She says, in *Earth Horizon*, that she knew "that the land of Inyo would be desolated, and the cruelty and deception smote her beyond belief. There was nothing more for her in Southern California." Before she left Inyo, she made two prophecies. One, that Los Angeles would some day feel the moral responsibility for its acts, came true, she felt, when dynamiting of the aqueduct led to forced arbitration twenty years later. The other, that the City ("the City" is always Los Angeles to Inyo people) would be destroyed by the land itself, is a prophecy—stated in somewhat cryptic terms—that has not yet come true.

When Mary Austin wrote *The Ford*, published in 1917, she drew upon her experiences in Owens Valley, merging them with many of the impressions she held of the southern San Joaquin Valley, where she had lived before moving to Inyo. She laid the action of this realistic account of economic inequality and social unrest in "Tierra Longa," a fictitious valley which resembled both Owens Valley and the country around Bakersfield. The novel is a story of reclamation in the broadest sense. Among other things, it tells much about the failure of the people to unite to defend their future, and it paints a shaded rather than a black-and-white picture of the role of the strong man in developing a desert area. More confused in its theme and less forceful in its drama than Frank Norris' *The Octopus*, it nevertheless merits a place beside that novel as an account of man's effort to remake nature.

For the attempt to conquer aridity is indeed the theme of *The Ford*. As an introduction to this theme, Mary Austin describes vividly a Southern California drought. The young folks, helpless in their plight, could do no more than talk despairingly of the thousands of cubic inches of water, of the refreshing streams that would have been available had there been scientific irrigation. The rest of the book deals with attempts to get that irrigation.

The story is frequently interrupted by detailed and important digressions, detrimental to the flow of the narrative but of much interest. There was the oil boom in which everyone thought he was going to get rich, and everyone except T. Rickard went broke. There were the machinations of this same T. Rickard, whose efforts in the long run paid dividends for the entire community, but not without posing a moral problem. "It came over him again that the key to the Old Man's success was, after all, knowledge, knowledge of land and minerals, knowledge of law, and, more than everything else, knowledge of men, knowledge of everything except that strange, ineradicable quality of men called righteousness." There was the failure, time after time, of the farmers to get together for their own interests. The community sense was lacking. And, taken from Mrs. Austin's Owens Valley experiences, there were the devious methods used by Elwood in obtaining options to purchase the land, so that he, or his masters, would control the water supply. The people, assuming that he was working for the United States Reclamation Service since he was provided with official surveys, trusted Elwood and made it possible for him to take up options right and left. Actually, however, the surveys had been given him by a former employee of the Reclamation Service; and Elwood, no government employee, was, in fact, working to take up the land so that the water might be funneled into the city hundreds of miles away. Mary Austin tells us that Elwood had

> . . . looted the wilderness; he had led the river captive . . .
> He had climbed up Indian Gate and from thence he had
> had a vision; a vision of the river dammed and stored, not
> to unending fruitfulness, as Steven Brent had seen it, but
> of an arched, concreted aqueduct leading from the Gate
> to the city's faucets; a vision worthy of the most exalted
> cult of Locality.

In the end, however, the city found its water elsewhere, and the valley was saved. Thus, Tierra Longa escaped the fate of Owens Valley.

In some verses titled "The Spirit of the Desert" a budding

poet in San Diego expressed an article of faith that appeared often in the reclamation story:

Then with the petals, and pollen, and sand,
We built beautiful houses along the shore
Just alike for the rich and the poor.

The assumption that the irrigation age would provide alleviation of economic maladjustment was constantly cropping up in books of the time. Too much of a realist to expect any sweeping social changes, Mary Austin concerned herself, in *The Ford*, with the problem facing the little people in availing themselves of the benefits of irrigation. Without capital and without unity they were fighting an uphill battle for their betterment, but they had a chance Harold Bell Wright's seer, in *The Winning of Barbara Worth*, saw the Imperial Valley as a home for small farmers, heroes in the drama of man against nature. And Peter B. Kyne's Bob McGraw, in *The Long Chance*, considered himself to be a social benefactor. " 'I'm going to make thirty-two thousand acres of barren waste bloom and furnish clean, unsullied wealth for a few thousand poor, crushed devils that have been slaughtered and mained under the Juggernaut of our Christian civilization,' " he boasted. In Ednah Aiken's *The River*, the social prophet is Brandon, the newspaperman who had come down the river with John Wesley Powell, that fabulous visionary of the West whose plans for reclamation had been as daring as his explorations. Brandon preached a gospel of a new way of life, a new democratic society of small landholders, self-sufficient and reliant, which would be created by the concentrated and controlled agriculture made possible by irrigation. To him Riverside was "the unreal dream of the socialist come true," and the Imperial Valley was to be the poor man's paradise. Unaware of the time when absentee landlordism and peon labor would be twin curses of the Valley, he asserted with complete

[23]

confidence that the reclaimed land was to support a bit of Jeffersonian democracy.

Brandon was but echoing the ideas of William Ellsworth Smythe, sometimes called the Peter the Hermit of the. irrigation crusade, who expressed more vividly and effectively than anyone else the social hopes that accompanied the reclamation movement. Smythe, a Massachusetts boy, had early absorbed the faith of Horace Greeley in the future of the West and in the virtue of colonies organized along Fourieristic principles. Moving to Nebraska, he found his mission in life when the droughts of the early 'nineties caused widespread distress. Having seen something of irrigation in the course of a trip to New Mexico, Smythe, in his capacity as editor of a local newspaper, led a crusade for irrigation in Nebraska to save the farmlands. The movement spread rapidly and with great success. "To my mind," wrote Smythe, "irrigation seemed the biggest thing in the world. It was not merely a matter of ditches and acres, but a philosophy, a religion and a programme of practical statesmanship rolled into one." A man of great energy, clear mind, and unlimited optimism, he devoted the rest of his life to the cause. In 1891 he founded a periodical called the *Irrigation Age*, the same year he organized the first National Irrigation Congress, and in 1893 he came out to Los Angeles to lead the first International Irrigation Congress. He wrote a number of books on his subject, the most important of which were *The Conquest of Arid America* (1900) and *Constructive Democracy: The Economics of a Square Deal* (1905). After establishing a colony in Idaho on the basis of his ideals, he moved his headquarters to Southern California at the turn of the century, where he founded a number of colonies, edited the *California Farmer*, and contributed to numerous journals. For a considerable period he ran a monthly department in *Out West*. He also took an active part in politics as a progressive, he organized conventions and lectured all over the country, and he helped with a number of government surveys. In San Diego, where he lived for a long while, he was prominent in civic affairs and wrote a most creditable local history.

Smythe's thesis, as expressed in *The Conquest of Arid America* and in numerous other places, was that aridity was a great blessing. It was not an accident, in his opinion, that many of the older civilizations—Egyptian, Palestinian, Persian, Arabian, Aztec, Incan—had developed in lands of low mean rainfalls. And he was convinced that "the better half of the United States" lay west of the forty-ninth parallel, in the regions in which farmers could not depend on seasonal rains for their crops. His reasoning was cogent enough. The West was fortunately arid. The minerals and salts which had been leached out of the ground in rainy zones here lay rich for the farmer's use. "The valuable ingredients of the soil which are soluble have been washed out of the land in humid regions, like our eastern States, by the rains of the centuries. On the other hand, these elements have been accumulating in the arid soil of the West during the same centuries." Smythe believed that irrigation in itself was a fertilizing process, partly because the silt carried by irrigation water increased fertility. Most important of all, the Western farmer was not at the mercy of the weather. "In the whole range of human industry nothing is so crude, uncalculating, and unscientific as the childlike dependence on the mood of the clouds for the moisture essential to the production of the staple necessities of life . . . . Rain is the poor dependence of those who cannot obtain the advantages of irrigation," he asserted. The scientific irrigation farmer was no longer subject to the ravishes of drought and flood; he got his water when he wanted it and in the quantity he desired, and he was able to distribute it according to the varying needs of his crops. To Smythe it was a symbol that Eden was an irrigated land: "A river went out of

[25]

Eden to water the garden," he quoted. And he reminded his readers of the saying in Proverbs: " 'Make this valley full of ditches, for ye shall not see wind, neither shall ye see rain, yet this valley shall be full of water.' "

Smythe, the disciple of Greeley, was not satisfied with the conviction that irrigation produced more fruitfulness than seasonal rainfall but saw also in the practice a great opportunity for associative enterprise, indeed, a real necessity for cooperative organization. At the same time, he reasoned that irrigation made it possible for a family to be self-sustaining on a small plot without hiring labor; in fact, the large farm was out of the question. "The essence of the industrial life which springs from irrigation is its democracy. The first great law which irrigation lays down is this: There shall be no monopoly of land. This edict it enforces by the remorseless operation of its own economy . . . . A large farm under irrigation is a misfortune; a great farm, a calamity. Only the small farm pays." Moreover, the very smallness of the holdings would make it possible for the landowner to live close to an urban center. Thus the farmer would have the advantages not only of economic security but also of the proximity of cultural offerings.

Smythe's enthusiastic writings in *Out West* on the Owens River project seem somewhat pathetic. On the thousands of acres of San Fernando Valley to be watered with Sierra snows, proud and resourceful democrats were to live on an acre apiece, growing vegetables, small fruit, and poultry. It would be one great garden filled with beautiful homes. Electric cars would take the sturdy farmers in to Los Angeles to the theater or the opera whenever they wished to go. "The neighborhood of Los Angeles will supply the highest refinement which has ever come to the life of the common man." Ironic, indeed, when one learns that almost all of San Fernando Valley was bought up for a song by a few financiers before the Owens

[26]

Valley aqueduct was put in, and that the promoters of the valley (and the aqueduct) later sold to the common man at a thousandfold the cost.

Smythe never stopped at words; he put his ideas into operation. Down at San Ysidro, near the Mexican border, he started a "Little Landers" community in 1908. The Lower Otay Dam provided controlled irrigation. For an average price of five hundred dollars, well within the limits of the purse of the sturdy democrat, the settlers each bought his acre of farmland and his lot in town and pledged himself to improving them within six months of purchase. The village was built around a park, and life prospered, with "a little land and a living." Then, in 1916, the citizens of San Diego, plagued by years of drought, hired the famous rain maker, Charles M. Hatfield, to bring moisture out of the skies with his extraordinary paraphenalia of open tanks filled with secret mixtures. (It is said that he produced forty inches of rain in three hours on the Mojave Desert near Randsburg.) Hatfield set to work, and the rains poured down. They came so fast that San Diego was isolated from the rest of the world. A second effort followed, in spite of the protests of the city council, and Lower Otay Dam was washed out. With it went the community of Little Landers, victims of the haphazard ways of nature (aided by a magician) in the face of man's best scientific efforts.

And yet Smythe's spirit lives on. There are many in California who live on their small holdings, and many more who insist that the economic welfare of the state agricultural lands —such lands as those developed by the great Central Valley Project—depends upon a displacing of large holdings with small farms, thus encouraging individual initiative. Time will tell.

ROBB BERNARDO

Bernardo followed crops during the twenties and thirties, consistently espousing I.W.W. conceptions and slogans in his verse.

The Imperial Valley Strike

Way down in Imperial Valley
They're said to be closed up tight.
I'd give my whole sack of Bull Durham
To be in that valley tonight.
The bosses and cops in that valley
Axe-handled us out long ago.
Why should they pay white-man's wages
When they could exploit Mexico?

We cursed when they opened the Valley
To cholos who'd work for mere beans,
Working the small kids for nothing,
Truck loading with girls in their teens.
But it meant plenty cash to the Valley,
And slave-agents also smelled riches;
And now that they're sweating this crop out
One laughs at the smart sons of bitches.

The melons that grow in the Valley
Are going to be picked by good men;
I used to get sore at those Mexes,
But probably won't be again.
They've set up a strong Federation,
Demanding scrip-payment repeal.
It'll be Solidarity next time, I hope,
And the grand One Big Union ideal.

[28]

In Honor of Labor's Dead

We meet in this green field today
To honor comrades gone their way,
Victims of struggles long,
To end Greed's wrong.
They died from many shots and blows
Dealt out by cruel or foolish foes
Who've robbed us blind
Too long, too long a time.

By holdback, cutting, company store,
Recruiting doubled o'er and o'er,
They beat these victims flat
And killed them after that.
But I do not come here to curse
The deputies, finks, or Burns dicks worse,
Or curse the owning class;
In time all this will pass:

Though bosses like James Cohn and Durst
Just laughed at hunger, sickness, thirst,
And shamed our kids and wives
And took these brothers' lives;
Though Wheatland and Visalia ran
With blood of many a working man,
Fresno jailed us in ire,
Sacto used whips and fire.

No, I stand up here just to say
That Solidarity today
Will make our Union dreams
True sooner than it seems;
And, finishing, to bare my head
In honor to these martyred dead
Who in these fields did fall,
Doing honor to us all.

Dead Man

By JAMES M. CAIN

Among Cain's best-known Southern California novels
are *The Postman Always Rings Twice* (1938), *Mildred
Pierce* (1941), and the extremely successful *Double In-
demnity* (1944). It has been estimated that the three
moving pictures made from these books earned some
twelve million dollars, only about one hundred thousand
going to the author. Cain's writings are much admired in
foreign countries, and such important writers as Camus,
Simenon, and Ben van Grevenbrock are said to be partly
his imitators.

He felt the train check, knew what it meant. In a moment,
from up toward the engine, came the chant of the railroad
detective: "Rise and shine, boys, rise and shine." The hoboes
began dropping off. He could hear them out there in the dark,
cursing as the train went by. That was what they always did
on these freights: let the hoboes climb on in the yards, making
no effort to dislodge them there; for that would have meant a
foolish game of hide-and-seek between two or three detectives
and two or three hundred hoboes, with the hoboes swarming
on as fast as the detectives put them off. What they did was
let the hoboes alone until the train was several miles under
way; then they pulled down to a speed slow enough for men to
drop off, but too fast for them to climb back on. Then the
detective went down the line, brushing them off, like cater-
pillars from a twig. In two minutes they would all be ditched,
a crowd of bitter men in a lonely spot; but they always cursed,
always seemed surprised.

He crouched in the coal gondola and waited. He hadn't
boarded a flat or a refrigerator with the others, back in the Los
Angeles yards, tempting though this comfort was. He wasn't

[30]

long on the road, and he still didn't like to mix with the other hoboes, admit he was one of them. Also, he couldn't shake off a notion that he was sharper than they were, that playing a lone hand he might think of some magnificent trick that would defeat the detective, and thus, even at this ignoble trade, give him a sense of accomplishment, of being good at it. He had slipped into the gond not in spite of its harshness, but because of it; it was black, and would give him a chance to hide, and the detective, not expecting him there, might pass him by. He was nineteen years old, and was proud of the nickname they had given him in the poolroom back home. They called him Lucky.

"Rise and shine, boys, rise and shine."

Three dropped off the tank car ahead, and the detective climbed into the gond. The flashlight shot around, and Lucky held his breath. He had curled into one of the three chutes for unloading coal. The trick worked. These chutes were dangerous, for if you stepped into one and the bottom dropped, it would dump you under the train. The detective took no chances. He first shot the flash, then held on to the side while he climbed over the chutes. When he came to the last one, where Lucky lay, he shot the flash, but carelessly, and not squarely into the hole, so that he saw nothing. Stepping over, he went on, climbed to the box car behind, and resumed his chant; there were more curses, more feet sliding on ballast on the roadbed outside. Soon the train picked up speed. That meant the detective had reached the caboose, that all the hoboes were cleared.

Lucky stood up, looked around. There was nothing to see, except hot-dog stands along the highway, but it was pleasant to poke your head up, let the wind whip your hair, and reflect how you had outwitted the detective. When the click of the rails slowed and station lights showed ahead, he squatted down again, dropped his feet into the chute. As soon

[31]

as lights flashed alongside, he braced against the opposite side of the chute: that was one thing he had learned, the crazy way they shot the brakes on these freights. When the train jerked to a shrieking stop, he was ready, and didn't get slammed. The bell tolled, the engine pulled away, there was an interval of silence. That meant they had cut the train, and would be picking up more cars. Soon they would be going on.

"Ah-hah! Hiding on me, hey?"

The flashlight shot down from the box car. Lucky jumped, seized the side of the gond, scrambled up, vaulted. When he hit the roadbed, his ankles stung from the impact, and he staggered for footing. The detective was on him, grappling. He broke away, ran down the track, past the caboose, into the dark. The detective followed, but he was a big man and began to lose ground. Lucky was clear, when all of a sudden his foot drove against a switch bar and he went flat on his face, panting from the hysteria of shock.

The detective didn't grapple this time. He let go with a barrage of kicks.

"Hide out on me, will you? Treat you right, give you a break, and you hide out on me. I'll learn you to hide out on me."

Lucky tried to get up, couldn't. He was jerked to his feet, rushed up the track on the run. He pulled back, but couldn't get set. He sat down, dug in with his sliding heels. The detective kicked and jerked, in fury. Lucky clawed for something to hold on to, his hand caught the rail. The detective stamped on it. He pulled it back in pain, clawed again. This time his fingers closed on a spike, sticking an inch or two out of the tie. The detective jerked, the spike pulled out of the hole, and Lucky resumed his unwilling run.

"Lemme go! Why don't you lemme go?"

"Come on! Hide out on me, will you? I'll learn you to hide out on Larry Nott!"

"Lemme go! Lemme—"

Lucky pulled back, braced his heels, got himself stopped. Then his whole body coiled like a spring and let go in one convulsive, passionate lunge. The spike, still in his hand, came down on the detective's head, and he felt it crush. He stood there, looking down at something dark and formless, lying across the rails.

II

Hurrying down the track, he became aware of the spike, gave a toss, heard it splash in the ditch. Soon he realized that his steps on the ties were being telegraphed by the listening rail, and he plunged across the ditch to the highway. There he resumed his rapid walk, trying not to run. But every time a car overtook him his heels lifted queerly, and his breath first stopped, then came in gasps as he listened for the car to stop. He came to a crossroads, turned quickly to his right. He let himself run here, for the road wasn't lighted as the main highway was, and there weren't many cars. The running tired him, but it eased the sick feeling in his stomach. He came to a sign that told him Los Angeles was 17 miles, and to his left. He turned, walked, ran, stooped down sometimes, panting, to rest. After a while, it came to him why he had to get to Los Angeles, and so soon. The soup kitchen opened at seven o'clock. He had to be there, in that same soup kitchen where he had had supper, so it would look as though he had never been away.

When the lights went off, and it came broad daylight with the suddenness of Southern California, he was in the city, and a clock told him it was ten minutes after five. He thought he had time. He pressed on, exhausted, but never relaxing his rapid, half-shuffling walk.

It was ten minutes to seven when he got to the soup kitchen, and he quickly walked past. He wanted to be clear at

[33]

the end of the line, so he could have a word with Shorty, the man who dished out the soup, without impatient shoves from behind, and growls to keep moving.

Shorty remembered him. "Still here, hey?"

"Still here."

"Three in a row for you. Holy smoke, they ought to be collecting for you by the month."

"Thought you'd be off."

"Who, me?"

"Sunday, ain't it?"

"Sunday? Wake up. This is Saturday."

"Saturday? You're kidding."

"Kidding my eye, this is Saturday, and a big day in this town, too."

"One day looks like another to me."

"Not this one. Parade."

"Yeah?"

"Shriners. You get that free."

"Well, that's my name, Lucky."

"My name's Shorty, but I'm over six feet."

"Nothing like that with me. I really got luck."

"You sure?"

"Like, for instance, getting a hunk of meat."

"I didn't give you no meat."

"Ain't you going to?"

"Shove your plate over quick. Don't let nobody see you."

"Thanks."

"Okay, Lucky. Don't miss the parade."

"I won't."

He sat at the rough table with the others, dipped his bread in the soup, tried to eat, but his throat kept contracting from excitement and he made slow work of it. He had what he wanted from Shorty. He had fixed the day, and not only the day but the date, for it would be the same date as the big

Shriners' parade. He had fixed his name, with a little gag. Shorty wouldn't forget him. His throat relaxed, and he wolfed the piece of meat.

Near the soup kitchen he saw signs: "Lincoln Park Pharmacy," "Lincoln Park Cafeteria."

"Which way is the park, Buddy?" If it was a big park, he might find a thicket where he could lie down, rest his aching legs.

"Straight down, you'll see it."

There was a fence around it, but he found a gate, opened it, slipped in. Ahead of him was a thicket, but the ground was wet from a stream that ran through it. He crossed a small bridge, followed a path. He came to a stable, peeped in. It was empty, but the floor was thickly covered with new hay. He went in, made for a dark corner, burrowed under the hay, closed his eyes. For a few moments everything slipped away, except warmth, relaxation, ease. But then something began to drill into the back of his mind: Where did he spend last night? Where would he tell them he spent last night? He tried to think, but nothing would come to him. He would have said that he spent it where he spent the night before, but he hadn't spent it in Los Angeles. He had spent it in Santa Barbara, and come down in the morning on a truck. He had never spent a night in Los Angeles. He didn't know the places. He had no answers to the questions that were now pounding at him like sledge-hammers:

"What's that? Where you say you was?"

"In a flophouse."

"Which flophouse?"

"I didn't pay no attention which flophouse. It was just a flophouse."

"Where was this flophouse at?"

"I don't know where it was at. I never been to Los Angeles before. I don't know the names of no streets."

[35]

"What this flophouse look like?"

"Looked like a flophouse."

"Come on, don't give us no gags. What this flophouse look like? Aint you got eyes, can't you say what this here place looked like? What's the matter, can't you talk?"

Something gripped his arm, and he felt himself being lifted. Something of terrible strength had hold of him, and he was going straight up in the air. He squirmed to get loose, then was plopped on his feet and released. He turned, terrified.

An elephant was standing there, exploring his clothes with its trunk. He knew then that he had been asleep. But when he backed away, he bumped into another elephant. He slipped between the two elephants, slithered past a third to the door, which was open about a foot. Out in the sunlight, he made his way back across the little bridge, saw what he hadn't noticed before: pens with deer in them, and ostriches, and mountain sheep, that told him he had stumbled into a zoo. It was after four o'clock, so he must have slept a long time in the hay. Back on the street, he felt a sobbing laugh rise in his throat. *That* was where he had spent the night. "In the elephant house at Lincoln Park."

"*What?*"

"That's right. In the elephant house."

"What you giving us? A stall?"

"It aint no stall. I was in the elephant house."

"With them elephants?"

"That's right."

"How you get in there?"

"Just went in. The door was open."

"Just went in there, seen the elephants, and bedded down with them?"

"I thought they was horses."

"You thought them elephants was horses?"

"It was dark. I dug in under the hay. I never knowed they

[36]

was elephants till morning."

"How come you went in this place?"

"I left the soup kitchen, and in a couple of minutes I came to the park. I went in there, looking for some grass to lie down on. Then I come in this here place, looked to me like a stable, I peeped in, seen the hay, and hit it."

"And you wasn't scared of them elephants?"

"It was dark, I tell you, and I could hear them eating the hay, but I thought they was horses. I was tired, and I wanted some place to sleep."

"Then what?"

"Then when it got light, and I seen they was elephants, I run out of there, and beat it."

"Couldn't you tell them elephants by the smell?"

"I never noticed no smell."

"How many elephants was there?"

"Three."

III

He brushed wisps of hay off his denims. They had been fairly new, but now they were black with the grime of the coal gond. Suddenly his heart stopped, a suffocating feeling swept over him. The questions started again, hammered at him, beat into his brain.

"Where that coal dust come from?"

"I don't know. The freights, I guess."

"Don't you know it aint no coal ever shipped into this part of the state? Don't you know that here all they burn is gas? Don't you know it aint only been but one coal car shipped in here in six months, and that come in by a misread train order? Don't you know that car was part of that train this here detective was riding that got killed? *Don't you know that?* Come on, out with it, WHERE THAT COAL DUST COME FROM?"

Getting rid of the denims instantly became an obsession. He felt that people were looking at him on the street, spying the coal dust, waiting till he got by, then running into drugstores to phone the police that he had just passed by. It was like those dreams he sometimes had, where he was walking through crowds naked, except that this was no dream, and he wasn't naked, he was wearing these denims, these tell-tale denims with coal dust all over them. He clenched his hands, had a moment of terrible concentration, headed into a filling station.

"Hello."

"Hello."

"What's the chances on a job?"

"No chances."

"Why not?"

"Don't need anybody."

"That's not the only reason."

"There's about forty-two other reasons, one of them is I can't even make a living myself, but it's all the reason that concerns you. Here's a dime, kid. Better luck somewhere else."

"I don't want your dime. I want a job. If the clothes were better, that might help, mightn't it?"

"If the clothes were good enough for Clark Gable in the swell gambling house scene, that wouldn't help a bit. Not a bit. I just don't need anybody, that's all."

"Suppose I got better clothes. Would you talk to me?"

"Talk to you any time, but I don't need anybody."

"I'll be back when I get the clothes."

"What's your name?"

"Hook's my name. Oscar Hook."

"Thanks, Mr. Hook. But I'm coming back. I just got a idea I can talk myself into a job. I'm some talker."

"You're all of that, kid. But don't waste your time. I don't need anybody."

"Okay. Just the same, I'll be back."

He headed for the center of town, asked the way to the cheap clothing stores. At Los Angeles and Temple, after an hour's trudge, he came to a succession of small stores in a Mexican quarter that were what he wanted. He went into one. The storekeeper was a Mexican, and two or three other Mexicans were standing around, smoking.

"Mister, will you trust me for a pair of white pants and a shirt?"

"No trust. Hey, scram."

"Look. I can have a job Monday morning if I can show up in that outfit. White pants and a white shirt. That's all."

"No trust. What you think this is, anyway?"

"Well, I got to get that outfit somewhere. If I get that, they'll let me go to work Monday. I'll pay you soon as I get paid off Saturday night."

"No trust. Sell for cash."

He stood there. The Mexicans stood there, smoked, looked out at the street. Presently one of them looked at him. "What kind of job, hey? What you mean, got to have white pants a white shirt a hold a job?"

"Filling Station. They got a rule you got to have white clothes before you can work there."

"Oh. Sure. Filling station."

After a while the storekeeper spoke. "Ha! Is a joke. Job in filling station, must have a white pants, white shirt. Ha! Is a joke."

"What else would I want them for? Holy smoke, these are better for the road, aint they? Say, a guy don't want white pants to ride freights, does he?"

"What filling station? Tell me that?"

"Guy name of Hook, Oscar Hook, got a Acme station, Main near Twentieth. You don't believe me, call him up."

"You go to work there, hey?"

[39]

"I'm *supposed* to go to work. I *told* him I'd get the white pants and white shirt, somehow. Well—if I don't get them I don't go to work."

"Why you come to me, hey?"

"Where else would I go? If it's not you, it's another guy down the street. No place else I can dig up the stuff over Sunday, is there?"

"Oh."

He stood around. They all stood around. Then once again the storekeeper looked up. "What size you wear, hey?"

He had a wash at a tap in the back yard, then changed there, between piled-up boxes and crates. The storekeeper gave him a white shirt, white pants, necktie, a suit of thick underwear, and a pair of shoes to replace his badly-worn brogans. "Is pretty cold, night-time, now. A thick underwear feel better."

"Okay. Much obliged."

"Can roll this other stuff up."

"I don't want it. Can you throw it away for me?"

"Is pretty dirty."

"Plenty dirty."

"You no want?"

"No."

His heart leaped as the storekeeper dropped the whole pile into a rubbish brazier and touched a match to some papers at the bottom of it. In a few minutes, the denims and everything else he had worn were ashes.

He followed the storekeeper inside. "Okay, here is a bill. I put all a stuff on a bill, no charge you more than anybody else. Is six dollar ninety-eight cents, then is a service charge one dollar."

All of them laughed. He took the "service charge" to be a gyp overcharge to cover the trust. He nodded. "Okay on the service charge."

[40]

The storekeeper hesitated. "Well, six ninety-eight. We no make a service charge."

"Thanks."

"See you keep a white pants clean till Monday morning."

"I'll do that. See you Saturday night."

"*Adios.*"

Out in the street, he stuck his hand in his pocket, felt something, pulled it out. It was a $1 bill. Then he understood about the "service charge," and why the Mexicans had laughed. He went back, kissed the $1 bill, waved a cheery salute into the store. They all waved back.

He rode a streetcar down to Mr. Hook's, got turned down for the job, rode a streetcar back. In his mind, he tried to check over everything. He had an alibi, fantastic and plausible. So far as he could recall, nobody on the train had seen him, not even the other hoboes, for he had stood apart from them in the yards, and had done nothing to attract the attention of any of them. The denims were burned, and he had a story to account for the whites. It even looked pretty good, this thing with Mr. Hook, for anybody who had committed a murder would be most unlikely to make a serious effort to land a job.

But the questions lurked there, ready to spring at him, check and recheck as he would. He saw a sign, "5-Course Dinner, 35 Cents." He still had ninety cents, and went in, ordered steak and fried potatoes, the hungry man's dream of heaven. He ate, put a ten-cent tip under the plate. He ordered cigarettes, lit one, inhaled. He got up to go. A newspaper was lying on the table.

He froze as he saw the headline:

"L. R. NOTT, R. R. MAN, KILLED."

IV

On the street, he bought a paper, tried to open it under a street light, couldn't, tucked it under his arm. He found Highway 101, caught a hay truck bound for San Francisco. Going out Sunset Boulevard, it unexpectedly pulled over to the curb and stopped. He looked warily around. Down a side-street, about a block away, were the two red lights of a police station. He was tightening to jump and run, but the driver wasn't looking at the lights. "I told them bums that air hose was leaking. They set you nuts. Supposed to keep the stuff in shape and all they ever do is sit around and play blackjack."

The driver fished a roll of black tape from his pocket and got out. Lucky sat where he was a few minutes, then climbed down, walked to the glare of the headlights, opened his paper. There it was:

L. R. NOTT, R. R. MAN, KILLED

The decapitated body of L. R. Nott, 1327 De Soto Street, a detective assigned to a northbound freight, was found early this morning on the track near San Fernando station. It is believed he lost his balance while the train was shunting cars at the San Fernando siding and fell beneath the wheels. Funeral services will be held tomorrow from the De Soto Street Methodist Church. Mr. Nott is survived by a widow, formerly Miss Elsie Snowden of Mannerheim, and a son, L. R. Nott, Jr., 5.

He stared at it, refolded the paper, tucked it under his arm, walked back to where the driver was tapping the air hose. He was clear, and he knew it. "Boy, do they call you Lucky? Is your name Lucky? I'll say it is."

He leaned against the trailer, let his eye wander down the street. He saw the two red lights of the police station—glowing. He looked away quickly. A queer feeling began to stir inside him. He wished the driver would hurry up.

Presently he went back to the headlights again, found the notice, re-read it. He recognized that feeling now; it was the old Sunday-night feeling that he used to have back home, when the bells would ring and he would have to stop playing hide in the twilight, go to church, and hear about the necessity for being saved. It shot through his mind, the time he had played hookey from church, and hid in the livery stable; and how lonely he had felt, because there was nobody to play hide with; and how he had sneaked into church, and stood in the rear to listen to the necessity for being saved.

His eyes twitched back to the red lights and slowly, shakily, but unswervingly he found himself walking toward them.

"I want to give myself up."

"Yeah, I know, you're wanted for grand larceny in Hackensack, New Jersey."

"No, I—"

"We quit giving them rides when the New Deal come in. Beat it."

"I killed a man."

"You—?... When was it you done this?"

"Last night."

"Where?"

"Near here. San Fernando. It was like this—"

"Hey, wait till I get a card.... Okay, what's your name?"

"Ben Fuller."

"No middle name?"

"They call me Lucky."

"Lucky like in good luck?"

"Yes, sir....Lucky like in good luck."

[43]

I Horn into Hollywood

By WILL ROGERS

This much-beloved actor and folk-humorist was born in
the Indian Territory of Oklahoma in 1879. After working
in Wild West shows and in vaudeville he began in 1919 to
contribute character-parts, often described as "mirror-
reflections of his own personality" to the movies. He died
in an Alaskan air crash in 1935, leaving behind him the
materials for his autobiography.

I have been asked to tell something of these bucking
pictures and as I have been in only one I know all about it.
I horned into this El Dorado a little different from most of
them. I had been going along peacefully working for a living
on the stage and really felt a little hurt that I had never been
offered a job in them.

One day Mrs. Rex Beach, who you hear very little of but
who is really the Ram Rod of the Beach outfit, Mrs. Beach,
after a late supper consisting of a Rarebit, had a very bad
night and thought of some terrible things. She arose early and
commanded James to taxi out the favorite Limouzine and give
it the gun for where I was bedded down for the mosquieto
season on Long Island.

I had just started in licking on my third Kid and I was a
little vexed at being thrown behind in my daily routine.

Well, she climbed out of this royalty on the "Spoilers"
and chirped above the wail of young rope throwers, "Will,
you are going into the Flickering photos." Now I live at the
same town and its not a coincidence on the island where the
Asylum is located, so I winked at her chouffer and said, "You
brought this Woman to the wrong house."

Now, I tried to tell the lady that I had never bothered
anybody and never annoyed over one Audience at a time and

that these were war times and a man could be arrested for treason as treason meant any thing that causes pain to our people thereby giving aid to the enemy. But she still insisted that the people of Olagah, Okla, and Higgens, Texas would grow up in ignorance if I did not enlighten them with my Art on the old muslin, said education for which they could obtain for a jitney and tax.

I told her that I couldent afford to earn any more, that I was just on the verge of the Income Tax now, all that saved me was that the Gov allowed two hundred for each child and my children and my income just come out even, and that I would have to speak to my wife and see if we could afford to increase our income.

I told her that I had heard that some of these Movable Actors sometimes appeared personally at the Theatre where their pictures were showing. She said, yes, some of them do but most of them dont or wont. She says you wont have to and I would advise you not to let them know even where you live.

Of course she had one corking good argument, that Caruso and myself were the last two singers to go in and look what it would mean to Caruso when someone, after looking at his picture, asked him why he went in. He could say, "Well, Will went in, us artists have to stick together." I showed her that Caruso had used up his only means of publicity getting married and was going into the movies and that the first thing you know he would be back singing again. I wanted time to think it over but she kept insisting she must know at once as she said if it got nosed around Fairbanks and Chaplin might get to me with a bigger offer.

Will's first picture was Laughing Bill Hyde, *made in the summer of 1918 at Goldwyn's old Fort Lee Studio in New Jersey, while he was still with the Follies. That Fall Goldwyn put him under exclusive contract and the following spring sent him to California. The family later moved out and California became their permanent home. Will wrote about his first experience there.*

First Day on the Set.

When a big burly nabbed me by the coat tail and yanked me back and said, "You poor boob, I saved your life. Thats Miss Geraldine Farrar taking close ups for the hell cat." I had heard what she did to Caruso one time and I thanked him. I watched her a while in hopes she would sing, but I tell you what she did have, she had an orchestra playing appropriate music in all of her scenes.

This man said he would show me where I belong, so we passed through an Irish farmhouse of Tom Moores, stopped to see May Marshes Propagander picture choking the Kaiser. We passed through Metropolitan Opera House and Cheyenne Joes saloon on the way to my gang. By the time I got there they thought I had given up the picture and gone back home.

It was now ten thirty and I thought I was late. We took the first scene at exactly three forty five in the afternoon. The Director says, "Now, Will, we are going to take the scene where your old pal dies. You have broken out of jail and he gets hurt and you are bringing him into the Doctors office at night to get him treated and he dies. Its the dramatic scene of the whole opera." I says, "But I havent got out of Jail yet." He says, "No, you wont for a couple of weeks yet. Besides the Jail is not built yet."

Thats the first time I learned that they just hop around any old way. We took a scene the start of a fellow and I fighting out doors and a lot of rainy weather come and a week later he knocked me down in the same fight. I thought we were trying to beat the European war record.

The Director says, "Have you ever had any Camera experience?" I said only with a little Brownie No 2 I used to have. He says, "Any moving Picture experience." I told him I worked with Miss Norman once but I dident know how it turned out. He warned me that if I was thinking a thing the camera would show it. I told him I would try and keep my thoughts as clean as possible.

Telegram sent when Sam Goldwyn wanted to change the name of Jubilo:

OCTOBER 17, 1919
SAMUEL GOLDWYN
469 FIFTH AVENUE
NEW YORK CITY NY
THOUGHT I WAS SUPPOSED TO BE A COMEDIAN BUT WHEN YOU SUGGEST CHANGING THE TITLE OF JUBILO YOU ARE FUNNIER THAN I EVER WAS. I DONT SEE HOW LORIMER OF THE POST EVER LET IT BE PUBLISHED UNDER THAT TITLE. THAT SONG IS BETTER KNOWN THROUGH THE SOUTH BY OLDER PEOPLE THAN GERALDINE FARRAR'S HUSBAND. WE HAVE USED IT ALL THROUGH BUSINESS IN THE PICTURE BUT OF COURSE WE CAN CHANGE THAT TO "EVERYBODY SHIMMIE NOW." SUPPOSED IF YOU HAD PRODUCED THE MIRACLE MAN YOU WOULD HAVE CALLED IT A QUEER OLD GUY. BUT IF YOU REALLY WANT A TITLE FOR THIS SECOND PICTURE I COULD SUGGEST JUBILO. ALSO THE FOLLOWING:

A POOR BUT HONEST TRAMP
HE LIES BUT HE DONT MEAN IT
A FARMERS VIRTIOUS DAUGHTER
THE GREAT TRAIN ROBBERY MYSTERY
A SPOTTED HORSE BUT HE IS ONLY PAINTED
A HUNGRY TRAMP'S REVENGE
THE VAGABOND WITH A HEART AS BIG AS HIS APPETITE
HE LOSES IN THE FIRST REEL BUT WINS IN THE LAST
THE OLD MAN LEFT BUT THE TRAMP PROTECTED HER
WHAT WOULD YOU HAVE CALLED THE BIRTH OF A NATION?

WILL ROGERS

[47]

Ad for Jubilo:

Now I was asked to write my own add, Now that is a pretty tough job Cause after my telling you what a picture we have you will think I am a little egotistical, At that I am glad they asked me to write it instead of paying for it. Jubilo means a song, an old-time Negro Camp Meeting song IN THE LAND OF JUBILO, I sing this song but fortunately the voice dont register on the film so you need not stay away on that account.

It was originally before we got ahold of it a very good story and appeared in the Saturday Evening Post (I get nothing extra for mentionning their name) This character Jubilo is a tramp, Well after Mr Goldwyn saw me several times in my street clothes he said there is the fellow to play the tramp.

Now this picture is just as long as any other 5-reel picture and takes up just as much time as a regular picture does, Another thing exibitors need have no fear of it conflicting with anything else on their programs, As it cant interfere with anything and nothing can hurt it, In one respect our picture is as good as lots of others, We have a Cast that can act and a Star that can not, an unusual combination in this business. We only have one Villain in the picture so you have no trouble telling who is doing all the dirty work. You know come to think of it it aint such a bad picture at that, it has Father, Girl, Villain who makes play for girl, Tramp Hero, dirty but honest. Pickford, Fairbanks and all of them have the same layout and get real doe for theirs, Story, theres no use telling you wise Birds. Same as usual. Looks bad for the Hero right up to the last Close Up, First reel introduces Hero dividing last crum of bread with dog, which they all do in the movies but nobody ever did in real life, Second reel looks bad for hero, Third reel looks even worse for Hero, Fourth reel evidence all point to

[48]

Hero being the robber, Villain looks slick and satisfied, End Reel 5 the winners, The tramp wins 100 percent HERO, Villain 2 and three quarters.

The directions was very good when you consider the director wore no Puttees or riding breeches.

The Photography was mostly shot in focus, the Camera used was a Brownie No 2.

The Sets, Goldwyn really spread themselves in this picture, there is one scene with mountains in the background that if you had to build it would have cost a million dollars, To give you an Idea we traveled over 2 miles from the studio to get it.

Interior Sets there is a Barn showing real hay, No fake stuff but real Hay and a Kitchen Scene that I'll bet dident cost a cent under 25 dollars but very realistic dirty dishes in the sink and everything. Theres an eating scene. (Well to give you an idea how good I did it we had to wait for the war to be over or Hoover would never let such eating pass.)

In "Jubilo" Ben Ames Williams wrote the finest story it was ever my privilege to work in. It was the only Story ever made out here where there was no Scenario made. We just shot the scenes from the various paragraphs in the Story in the Saturday Evening Post. When we took a Scene we just marked it off and went on to the next. I think, and Williams verified it, that it was the only story ever made that was absolutely filmed as it was written, and here is the big Novelty to it. We dident change his main Title either. They will film the Lords Supper and when it is made, figure out that it is not a good release Title and not catchy enough, so it will be released under the heading, "A Red Hot Meal," or "The Gastronomical Orgy."

In .1919 one of Will's movie fans sent him twenty-five cents in stamps to pay for a photograph. About six weeks later

[49]

when Will happened to read the letter he returned the stamps with this note:

My dear Sir:
I thank you for the use of your money. I havent got a picture of myself. If I did have it wouldent be worth two-bits. If I did have one, I'd give you two bits to keep it.
Yours,

Will Rogers

In 1919 Will wrote his famous fourteen points on the moving picture business in Wid's Yearbook, *published by the* Film Daily.

President Wilson and I each have fourteen points. He took his to Paris where they not only saw his fourteen but raised him twelve more, I brought my fourteen points to the coast. The first five and principal of mine a wife and four children in itself constitutes a novelty in this business, that is provided you still live with them.

Point number six: I heard there was a movement on to revive moving pictures.

Point Number seven: Producers decided to make fewer and worse pictures. They may make fewer but they will never make worse.

Point number eight: I hold the distinction of being the ugliest man in pictures.

Point number nine: Caruso and I and Jesse Willard were the last to go in.

Point number ten: Goldwyn figured by getting a good cast and a great story, it would about offset the action of the star.

Point number eleven: I can't roll a cigarette with one hand and can't whip but one man at a time (and he must be littler than I am).

Point number twelve: I made a picture last year and some theatres bought it. So they figured if I made another one they could double the sale on this one. Get two to use it.

Point number thirteen: Moving pictures are the only way in the world that you can play and tour and not have to worry about hotels.

Point number fourteen: It's the only business where you can sit out front and applaud yourself.

Will Rogers

In 1920 Will wrote his suggestions on how to improve the Moving Picture industry. His suggestions might be read with profit, from time to time, by the industry. Here they are:

Use your audience for a Press Agent instead of hiring one.

Don't tell your audience what your picture cost, they know what they were stung by the price of admission.

How can you make five movies a year of over four million different pictures each when it took Rembrandt five years to make one still?

You hear it asked, Are Movie audiences getting smarter? The answer is No. Ain't more people going to Movies than there ever was?

There is only one thing that can kill the Movies, and that is education.

What Movies need is another name for an All-Star Cast.

What the Picture business needs is a picture.

What the Movie audience needs is endurance.

What the Movie actor needs is better doubles (so they can do better stunts).

What the weeping Movie heroine needs is glycerine that won't stay in one place, but will run down the face.

What the entire industry needs is a sense of humor.

[51]

If the Movies want to advance, all they have to do is not to get new stories but do the old ones over as they were written.

Producers say Pictures have improved, but they haven't. It's only audiences have got used to them.

You can't spring a new plot on an audience the first time and expect it to go. It takes a Movie audience years to get used to a new plot.

Moving Picture audiences are just like an old gold miner, they will keep on going and going for years hoping against hope to eventually some day strike a picture.

The finish of the Movies will be when they run out of suggestive titles.

Movies Patron coming out of Theatre was asked, How's the feature? "I guess it's good, but I didn't see one."

A plot that will make money and that could be elaborated by an imaginative director into a big feature is a little Bo-Peep.

Some say, What is the salvation of the Movies? I say run em backwards. It can't hurt 'em and it's worth a trial.

Some Cinics ask, Is Movies really an Art yet? Yes, selling them is. Will the industry live? Not unless a Mid-Wife comes. We can't tell yet, it's like a newly born cat, we've got to wait nine days to see if it will open it's eyes.

Which one of the Arts will it supplant? It must have been Literature, as there hasn't been any in a long time (if it hadn't been for my book).

Pictures are getting so long that the life of a moving Picture fan is four features.

The average life of the movie is till it reaches the critic.

The average life of the movie hero is till he is found out.

One time out here in the old silent day pictures, it was in 1919, we made about three pictures up at a place near Mohave, Called-darnsburg. It has a big old mine, and Irene

Rich was with us. She was just a breaking in as a leading lady. In those days I was one of the love interest. (Nowadays I just have to fix it for some young ones. They wont let me have anything to do with it personally. I guess its just as well, I never was so hot as a screen lover.) But in those days your age never mattered. Audiences figured that old people fall in love too, but now thats all out. Modern audiences think that old folks are just to be the fathers and mothers of the young ones. And too in one of those same pictures was Margaret Livingston, who is now Paul Whitemans's wife. She is the one that made him quit eating so much. The way she did it she would let him order whatever he wanted and then she had a string tied to it and she would pull it away from him, and he got thin grabbing at it. I was one time to rescue her out of the water.

Well we had to go another two hundred miles to find a stream. You know this water thing out here aint just water, its gold. Well I was supposed to swim in on a horse and rescue her, and as I dragged her ashore pull her up on my horse and run to the doctors with her. Well say you get on dry land and try to stay up on your horse and pull a fair size old gal up on there with you, when she is supposed to be plum dead, and then wet to boot! Say, she had to reduse before I could get her up there. There is nothing heavier than a person that is wet, even a little person. You dip one of Singers Midgets in the water and let him soak awhile, and I bet you Dempsey wouldent lift him up in front of him.

Another time I was supposed to get on a bucking horse in a corral and he was supposed to buck out of the gate and down to the creek, where he was to throw me off into the water. Then the leading lady was supposed to come up and see me as I was crawling out of the water, and I was to register embarrassment and try to conceal my wetness at the same time. It was in the wintertime when we took it. The fellow that wrote this little byplay in the scenario did so in a nice warm dry room.

Well, I got on the horse and got almost to the gate, when he bucked me off. We caught him and did it over again. And the next time I stayed with him until he got out of the gate and that was all.

The director said, "That's no good. You'll have to try it again. You are supposed to stay on until you get to the creek and then get bucked off."

I says, "Say, listen, if you want me to do this scene, you get a corral that's nearer the creek; or better still, find some creek that's nearer a corral."

Under his contract with Sam Goldwyn Will made the following moving pictures: Laughing Bill Hyde; Almost a Husband; Water, Water Everywhere; Jubilo; The Strange Boarder; Jes' Call me Jim; Cupid, the Cowpuncher; Honest Hutch; Guile of Woman; Boys will be Boys; An Unwilling Hero; Doubling for Romeo; *and,* A Poor Relation.

The Ballad of William Hickman

Marion Parker, aged eleven, was kidnapped and butchered by the Los Angeles youth Hickman on December 15, 1927. Hickman demanded a ransom of $1500 dollars, met with Marion's father for this purpose, and, just before driving away, tossed chunks of Marion's flesh out of the car window for the father to retrieve. The exquisite cruelty of this act made the crime more exciting than most, and a ballad circulated in California and other states, preserving an ill name after the execution of its owner at San Quentin in 1928.

Right here in California bright and gay, and gay,
A family wrapped up little gifts for Xmas day.
One of them was Marion, such a pretty child,
All the folks on that block loved her pretty smile.

She went out next morning, here in bright L.A.
Going to her grade school just a couple blocks away.
She got to her school all right, but a dirty fiend
Got her in his jalopy and drove her from the scene.

He wrote her daddy a ransom letter for a thousand five,
But also thought poor Marion might talk if left alive.
So this dastard took a shiv and cut her joints away,
It was the cruelest thing e'er done, here in old L.A.

Her daddy he was honest, he brought the cash along;
If only Hickman also was, nothing would be wrong.
He sat there in his fine car, tossed out ears and eyes;
The father he was weeping, distressed by Hickman's lies.

If he had only been more fair and had not cut her dead,
He might have got a better car and never be afraid.
But some men are so cruel, nothing does them touch:
He was a hard-hearted skunk, so he is in Dutch.

The Jury found him guilty then, murder first degree,
Never will this poor youth his darling mother see.
He's up in old San Quentin now, thinking of his mom;
When he could be a free man here in L.A. so warm.

The father he was honest; why wasn't Hickman too?
He had no call to kill her, poor Marion so true.
She was probably as brave as any girl could be;
If he had asked, she'd keep shut, on who did that deed.

He was not a Negro, I am glad to say.
He was white as she was, this girl so young and gay.
I'm tired of all the lies they tell, here in L.A.,
Saying that the African again should go away.

Africans are just as good, neath California skies,
As anyone, and many did, for their country die.
So never knock but boost Los Angeles so fair,
With the pretty girls all round, happy to be there.

The Blond Dog

By LOUIS CLYDE STOUMEN

Stoumen came to Hollywood from Bucks County, Pennsylvania, in the thirties. "The Blond Dog" happens to be
the first short story he published. In addition to fiction
and articles, he has several successful filmscripts to his
credit.

My Essex had a leak in its water pump and I wasn't ten
minutes out of Hollywood before the radiator started to steam.
Up in Laurel Canyon there are no gas stations. Since I couldn't
afford a better car than the Essex, I couldn't afford a cracked
block. The car needed water fast.

As soon as I topped the rise I shifted into neutral, coasted
on the downgrade, and turned the wheels into the first private
driveway I saw. It was narrow, curving road of smooth tarvia,
enclosed on both sides by vine-covered stone walls at least six
feet high. Momentum carried me rapidly around the curve toward a house.

I still don't understand where the dog came from. He
couldn't have come through the stone walls, and I doubt he
came over them. I didn't see him come down the drive ahead
of me. There was a flash of white, and he was under my wheels
before I knew it, screaming like a hurt woman.

The emergency brake threw me hard against the steering
wheel, but I was out of the car before it stopped rocking.

The dog was a large Russian wolfhound, a beautiful
silky-haired blond animal. He had been hit in the hind-
quarters, perhaps had his spine crushed, and now he struggled
grotesquely five feet back of my car. He tried to get to his
feet, but his hind legs and haunches lay limp and broken on
the roadway, and he managed only to raise his great racer's
chest onto his forelegs and to point to the sky his long blond

snout in a soprano scream of agony.

The dog's terrible cry bounced from green wall to green wall in the narrow roadway, like a fire siren in a phone booth.

Hitting somebody's dog with my car was unpleasant enough, but the sudden sound of his pain was terrifying. I trembled so my legs could hardly hold me up. And as the sound continued, I rushed about the road searching for a club or a stone to put the animal out of his misery. There was nothing.

I couldn't bear the dog's writhing and the sound of his screams. I jumped into the Essex and lunged it backward over the hurt animal. There was a soft bump under a rear wheel and then under a front wheel, and the pitch of the dog's scream lowered with each impact. I drove forward over the body once more. The cry stopped as if a blaring radio had been switched off.

I braked the car and my fingers were barely able to find the ignition key and turn it off.

Through the windshield I saw a woman come running up the driveway from the house. She was dressed in white play clothes, and her long blonde hair flashed in the sun. She ran like a professional sprinter—so fast that she banked on the turn.

"I saw you!" she shouted. She was hysterical. "I saw you purposely drive over my dog!"

Before I could answer, she flung open the door of the car and, with a strength surprising in one so young and slight, took my arm and pulled me from my seat out onto the driveway.

She slapped my face on one side then the other, and I stood there weak and shaken and took it. As she swung for the third time, I raised my arm to protect my face and took the blow on the back of my hand. The woman had long fingernails, and I felt them rip over my skin. I turned the hand and saw blood.

Then the woman was crying, and all the strength was gone out of her. Her shoulders hunched up and her hands covered her face and she sobbed, "Poor Prince Igor! Poor, happy, lovely dog!"

She raised her face to me again and said low in her throat, more as accusation than question, "why did you do it?"

I explained about the Essex needing water, and how it had been an accident, and why I had run the car over the dog again.

She looked at me through tears, only half believing, then took two steps toward the back of the car and looked at the remains of the dog.

Her body trembled, and I saw her sway. I reached out and took her about the waist. She didn't faint, but she let me hold her and pat her shoulder and she buried her face on my chest, sobbing again, uncontrollably, like a child. I turned her about and walked her toward the house, still patting her shoulder comfortingly through its sheath of loose blonde hair.

It was a low one-story house of modern design. I noticed an entire wall of glass, some cement surfaces, and the use of redwood for the roof and doorway.

Inside, I sat her down on a fat chartreuse chair. She sank into it limply, sobbing into her hands. I walked back through the house looking for someone to take care of her.

Two bedrooms, a library, a kitchen, two bathrooms, an open dining patio and an attached garage housing a new station wagon were all empty. Off the patio was a small swimming pool, and beyond that a bungalow that might have been servants' quarters.

I called, "Anybody home?" There was no answer.

When I got back to the living room the woman was herself again. She stood cool and lovely, only a little red-eyed from crying, by a black lacquer cabinet. She wore a white play skirt and a white bra, and she was pouring something from a silver decanter into two goblets of purple glass.

It was then I recognized her. I had seen her often on the screen. The long silver-blonde hair that waterfalled about her shoulders was her film trade-mark. I had admired her performances for some years.

She extended one of the purple goblets and I took it.

"Thanks," I said. "You know, I just recognized you. You're Lucy Warner—I've been a fan of yours for years!"

"Not too many years, I hope," she shrugged. "I loved Prince Igor. I've had him since he was a puppy. But I understand now how it happened. He was such a friendly dog, always running up the driveway to welcome anyone who drove in."

I lifted my glass to her, then drank. Scotch.

"Who are you?" she asked.

I fished a card from my wallet and passed it to her.

GRANT WILKINSON
Pretty Pictures
732 1/2 El Caribao Drive
Hollywood 38   HO 9-2722

That "Pretty Pictures" pitch was my wife's idea. She thinks it's cute and helps me get trade. I think it stinks.

"A photographer?" she asked.

"Yes."

"What sort of work do you do?"

"Anything I can get. Babies, weddings, portraits, store fronts. I was just on my way now to deliver some architectural prints to a customer down the canyon. Pictures of his house."

I told her the name and she knew it.

We chatted about ten minutes and each had a second

drink. I told her how much I had enjoyed her work in pictures, and she liked that.

"About the dog," I said, "How much . . ."

"Never mind that. Prince Igor can't be replaced with money."

"Well, how about letting me bury him?"

"Thank you. But don't bother about that either. My gardener is due here later this afternoon. He'll do it. You've had enough unpleasantness for one day."

"I'm terribly sorry it happened," I said. "You've been swell about it all." I got up to go.

"Don't you want some water for the car?"

"Well," I said, "it can wait till—"

"It's no trouble. You'll want to leave by the other gate anyway. Bring the car to the door."

When I drove up, she was standing by the door holding a yellow oversize ceramic pitcher gracefully in both hands.

I took the pitcher from her, set it down, opened the Essex' hood and started to pour.

"Those pictures I mentioned are on the front seat if you care to look," I said. "Open the camera case. They're in an envelope on top of the camera."

She got the envelope, took out the 8 by 10s, and shuffled through them. "Oh, I *like* these," she said. "Such clean dramatic work."

"Thanks."

"You know, I'd like you to make some like these of my house."

"Sure. Anytime you say."

"The sun is fine now," she said. "If you feel like working after what happened."

I put down the hood. "OK," I said.

My fingers were still a little shaky. But I set the Graphic on a tripod and used a cable release.

[61]

The house was the most interesting I'd ever photographed. Large spacious rooms, with a view from each room. Clean lowslung lines. She told me it was designed by Frank Lloyd Wright. I shot both sides of six holders as she stood by, watching and interested. In four of the shots I posed her in doorways and window areas.

"You've been very kind," I said when I was finished. "I'll mail you the prints by the end of the week." I jotted down her house number in my notebook.

She offered me her hand, and when I took it she smiled and wrinkled up the corners of her eyes in that friendly way she does sometimes on the screen. A lock of her blonde hair fell over her forehead. I drove out the other gate and delivered the architectural prints to my customer.

About two o'clock that morning my doorbell rang. I wasn't asleep. I couldn't sleep that night. I eased quietly out of bed, trying not to wake Maria, and threw a robe over my pajamas.

At the door were two policemen.

"You Grant Wilkinson?" one of them asked.

"Yes."

"Go put on your clothes. You're under arrest."

"You must be looking for someone else," I said. "I haven't done anything. What's the charge?"

"You ought to know."

"I don't know, officer."

"Quit your stalling, Wilkinson," said the second cop. "You're wanted on suspicion of murder." He named her name. I almost fell over.

"Listen," I managed to say, "I was at her house this afternoon, but—"

"Save it," the first cop put in. "You'll have time to talk."

They didn't let me out of their sight. They followed me right into the bedroom and watched me get dressed.

[62]

"We're sorry, ma'am," one of the cops said to Maria. "Excuse us. Line of duty." Maria cringed in the bed, the blanket up to her black wide eyes.

"It's nothing," I told her. "There must be some other Grant Wilkinson in this town. You stay right here in bed; and, as soon as I set everything straight, I'll phone you."

When we moved to go, Maria hopped out of bed, with a little cry, and ran to me, not bothering to throw a robe over her night dress in front of the cops. She held on to me, and I had to pull away to follow the cops.

At the Hollywood station house on Wilcox Avenue they unlocked the handcuffs, took my fingerprints, and booked me for murder. Nobody there had any ears when I insisted they were making a mistake.

Handcuffs again and back into the radio car.

"Where are we going?" I asked the man I was chained to.

"You'll find out."

"It's all a mistake. There was a dog—"

"You'll have time to talk," he interrupted. "You're probably the only guy's made a mistake.

They drove around to the back of City Hall and took me inside. We went up in an elevator. Behind the door marked Homicide Bureau a soft-spoken detective in plain clothes told me the best thing I could do for myself was to tell the whole story and tell it straight.

I said that was exactly what I wanted to do. I told the whole story, truthfully just as I am now. A lieutenant in uniform listened in. A third cop took down everything I said on a small quiet black machine.

"Fine," said the plain-clothes man when I'd finished. "Only one thing wrong with your story. That big white dog is still the picture of health. But the dame is dead. The gardener found her body in the driveway, run over two or three times like you said. A mess. The dog was nuzzling it and whining."

For a moment I couldn't find words. I could hardly breathe. Then the words came in a rush.

"I can't believe it," I said. "There must have been a pair of those Russian dogs. I know I killed a dog, but you don't charge a man with murder for killing a dog. Someone else must have driven a car down that driveway later and struck her down by accident, the same way I struck the dog. That's it! She was out in the driveway looking at the dog's body again, and that's when someone else struck her down. That driveway is blind! It isn't safe! I know—"

"Why did you kill her?"

"I didn't! I—"

"This your card?" He unwrapped it carefully from a white handkerchief.

"Yes. Like I told you, I gave it to her when—"

"Beautiful woman, wasn't she?"

"She was alive when I—"

"What did you bang her on the head with before you carried her to the driveway?"

"I didn't! She—"

"Better talk now, Wilkinson. You're in bad trouble. The coroner's report hasn't come up yet, but it'll have all the answers."

"No, I—"

"Why don't you make a statement? Tell us the truth. Tell us now what we'll find out anyway, and we'll let you alone."

"I told you what happened! I gave you my statement! I killed the dog, sure. Not her. She's a swell person. We talked. She gave me a drink. I made pictures for her."

"Sure, sure. You run down her dog and then she asks you in for a drink. Even has you take snapshots for her. *Where are those pictures?*"

"Home. At my place. I developed the negatives as soon as I got back, and before I went to bed I made the prints. They're

[64]

on tins now."

"Whaddaya mean, 'tins'?"

"Ferrotype tins. They're thin sheets of chrome-plated metal you dry glossy prints on. Makes them shiny."

"Your studio is right where you live?"

"Yes."

The lieutenant lifted a telephone to his mouth, said, "Martinez," and put it down.

A large cop with a mustache came to the door. "Go to this address," the lieutenant said, showing him my card in the handkerchief. "You'll find a woman there. This Wilkinson's wife. Ask her to show you where the picture tins are. Take the pictures off the tins and bring them back. Tell the woman we need them for evidence that might help her husband."

"They're not likely to be dry yet," I said. "Peel them off easy, or they'll tear. If they don't come off easy, bring the tins back with the prints on them."

"That's right," said the lieutenant.

The officer went out. I felt better. "She's in some of the pictures herself," I said. "She couldn't be dead and in the pictures, too. You'll see."

"Sure we'll see," said the man in plain clothes. "And what will that prove? Only that you were there. You couldn't have made the pictures and *then* killed her, could you?"

They walked me across Spring Street, in handcuffs again, to the Hall of Records building and put me in a cell of the county jail. One of the cells a few doors up on my side housed a "wino" who was singing the *Marine Corps Hymn* in a happy drunken voice. "Shuddup!" my jailor told him on his way out.

There were other sounds. Night sounds from the street outside. The whirring of rubber tires. The rattle of a loose fender. The distant laughter of a girl. Under me the iron cot squeaked. Someone in a cell across the aisle snorted suddenly

[65]

in his sleep. From somewhere came the chirping of a bird (was it already dawn?). There was a fast muffled oppressive drumbeat. My pulse; I trembled with cold, though it was a warm night.

"All right! Let's go!"

It was my jailer. Somehow I had fallen asleep. I shuffled out the cell door and he followed half a step behind, holding my elbow the way a man helps a woman across a street. We walked down the corridor, turned a corner, and entered a long, narrow room. It contained a few chairs, a table, a battered metal desk and an overflow of cops.

Against the far wall was a bench, and set up on the bench, leaning against the wall, were my tins. The prints were still stuck to them. Three 18 by 22 tins with the white backs of four 8 by 10 prints showing on each of them.

"These the ones?" the plain clothes man asked me.

"Yes."

"Take them off."

"They don't seem to be dry yet," I said. "If—"

"Take them off!" said another cop. "This is a murder case."

I slid a fingernail under the corner of the first print. It peeled off without much trouble. It was a long shot of the back of the house taken from the swimming pool, one of the ones in which Lucy Warner wasn't posed. One of the cops took it from my hand.

The second print stuck, but I pulled it off anyway, cracking the emulsion but not tearing the print. It was a closeup of the redwood front doorway, the one I had posed her in with her shoulder against . . .

But Lucy Warner wasn't in the picture! On the threshold of that open doorway stood the blond dog!

I wasn't able to take the rest of the prints off myself. The cops took them off and laid them out on the table in front of me. I lifted my head from the table and looked at the pictures. They were my shots all right. I'd recognize my style of work anywhere. They were my pictures just the way I made them, except that in the four shots in which I know I posed Lucy Warner, the dog stood instead. She was not in any of the pictures.

"All right, Wilkinson," said the plain-clothes man, "you can cut the bull now and start talking."

"I've told you everything."

"Why did you kill her?"

"I didn't kill her! I killed a dog. Just a dog!"

"How did you know she was alone?"

"I didn't even know she lived there. My car—"

"What did you crack her on the head with before you carried her to the driveway?"

"I didn't!"

"What do you know about that Black Dahlia murder last winter?"

"Nothing! I—"

"Do you know where the Twelve Palms Motel is on Sunset?"

"No."

"That's where that high school girl was found last week. Strangled. Remember it now?"

"No! No!"

"How did you get the dog to stand still for his picture?"

"I didn't photograph the dog. I photographed Lucy Warner."

"Why did you kill her? How did you do it?"

"I didn't do it!"

"How did you kill her?"

The State of California threw the book at me. There had been a series of unsolved murders in Los Angeles and the officeholders were hot on giving the newspapers a conviction to play with for a change. The state charged murder in the first degree and demanded the death penalty. In California it's the gas chamber.

I had no money to defend myself. But the judge appointed an aggressive young lawyer who I thought fought hard and well for me. Main thing was, he believed in me.

Not that he ever exactly accepted my understanding of what happened that afternoon in Laurel Canyon. But I know he never felt me guilty of any crime. His first advice was that I plead temporary insanity, and he brought a psychiatrist to my cell to talk things over. We finally decided, on the basis of the psychiatrist's report, to enter a simple plea of not guilty.

The county district attorney was merciless. Plaster casts of alleged tire marks on the woman's body were entered in evidence, along with matching marks from the almost bald tires on my Essex. There were fingerprints from the purple goblets—both of them—and from my business card, the ceramic water pitcher, and the knob of the kitchen door. My prints, not hers.

The ex-husband of the actress testified. He was a handsome man wearing a black armband. The reason for their recent divorce, he said, was her insistence on living alone for occasional periods of several days at a time. She had once told him that to her the lens of a studio camera was the eye of fifty million people. After exposing herself to it during the shooting of each picture, she had said, she needed at least a week of complete solitude to regain her feeling of privacy.

The gardener testified in detail how he had found the body of the woman, with the dog nuzzling it and raising his snout to the sky in mournful whines.

The district attorney confronted me with the gardener and asked if I recognized him.

"No," I said.

"How did you know he was expected that afternoon? Did you wait outside on the highway and watch him discover the body?"

"No, I . . . she, she told me he was coming."

"That's all. Thank you."

The district attorney even had the blond dog brought to the courtroom. He led the dog on leash up to me as I sat on the witness chair.

"Is this the dog you say you killed?" he asked.

"It looks just like him," I said.

When I put out my hand the dog came to me. I was surprised at the unpleasant muttering that came from the packed courtroom when I patted the dog and fondled his ears.

"What is the dog's name?" asked the prosecutor.

"The name of the dog I killed was Prince Igor."

When I said the name the dog barked. A soft, friendly bark. There was a rumble of unpleasant murmuring from the spectators, who crowded every seat in the courtroom. The judge rapped his gavel.

"How do you know his name?"

"She told me. Lucy Warner said his name when—"

"Witness dismissed. Thank you."

My lawyer did the best he could against this chain of circumstantial evidence. He began by admitting that my car had struck down the actress in her driveway. He even admitted that the evidence seemed to show my car had backed and advanced over the body after it had been struck down.

But he affirmed, eloquently, I thought, that the state had failed to establish any motive for murder, and that all the evidence the state offered to prove murder was entirely circumstantial. He told the jury that what had happened was plainly an accident. A simple case of involuntary homicide.

My lawyer got an expert mechanic to drive my Essex along the same Laurel Canyon route I had taken that day. On the stand, the mechanic testified that, though he filled my car's radiator full of water before he began the trip, the water pump leak was so bad that the car began to steam before he reached the actress' driveway.

How I knew the dog's name, and how I knew the gardener was expected that afternoon, were two more problems for my lawyer. He had told the jury I never spoke to the woman, that the accident happened as I first drove into the grounds.

A movie magazine came to my rescue on this. The lawyer and my wife, Maria, rummaged through the pile of magazines lying about my studio, and came up with a copy of *Modern Screen* published just a month before the actress died. If she did die.

This magazine had a color photograph of the actress and the blond dog on its cover. Inside was an interview with the actress in which the dog Prince Igor was mentioned by name. The story also reported that since her divorce the actress had been living in her "Hollywood home" (no address given) entirely alone. Her only servant, the article said, was a gardener-handyman who lived nearby and came over every afternoon to work, to run errands and to feed the dog when she was working at the studio.

I decided right after my arrest that my only hope was to tell nothing but the truth. During questioning by the police, and on the stand during trial, I never once lied or withheld information. So when my lawyer showed me this copy of *Modern Screen* and asked if I'd read it, I told him truthfully I couldn't remember having read it. Since the magazine had been in my studio for a month, as he and Maria assured me it had, I agreed it was possible I had paged through it. But I could not honestly say (and did not) that I remembered reading it.

Nevertheless, my lawyer introduced the magazine in evidence the next day. Under his questioning I said again that I did not remember reading it, though I might have. I do read the movie magazines occasionally, mostly to study the current work of the studio still photographers.

The jury men and women (there were six of each) took the magazine with them that night to the hotel where they were quartered during the trial. The magazine may have done me some good. I don't know.

But the heart of my defense was the testimony of the psychiatrist my lawyer had first brought to my cell when he was advising that I plead temporary insanity. The psychiatrist spent altogether perhaps forty hours talking with me before the trial.

"Doctor Nicholson," my lawyer asked on the stand (Abner S. Nicholson, of Berkeley Medical), "please give your opinion as to the sanity of the defendant."

"It is my considered opinion that this man is rational and of at least normal intelligence," the psychiatrist said. "I found in his mind one limited area of a psychopathological pattern. But I would say, medically speaking, that on the whole his is the mind of a sane man. From the viewpoint of law, it is a mind capable of distinguishing right from wrong."

"Would you explain, doctor, just what you mean by a limited area of psychopathological pattern?" my lawyer asked. "How is it possible for a mind to be sane, both medically and legally, and still to exhibit abnormality?"

"In cases of true medical and legal insanity," the doctor replied, "the mind is afflicted with a basic pathology, some mania, delusion, anxiety, or obsession. This aberration is present in such a compulsive force that it channels the patient's over-all behavior into a pattern we know as madness.

"But such is not the case with the mind of Grant Wilkinson. The limited area of psychopathological pattern to which I referred is truly limited in Mr. Wilkinson's mind. It is com-

[71]

partmented off from the main stream of his consciousness. I found no clinical evidence that this aberration has contaminated his mind as a whole. It is, I repeat, a sane mind."

"Doctor Nicholson," my lawyer asked, "could you make a little clearer the difference between a true insanity and the limited aberration of which you speak?"

"I shall try. The basic distinction is perhaps one of origin, of cause. Your true manias and dementias have their roots deep in the patient's personal life. They go back in many cases to maladjusted childhoods, unhappy homes, and basic sex disturbances.

"But there are other patterns of pathological behavior that are not so deep-rooted in poor childhood adjustments. Normal and sane minds are perfectly liable to reveal sudden pathological symptoms as the result, for instance, of severe trauma of either a physical or an emotional nature. The most commonly known psychopathology of this sort is amnesia, or loss of memory. Amnesia can be caused by a blow on the head, by a sudden emotional shock, even by the high fever of malaria.

"No, I do not imply that Mr. Wilkinson is suffering from a simple amnesia. I do, however, testify that the limited aberration I found in Mr. Wilkinson's mind is of a nature somewhat akin to amnesia. I do testify that its cause is also similar —namely, a sudden accumulation of emotional shock."

My lawyer again: "Perhaps it would be easier for you to explain this, doctor, if you gave us your theory of just what happened, physically and in the defendant's mind, that afternoon in Laurel Canyon."

"I shall try," said the psychiatrist. "First of all, it is apparent to all of us here that a woman has died. The evidence shows, and the attorney for the defense admits, that she died under the wheels of the defendant's automobile. Yet the defendant himself affirms that such was not the case. He says his

[72]

car struck down a dog.

"I am convinced that what Mr. Wilkinson has told us is, for him, the truth. I am convinced that Mr. Wilkinson wholly believes in his own mind that his car struck down the dog and not the woman. This, then, is Mr. Wilkinson's *idée fixe*, his fixed delusion, the limited area of psychopathological pattern of which I speak.

"Now let us consider what might have happened that fatal day. Suppose the defendant did turn into the driveway for the reason that his automobile was in urgent need of water. Let us further suppose that the deceased woman was at that moment walking down the driveway with her back to the oncoming automobile. It might well have been that she did not hear the automobile's approach, for it was coasting out of gear at the time. And Wilkinson might well not have observed her. Perhaps his eyes were at that moment fixed on the water temperature gauge on the—"

"*Your honor!*" The district attorney was on his feet. "Your honor, I object to this line of questioning by counsel for the defense. Supposition and deduction from the evidence is the duty of the jury. Its practice by a witness is clearly improper. This witness is competent only to give medical testimony."

My attorney made a good reply: "Your honor, a man's life depends upon our establishing here the truth of what happened that day in Laurel Canyon. Not only the truth of physical events, but the truth of what happened in the defendant's mind. The qualifications of Doctor Nicholson as a medical expert are beyond question. And he feels, as do I, that he cannot give conclusive medical testimony without a discussion of the evidence."

The judge was silent for about ten ticks of my darkroom timer. Then he spoke: "The court will withhold its ruling. The witness may proceed with his testimony. If the testimony is

[73]

found to be irrelevant, the court will instruct the jury to disregard it, and will order it stricken from the record."

Doctor Nicholson continued: "I have suggested how the accident might have occurred. I do not bear witness that it did happen that way. Or even that it was an accident. But, working backwards from the results in clinical evidence of my examination of the defendant, I have reached the personal conclusion that that is what happened. The accident occurred just as Wilkinson described it—except, of course, that the woman died and not the dog.

"Now let us look into Wilkinson's mind. When he stopped his car too late, jumped out, and saw what he had done, he must have been horrified. Just as you or I would have been horrified.

"Previous medical testimony by the coroner has established that the first impact of the automobile crushed the woman's spine at its base. Such an injury might well have resulted in paralysis of the legs and lower part of the woman's body. It would not necessarily have resulted in loss of consciousness. It would surely have meant extreme agony.

"Thus, you see, it could well have been that the woman screamed in her terrible pain and attempted to raise the forepart of her body upon her hands. This is precisely the behavior Mr. Wilkinson ascribes to the dog which he insists was the victim.

"We see the woman lying in the roadway and trying in her agony to struggle to her feet. The sight must have terrified Wilkinson and filled him with unbearable guilt. The woman's continued screams provided further auditory stimuli to Wilkinson's panic-stricken mind. Finally, it is possible that at this moment Wilkinson recognized the deceased as an actress of great fame—a further surprise and shock.

"As the woman's screams continued to reverberate in the narrow driveway, Wilkinson's mind neared its limit of shock tolerance. Probably feeling that she was dying anyway, he turned in desperation to the only available means of silencing her screams and ending her misery. His automobile. He backed his automobile over her body and then ran forward over it once again, just as he related on the stand he had again driven over the dog.

"Now the full realization of what he had done came over him. There is a limit of emotional trauma beyond which a mind loses its balance. Wilkinson had reached his, and was on the verge of the same kind of hysterical madness which afflicts fear-driven soldiers on the battlefield.

"At this moment the dog Prince Igor might well have come running up the driveway in answer to his mistress' screams. Wilkinson's mind, casting about in panic for some means of maintaining its balance, immediately seized upon the likeness between the dog's white fur and the woman's white clothing and famous blonde hair, and transposed the two. His mind could not, this side of sanity, allow itself to believe what had actually happened. So it immediately accepted as truth the survival of the young woman and the death of the dog.

"Then," continued the psychiatrist, "still sane but with this one fixed delusion, he pacified the disturbed dog, made friends with it, actually believing the dog was the woman. He must have taken the dog to the house, found the liquor cabinet, and acted out the friendly gesture of having two sociable drinks with the deceased.

"But now some lingering awareness of what he had done must have struggled near the level of Wilkinson's consciousness. To lock this terror deep in his subconscious mind, he perhaps felt a need to perform some familiar and habitual act, to go through the motions of some normal activity so that his unreal understanding of the preceding events might also seem normal and true.

"Then it no doubt was that Wilkinson took up his camera

[75]

and made the twelve photographs now on evidence in this court. Handling his camera was a familiar habit pattern. He made the pictures almost automatically. The customary work eased his mind, made him feel everything was all right.

"When he had finished his work, what would have been more natural than for him to place his business card on a table? This was another professional habit pattern. And then he drove off to complete the original errand which brought him to Laurel Canyon—the delivery of a set of photographs to a customer. He left by the other gate, a victim of his mind-made fantasy that he had killed only a dog."

The judge split hairs. He ruled that the psychiatrist's testimony was admissible. But he cautioned the jury to make its own judgment of its value and to distinguish carefully as to what part of it was the testimony of an expert medical witness and what part was simply opinion.

Next day, the prosecutor brought to the stand two more psychiatrists, who had also talked with me in my cell, but more briefly than Doctor Nicholson. They agreed that I was sane. But they said they found no evidence of delusion. The district attorney told the jury that this meant I had invented my delusion for the purpose of feigning insanity and saving my "criminal" skin.

He even dug back into the 1932 yearbook of Hollywood High School to show the jury that I had been president of the high school dramatic club and was therefore, so he said, a skillful actor. So I don't know what good Doctor Nicholson's testimony did me.

In his summation to the jury the district attorney used the quality of my own professional work against me. Brandishing my twelve prints of the actress' house in the faces of the twelve jurors, and then passing out one print to each of them, he asked them to observe how sharp and attractive my pictures were.

"It took a steady hand to produce photography such as

this," he told the jurors. "Who except a man in full possession of his faculties could have produced photographs of such high caliber immediately after committing a deliberate and cruel murder? For this was murder. A cruel and cold-blooded crime of passion. The state has proven in this case that a crime of passion can be committed in cold blood. The state feels that you honorable ladies and gentlemen can only return with a verdict of guilty of murder in the first degree.

"As you know, California law gives you the option of recommending either life imprisonment or the death penalty. So unusually cruel and deliberate was this crime that the state does not hesitate to expect that you will in good conscience recommend the death penalty."

Well, you read the papers. You know the jury is still out, after four days.

What do I think about the case now? I must admit it's still no clearer in my mind than when the police got me out of bed that morning.

The woman is dead all right. I saw a picture of her body in the papers. A closer, more terrible, view was on evidence in court. It was her body. She's dead.

The blond dog is alive, too. I saw him in court. My lawyer checked with the dog-license bureau, and found there are exactly eighteen more grown Russian wolfhounds in all of Los Angeles county. He and my wife Maria tracked down the owner of each dog, and saw personally that each dog was still alive.

All the evidence seems to indicate that what Doctor Nicholson said might have happened, actually did happen. My car struck down the actress, and her screams and agony and the shock of recognizing her were all so terrible to me that my mind did a flip-flop and made me sure it was the dog I'd killed. Made me fool myself right up to now.

[77]

Yet against the weight of all evidence, a man must at last trust only the testimony of his own senses. *I know I killed the dog: I know I talked with the woman, and drank with her, and posed her when I made the pictures, and left her perfectly alive when I drove away.*

I also know that all three psychiatrists were right in agreeing I'm sane. I think clearly still. My conduct on the stand was reasonable. I love my wife in an achingly normal way. I'm perfectly rational. Hasn't the story I've just told you been straightforward? Has it sounded like the invention of a demented man?

There's only one bit of evidence left that I can't get myself to understand. Maybe it does mean I'm mad. Maybe, at least, I do have a fixed delusion.

You remember how I told you about the woman slapping me across the face after I'd killed the dog? She slapped me twice, and on the third swing I raised my arm to protect my face and got my hand scratched with her long fingernails.

Well, those scratches are all healed now. But the back of my hand still shows the scars. Here, look at it. See how long and deep and parallel those scratches were.

Well, I sit here wondering what the jury is going to do, and I keep studying those scars. They don't look to me quite like fingernail scratches. It worries me that they look almost like the claw marks of a dog.

Concerning a Woman of Sin

By BEN HECHT

> After a childhood in Racine and Chicago, Ben Hecht
> became one of the leading literati of the twenties. With
> Charles MacArthur he wrote the prizewinning play, *The
> Front Page* (1930); and he and MacArthur were afterward
> partners in their own movie company (1934). His many
> other involvements with the industry, plus his own ex-
> experience as a child prodigy (*per* violin) yielded material
> for such stories as "Concerning a Woman of Sin".

Every year or so a new conqueror appears in Hollywood
and, seizing it by the tail, swings it around his head. And for
the year or so this conqueror rides a gold elephant to work and
lives on a dream boat.

Sometimes there are two, three or four conquerors in
Hollywood all at the same time and all swinging it around their
heads. On such occasions the hostesses, bartenders and publicity departments of the cinema capital break down and the
neighbouring spas become crowded with convalescents.

This story is the account of one such conqueror who,
singlehanded, sent the mightiest of Hollywood to Arrowhead
Lake and Palm Springs to recover from the tumult of her conquest. Jerome B. Cobb, head of the great Empire Studios, was
one of those many refugees. The top Pharaoh was accompanied
by two nurses and an osteopath who toiled for several weeks
to bring Mr. Cobb back to sanity, or what passes for sanity in
the Cobb cosmos. An entourage of important Nobles kept Mr.
Cobb company taking hot mud baths and trying to shake the
impact of Daisy Marcher out of their nervous systems.

But before I can start this account of Daisy Marcher's
conquest of Hollywood it will be wise to explain a few things
about the movie capital. It has been my experience that it is

[79]

best to approach a tale of Cinemaland like an anthropologist and discuss the old tribal customs of the place so that the reader will be partly persuaded at least that one is not writing with an opium pipe in one hand. I will confine these preliminaries only to that phase of the movies which makes possible the unnerving advent of a Daisy Marcher.

In Hollywood a movie star receives from $100,000 to $150,000 for acting in a single picture. This chore occupies about ten weeks of the star's time, which means, on a basis of an eight-hour day, that the star receives roughly from $5 to $7 a minute for acting. This includes the many minutes (more than two-thirds of them) during which the star lies dormant in the dressing room; also the many minutes in which the star gets mad and won't act at all; likewise the many minutes during which the star is kept from the full practice of his or her art by infidelity, amnesia or a hangover.

Similar pots of gold are handed over to the top writers and directors of movies who are sometimes incapacitated for whole weeks at a time (while on salary) by being unable to think at all. But whether they are thinking or merely sitting staring at the wall these artists receive from $4 to $6 a minute. In fact, there is no one connected with the artistic side of movie-making—not excluding somebody called the producer who usually just comes along for the ride—who does not receive some staggering sum for his participation.

There are many reasons why we movie makers are so prodigiously rewarded for tasks that might well come under the head of trivia. I will skip most of them as having nothing to do with Daisy Marcher and offer only the one that is pertinent— the Hollywood Agent. Foremost in the forces that have skyrocketed the earnings of the movie artist has been this peculiar sleight-of-hand worker.

His emergence on the Hollywood scene some twenty years ago was occasioned by the fact that most of the movie artists

[80]

were unable to add or subtract and also needed someone to look up telephone numbers for them. From these humble beginnings the agent (the Great Agent) has risen to breath-taking heights. Although on the surface he has remained a stylish sort of mendicant hunting handouts for his finicky clientele, actually he has become one of the major headaches in the movie industry—and as such stands shoulder to shoulder with its leading Pharaohs.

The Great Agent has under his wing today bevies of stars and geniuses whose venality he has inflamed (a not difficult task) with purring tales of their worth. The peddling of these treasure troves is the simplest part of his labours. For it was the agent who first uncovered the Basic Principle of Hollywood. This is that the Pharaohs who run the studios measure their own greatness by the amount of money they are able to spend. There is, in fact, no other activity open to them. The Pharaoh who can spend the most money on stars and geniuses becomes automatically the most dazzling figure in the cinema capital. Thus the competition to run the studios into bankruptcy is an extremely hot one. That all the studios are not quickly ruined by these royal extravagances is due to a single factor out of their control.

The popularity of the movies has become almost equal to that of sex. And as in the case of the latter enterprise, no amount of extravagance, disappointment or mismanagement seems able to impair the success of the studio product.

Such a situation has enabled the agent to mature from a menial who originally looked up telephone numbers for his clients to a Power who thinks in them.

Yet nobody in Hollywood, least of all the movie artists whose incomes he has tripled, has ever a happy word for this magician. The industry regards him as a combination beggar and pirate who divides his time between harassing the Pharaohs for alms when they have no need of him and scuttling their studios when they have. And his clients are inclined to think of him as a quisling bent on selling them out to the Bosses and solely responsible for their decline in public favour.

Burdened by these calumnies, with a status wavering between that of a White Slaver and a crooked Senator, the Great Agent has nonetheless found a certain sweetness in his toil. For today he is richer than any one of his illustrious clients. He, too, is one of the conquerors of Hollywood, albeit a minor one. And the Pharaohs themselves, though they howl behind his back that he is a parasite and a highwayman, must greet him with the hand of royal fellowship.

Orlando Higgens, who is the villain of my story, has been my Hollywood agent for seventeen years. His depredations as my representative have been, however, modest ones. It was as Daisy Marcher's agent that Orlando succeeded in almost wrecking Hollywood. And, as Orlando himself says, if that be villainy, make the most of it.

Whatever other achievements I may have in Hollywood, Orlando is my true bid for fame. It was I who started him as an agent. He was originally a tall, scatterbrained and explosive financier, at least financier was what he called himself when I first met him in his twenty-fourth year. It developed his claim to the title of financier was based on a mania for borrowing money. Orlando was no sponger but at twenty-four he had been unable to figure out any other way of making his "million or two", except by raising it in small sums from former fraternity brothers who had gone to work. Men without vision, he called them.

We were sitting in my house one evening seventeen years ago discussing a trip around the world on a chartered yacht that Orlando had planned—to involve twenty-five congenial souls at $10,000 apiece, which would nicely cover all expenses —including his own salary as financier. Somehow during this discussion Orlando stole an unpublished manuscript of mine from my desk. Five days later he wired me from Hollywood asking me to wire him back immediately $1,500 as his ten per cent of its sale money. He had disposed of my manuscript (a foul one) to a movie studio. This was Orlando's first taste of porch climbing.

How it befell that my friend whose chief characteristics were an inability to tell the truth on any subject, an evasiveness worthy of a bank embezzler and a childlike abhorrence of all toil—how it befell that so giddy and incompetent a character could rise to the heights of Orlando Higgens, Inc., is a matter I will skip. For like most Hollywood facts the rise of Orlando Higgens belongs more to the field of magic than biography. I give you merely Orlando in all his grandeur just as mythology gave us Minerva who jumped fully dressed out of Jupiter's head. To cap the mystery, I will add that seventeen years of Huge Deals and Masterly Manipulations had in no way changed my friend. He was as incompetent, evasive and irresponsible a character as head of Orlando Higgens, Inc., as he had been in his lowlier days. Apparently his inability to remember anything—an inability bordering on amnesia—his habit of lying about everything to everybody and his chronic state of confusion were the very talents that had brought him success. These and possibly the fact that he was one of the nicest men I have ever known.

I was sitting in Orlando's office on one of those glaring Hollywood afternoons when everything, including your own soul, seems made out of shiny new stucco, when the telephone rang and Orlando's fourth secretary (there were six in all) informed him that a Miss Daisy Marcher wished to speak to him.

"Who the hell is Daisy Marcher?" Orlando inquired peevishly.

"She's an author," the secretary said.

"For God's sake," Orlando yelled, "do I have to talk to

every half-witted author who calls up? Tell her I'm busy."

He hung up and beamed at me.

"You used to like authors," I said, "before they made you rich."

"Before they drove me crazy," said Orlando. "I loved 'em, seventeen years ago. But I swear to you the way I feel now about authors I can't read a book any more. I know them too well. Talk about hams!" He shuddered. "Authors are worse than boy sopranos."

The phone rang. There were five differently coloured instruments on Orlando's fifteen-foot Italian antique desk and each had a different ring. After seven years Orlando was still unable to tell which ring belonged to which phone. He picked up two at a time and called out in a clipped efficient voice, "Hello. Who is it?"

"Mr. Sylvester for Mr. Higgens," Secretary Number Two answered on one of the phones. Orlando winked at me.

"This is going to be fun," he whispered. "*That* fathead!"

"Hello Syl," he chuckled into the phone, "nothing doing at Fox. Nope. No dice . . . Yep. I'll hop right on it. O. K. Goo'bye. Right . . . Goo'bye. What's that? No, Zanuck read it personally and thinks it stinks . . . Yep. Will do. Goo'bye."

Orlando hung up and cackled happily, as he always did when any of his clients were in despair.

"I can't sell that big know-it-all for peanuts," he grinned. "Did you read that last book of his? It turned my stomach."

"What's happened to Sylvester?" I asked. "He was pretty hot a while ago."

"Well, he ain't hot now," said Orlando with a snort.

One of the phones rang.

"Did I tell you Chick is in the conference room?" Orlando continued. "He moved in two days ago with a case of Scotch. Great fella." He looked proudly at the leather-panelled door of the conference room and chuckled.

"I though Chick was directing the Dietrich picture," I said.

"He is," Orlando beamed. "But he said he hit a snag and is going to drink himself out of it. Nobody knows where he is, so don't say a word." A larkish light filled Orlando's eyes and he murmured in an awed voice, "It's costing Empire a mint of money. If they don't find him by tomorrow they may even have to call the picture off."

I picked up the ringing telephone.

"Miss Daisy Marcher wishes to speak to Mr. Higgens," said Secretary Five.

"It's Daisy again," I said. Orlando's face reddened and he seized the instrument.

"What the hell is this?" he demanded. "I've got five secretaries" (he had six) "to see that I'm not disturbed. So they all keep bothering me. I told you to tell her I'm busy."

"We've told her that seven times," said Secretary Five. "I've hung up on her myself three times in succession and she keeps calling right back and asking to speak to you, as if nothing had happened."

"What do you know?" An admiring light came into Orlando's eyes. "A nut, huh?"

"I'm afraid so," said the secretary.

"Put her on," said Orlando.

"Is this Mr. Higgens?" a purring voice inquired.

"Yes, this is he," said Orlando.

"This is Daisy Marcher," the voice continued. "I would have called you up sooner but I have been ill with a fever and I could not get out of bed. Today is my first day up."

"Is that so?" Orlando beamed. "And how do you feel now, Miss Marcher?"

"Oh, I feel all right now," said Miss Marcher, "as long as I keep my muffler on around my neck."

"Well, thanks for letting me know about your health,"

[85]

Orlando chuckled. "Anything else on your mind?"

"Oh, yes," said Miss Marcher. "I am getting very impatient to know if you have sold my motion picture drama. That is why I called."

Orlando winked at me and whispered, "Some goddam foreigner. Probably a Hindu."

"What is the name of the drama?" he spoke into the phone.

"It is called *A Woman of Sin*," Miss Marcher said.

Orlando winced.

"Let you know tomorrow how it's coming along," he said.

"You've had it already two weeks," said Miss Marcher, "and I can't understand why it should take so long to sell."

"Oh, is it that good?" Orlando beamed.

"Yes indeed," said Miss Marcher. "I consider it the best motion picture drama that has ever been written."

"You don't say," Orlando purred, "Well, when you get your strength back drop in and we'll have a drink."

"Thank you very much," said Miss Marcher, "but I don't drink—ever."

"What, a great author like you doesn't drink! I can't believe it!" Orlando chuckled. "I bet you're soused to the gills right now."

"I think you are a horrid man," said the gentle voice, "an utterly nasty man and I am sorry I selected you to be my agent."

There was a bang. Miss Marcher had hung up. Orlando sat glaring at the instrument. Miss Betha Flannigan entered and walked to her desk in the corner. As Secretary Number One, Miss Flannigan shared the Higgens sanctum.

"What the hell do you mean by letting half-wits like that send us scripts?" Orlando demanded of her. "Did you hear that title? *A Woman of Sin!* My God, are we sending out junk like that!"

The round-faced Miss Flannigan, who had no idea of what Mr. Higgens was talking, answered soothingly.

"I'll have it checked right away."

"Fire that manuscript right back at her as fast as you can," Orlando growled. "A *Woman of Sin*. It turns your stomach—just the title."

"I'll double check," said Miss Flannigan firmly.

A phone rang.

"That's your private phone," said Miss Flannigan.

Orlando paled. Only his current sweethearts and his most important clients were permitted to call on this number. Any one of them meant trouble. He picked up the instrument and spoke guiltily into it. "Hello." A voice rumbled back. "Right," Orlando answered with a snap, "Will do. Yep. Immediately. Yep. Is that so? Will do. Take care of it right away."

He hung up with relief.

"That was Chick," he said.

"I thought he was in the conference room," I said.

"He is." Orlando stood up glaring at the leather-panelled door. "He called from there. He says he's dying and I should get him a doctor. Come on, let's go to lunch."

"Shall I send for a doctor?" Miss Flannigan asked.

"Good God, no," Orlando said "And don't stay out for lunch so long because I get all mixed up when you're away."

It was four o'clock when we returned. I had decided to spend the rest of the day on Orlando's office divan, it being the coolest place in town. Orlando entered his office with a business-like "What's new?" to Miss Flannigan.

"Mr. Chick Howser has left," she said. He looked disappointedly at the leather-panelled door. It was open. "Paramount called," Miss Flannigan continued, "and Mr. Goldwyn wants you to call him immediately on your return. Mr. Zanuck says he'll see you at 2 A.M. in his office. And Mr. Blue called."

"Freddie Blue, eh?" said Orlando with a frown. "Hm. No likee."

Freddie Blue was part of Jerome B. Cobb's hierarchy. There were several figures closer to the throne of the Pharaoh but Freddie was Shock Troops.

"Get me Blue," said Orlando. "Something's up. They probably found out about Chick camping here. Am I going to get hell! How did he sound, Flannigan?"

"Very eager," said the secretary. "He's on the wire now."

"Hello," Orlando chirped heartily. "Freddie? How's the world's greatest ladies' man? . . . Never mind. I've heard plenty . . . Fine . . . Great . . . Listen, how about a hearts game tonight? . . . Okeydoke. Tomorrow's a date . . . What's new, Freddie? . . . What! What's that!" Orlando's eyes opened wide. "You don't say! Glad to hear it. She's a great girl. Brilliant as hell. Sure, we're handling Daisy. Been keeping her under cover for months, sort of coaching her. Yep! Right. Get hold of her immediately. Call you right back . . . Yep . . . Yep . . . Goo'bye."

He hung up.

"Well, I'll be damned," he said blankly and turned to Miss Flannigan. "Get hold of that half-wit what's-her-name— that Hindu or whatever she is."

"Daisy Marcher," Miss Flannigan suggested.

"That's right," said Orlando. "I'm kind of stunned. Empire is buying *A Woman of Sin*. Can you beat that!"

Miss Flannigan spoke into her private phone, an ordinary black one.

"Have Mr. Horowitz contact Daisy Marcher right away," she said. "Mr. Higgens wants to speak to her personally. It's important."

I didn't know as I dozed off on the divan that one of the greatest calamities ever to threaten Hollywood had been officially launched.

Orlando arrived at my hotel shortly after midnight. I was just leaving my room. The producer of the picture on which I was working had decided we needed a new ending. He was waiting in the studio for me with the director, and my presence there was a matter of life and death, he insisted.

"Forget about Walter," said Orlando when I started to explain. "I'm in a hell of a pickle. In fact, I've been going crazy all day."

We started out of the hotel together.

"I can't find that half-wit Daisy Marcher," said Orlando. "I've called seven hundred people. Nobody every heard of her. And Empire's gone nuts about *A Woman of Sin.* Stark, raving nuts. Freddie Blue's been hounding me to close the deal. And Mike Devlin's been hounding me too."

I was impressed. Mike Devlin was Mr. Cobb's royal right hand. He had in his youth gone nine rounds with Jack Johnson and then retired from the ring and cast his lot with the motion picture industry, beginning as a masseur. How so honest and humanly worthy a character as Mike Devlin had ever climbed the shenanigan heights of Hollywood was always a mystery to me. It may have been with his fists.

"I'd like to read that script," I said.

"So would I," said Orlando. "There isn't a copy in the office. It got sent over to Empire by some mistake. Some bumble-head put the wrong script in an envelope. I'm going to fire half the staff tomorrow. You can't run a business that way."

"A fascinating situation," I said, "genius rising above the handicaps of an agent."

"Genius, my eye!" Orlando snorted. "J. B. Cobb's gone crazy—that's all there is to it."

"What's he got to do with it?" I asked.

"He read it," Orlando said. "That's part of the whole mistake. Once you start a mistake it keeps on. That damn

[89]

script got on his desk, somehow." He chuckled. "The title must have attracted him."

The thought of Mr. Cobb reading a manuscript was truly astonishing. Mr. Cobb never read manuscripts nor concerned himself with any of the details of movie-making. It was his function to preserve a fresh, unused mind so as to be able to harass all the Nobles under him when they did wrong. Nobody could harass Mr. Cobb for the reason that he never did anything. And there was no questioning his genius because he was getting constantly richer and more powerful.

"He read it," Orlando repeated, "and it went to his head like a shot of hop. I'm betting that script is pure drivel."

Jerome B. Cobb was standing on the kerb outside the hotel waiting for his palanquin. Two Wazirs were in attendance. Mr. Cobb looked at me coldly but his heavy face lighted at the sight of Orlando Higgens.

"I want to talk to you, my boy," he smiled.

The two Wazirs immediately hailed Orlando with shouts of camaraderie.

"You have done a lot of things I haven't approved of," the Pharaoh began in measured tones, "such as selling me material which was nothing but low grade rubbish. And holding me up for it."

"Oh, come now, J. B.," Orlando protested. "In the first place I didn't sell it to you. I sold it to Empire."

"I am Empire." Mr. Cobb quivered and then controlled himself. "Now please don't interrupt me because I am going to say something of importance to you. I consider that you have finally redeemed yourself in my eyes by sending us this new story."

"A Woman of Sin," Orlando beamed.

"I will be frank with you," said Mr. Cobb. "I read the story myself, busy though I am. And I'm glad I did. Because God knows it might have slipped by us. My boy, I consider that story not only a great masterpiece but one of the greatest pieces of box office entertainment we have ever made. I'm going to shoot it without a single change and I am going to make it an all-star production."

"I'm glad you like it," Orlando purred.

"Like it!" Mr. Cobb raised his voice to a shout. "I'm crazy about it! By God, it's what this country needs— a great sex story." The Pharaoh turned a stony face suddenly on Orlando.

"I want that deal closed by tomorrow at ten," he said, "and if you try any Orlando Higgens tricks with any other studios, I'll ruin you. I'm telling you openly and above-board."

"What the hell you talking about?" Orlando said peevishly. "I would have closed the deal today except for that damned writer."

"What writer?" Mr. Cobb demanded darkly. His thought was unused to delving this low in the movie business.

"Daisy Marcher," said Orlando.

"What's the matter with her?" asked Mr. Cobb.

"She's asking too much money," said Orlando. "And I simply don't want to stick Empire. It's bad business for me in the long run, J. B. I've been arguing my head off with her."

"How much does she want?" Mr. Cobb asked coldly.

"It's preposterous," Orlando feinted, "but I can't budge her."

"How much?" Mr. Cobb shouted.

"Seventy-five thousand dollars," said Orlando in a contrite voice. "And frankly, J. B., I don't think that script is worth it. No script is."

"It's a deal," said Mr. Cobb quietly. He turned to one of the Wazirs. "Get Blue on the phone immediately and tell him that seventy-five thousand dollars is the price we will pay for A Woman of Sin."

He held out his hand to Orlando.

[91]

"We'll shake hands on it like old friends," Mr. Cobb smiled, "and remember we got witnesses."

Orlando's phantom bonanza fascinated me and I hurried to his office as soon as I could get off the set on which our new ending was being shot. It was noon. I found the three outer Higgens salons in turmoil. Phones were ringing and voices barking in all corners.

Orlando was pacing in his sanctum, his coat off, his suspenders moist and a gleam on his face.

"I haven't slept a wink," he greeted me.

"Find her?" I asked.

"No. I sicked a detective agency on her at seven this morning," he grinned.

"How about the Screen Writers' Guild?" I suggested.

"Those fatheads," Orlando sneered. "They never heard of her. I've been tracking her down from every angle. She's a myth, that's all."

"How about telling Freddie Blue the truth?" I said.

Orlando laughed contemptuously.

"For one thing they'd never believe me," he said. "They'd think I was trying to pull something crooked. Besides," he added, "I haven't got her signed up yet."

"Mr. Cobb on the phone," Miss Flannigan announced. "The green one."

"Hello, J. B.," Orlando began quickly. "Listen, I've been talking to Miss Marcher half the night like a Dutch uncle. But I can't get her to see it our way . . . Yep. Yep. . . . Nope . . . Nope. . . . Listen, J. B., she absolutely refuses to sign any contract that doesn't give her a percentage of the gross over and above the seventy-five grand. . . . Yep. Right." Orlando raised his voice to a righteous scream. "I told her it was absolute lunacy," he cried, "and that I thought she was behaving like an absolute stinker." His wrath subsided as he listened with a business-like frown to Mr. Cobb's bellows. When he spoke again it was in a sad voice. "that's exactly what I've been begging her to do, J. B.," he cooed, "go over and talk it out with you. And that you were the fairest man in Hollywood. But she spit in my eye and told me to go to hell and we *both* almost lost her. . . Nope. Nope. Listen, J.B., all I know is that she just simply won't go see anybody connected with a studio. She hates movie executives or something. It must be some kind of a curious quirk."

Orlando listened with a suffering expression. Then he spoke again. "J. B., honestly I'm going nuts with this," he said. "These goddam writers drive you crazy . . . What? How much? . . . Now wait a minute, J. B. I can't stick you like that. I'll try my damnedest to get it for the seventy-five grand like we agreed and shook hands on. Yet. Right. I'll tell her. Will do. Call you back."

Orlando hung up the instrument and sat looking moodily at a Picasso on the wall.

"This damn business really exhausts you," he said and added thoughtfully after a breather, "He offers one hundred thousand and will go higher."

"How long can you keep this up?" I asked.

"Frankly, I don't know." A grin brightened Orlando's face. "But I've got an idea! Flannigan, get me Freddie Blue." He sat humming and staring at me with a larkish beam. "You know, this is a very interesting situation," he said.

"Mr. Blue is on the red phone," Miss Flannigan announced.

"Freddie," Orlando cried. "Listen, honeyboy, you've got to help me. Yet, I've talked to J. B. But I want you to do this for him and me both. I want Empire to put out a story that they're buying *A Woman of Sin*. . . . I know it's against the rules but it's our only hope. If that silly fathead Marcher sees her name in the papers it'll soften her up. . . No, use psychology, Freddie—it won't make her worse! I tell you I know her

[93]

like a book. She's fame-hungry. It'll show her you people are sincere. . . . O. K. Thanks. That's a pal. . . . Right. Yep. Absolutely. Call you back."

Orlando hung up and beamed.

"That'll smoke her out," he said. "Come on, let's go swimming. It's hot as hell." He turned to Miss Flannigan. "You know where to find me if that hambo Marcher turns up."

"This is a great town," said Orlando happily as we drove to the beach, "the only place left where a fella can use his wits."

The movie columns the next morning carried enfevered accounts of Empire's new project—the production of the screen drama *A Woman of Sin,* considered by Mr. Cobb the greatest study of human emotions ever attempted by the cinema. The picture was going to be blessed with an all-star cast. At the tail end of the publicity stories, which recounted mainly the brilliance of Jerome B. Cobb as a master showman, was a single line identifying the author of the screen drama as a newcomer named Daisy Marcher. This was an unusual break for Orlando, for it is rarely that a writer, unless he is adept at blowing his own horn, figures in the symphony of adulation that cinema critics offer to the industry.

I reached the Higgens office at two o'clock. Orlando was having lunch at his desk.

"Kind of exciting eh?" he beamed at me.

"Daisy turned up yet?" I asked.

"Nope." Orlando chewed thoughtfully on his food. "I've got a theory she's dropped dead somewhere."

"Mr. Cobb is on the phone," said Miss Flannigan, "the blue one."

"Tell him I'm in conference with Miss Marcher," said Orlando. He resumed his thoughtful chewing.

"What makes you think Daisy dropped dead?" I asked.

"Drink," said Orlando. "She was drunk as a coot when

[94]

she called me. You remember. And she said she's been laid up with a cold. Well, you take a lush like that and give her influenza, and they never recover. Flannigan, get me all the obituary columns for the last four days. I want to look them over." Orlando beamed at me. "That's irony, isn't it?" he chuckled. "To end up in a drunkard's grave, with fame and fortune as your pall bearers. Real irony. Make a great movie."

Orlando kept on chewing. The phone rang.

"Miss Daisy Marcher to see you," Miss Flannigan announced and her voice had dropped a little of its coolness.

Orlando turned and stared at her.

"No kiddin'," he said softly. "Where is she?"

"In the waiting room with Mr. Horowitz," said Miss Flannigan.

"Have her come right in—and be sure she's alone," Orlando ordered. "It smoked her out, just as I figured it would. They're all hams, drunk or sober."

He had no more than finished this statement when the door started opening. The three of us looked expectantly. It seemed to open rather mysteriously.

"Come in, come right in," Orlando called in a saccharine voice.

A child with blonde hair falling over her shoulders appeared. It was an unusually small child. It wore a sort of Scotch dress about a foot long and its legs seemed bare to the waist. On the top of its head stood a large, pink hair ribbon. The tot regarded us with a pair of frowning and unwavering eyes.

"What do *you* want?" Orlando asked peevishly.

"I'm Miss Marcher," said the child in a slightly awed voice.

"Well, tell your mother to come in and you wait outside like a good little girl." Orlando smiled winningly. But his nerves were jangled. Turning to his secretary, he added, "Damn it, Flannigan, can't I have this office run the way I

[95]

want to? How many more secretaries do I need?"

"I have no mother," said the little visitor. "I am an orphan." She looked about her solemnly and inquired, "Which one of you is Mr. Orlando Higgens?"

"I am Mr. Higgens," said Orlando slowly. "Why?"

"Is that so?" said the child. "Oh dear, oh dear—that's too bad."

"It is, eh?" said Orlando testily.

"Yes, it is, indeed," said the child whose tone had now become firmer. "Because I don't think I'm going to like you."

"Why not?" I asked, always interested in character analysis of Orlando.

The little visitor flashed a smile at me.

"Because he has red-rimmed eyes," she said, "and an insincere look."

Orlando was staring with his mouth open. Repartee failed him.

"So you're Daisy Marcher?" he asked finally.

The child nodded.

"Well, that's very interesting." Orlando jeered at the tot. "And I suppose you're also the author of *A Woman of Sin.*"

"Yes, I am," said the child. "Indeed I am."

"You're nuts!" Orlando exploded and leaped to his feet. "Do you know what happens to little girls who tell lies—dirty, rotten lies?"

Daisy sniffed.

"Oh, don't be silly," she cried. "I can't bear silly men."

"God Almighty!" Orlando cried. "What is this? Is this a gag or something? This is the damnedest, most idiotic thing that ever happened!"

"I wouldn't swear in front of the child," Miss Flannigan said.

"You keep out of this," Orlando roared.

"Oh, I don't mind at all," Daisy's gentle voice stopped

him. "I am used to profanity. People always swear at me."

"I'll betchya," said Orlando witheringly.

"Especially if they got red-rimmed eyes," said Daisy.

Orlando pulled himself together.

"Listen," he said haughtily, "I am not in the habit of quarrelling with babies."

He walked around the table and, lifting Daisy to its top, stood looking fiercely into her eyes.

"What I want to know is," he continued coldly, "are you actually the author of *A Woman of Sin*? Cross your heart and hope to die."

Daisy solemnly crossed her heart and answered,

"Hope to die. Yes, I am."

"Yes, you are what?" Orlando was not to be taken in by half oaths.

"I am the author of *A Woman of Sin*," said Daisy, "hope to die."

There was a hush in the office. Miss Flannigan tittered. No one spoke. The little visitor remained on the table top swinging her legs and fluttering her eyelids. She seemed very happy now. Orlando broke the silence.

"That hair ribbon is what kills me," he said hoarsely. "Take it off."

"What for?" Daisy asked.

"It gets me nervous," said Orlando.

"Oh, but it makes me look taller," Daisy smiled. "My mother gave it to me."

"I thought you were an orphan."

"On her deathbed," said Daisy, "when I was a little girl."

"Listen"—Orlando's voice was firm and he seized the tot by her pipestem arms—"I want the truth. About everything. You're an orphan, eh?"

"Yes," said Daisy. "My father ran away with another woman who afterwards stabbed him to death in a saloon brawl.

[97]

And my mother hanged herself because of a broken heart."

"I thought you said she died in bed," Orlando snarled.

"Oh, yes," Daisy agreed. "They cut her down and she lingered because her neck hadn't been broken. Only twisted."

The child swung her legs over the table edge and sighed, "I've been through a lot."

"Never mind about that," said Orlando peevishly. "Where do you live?"

"Oh, in the hills," Daisy waved a little hand. "I like the wilderness."

"I suppose you live in the hills all alone," Orlando sneered, "like a hermit."

"Not altogether," said Daisy. "Because my grandmother is there."

"Now we're getting somewhere." Orlando beamed at me. "What's your grandmother's name and what's the address?"

Daisy frowned and was silent.

"You're just wasting my time, damn it," Orlando cried. "Where does your grandmother live?"

"It wouldn't do you much good to meet her," said Daisy softly.

"Why not?" Orlando demanded.

"Because she's an Indian," said Daisy, "and like most Indians she doesn't care to talk very much. She goes for a whole year sometimes without saying a word. Her name is Minitonka. And she's very old. A hundred and ten, I think, anyway. So you see you will be wasting your time talking to her."

Orlando listened spellbound.

"Jee-rusalem!" he cried. "You're the damnedest liar I ever met!"

The child started climbing breathlessly down from the table.

"How dare you!" she cried. "After I crossed my heart and

hoped to die and everything, and now you call me a liar!"
"Shut up or I'll spank you!" Orlando's face was red.
"Why, of all the nasty men I ever met"—Daisy screamed
and started for the door.

"No, you don't!" Orlando grabbed her. "Come on,
Flannigan. We're taking this brat home and finding out the
truth about her if I have to skin her alive."

We learned a number of things in the next hour.

Daisy Marcher lived in a modest apartment over a grocery store with a stout and amazingly coy mother, who had
never hanged herself. Daisy's critical sense had apparently invented the hanging. There was no grandmother and there were
no Indians. Daisy's father, whose picture was shown us, had
been a Methodist clergyman until he succumbed to pneumonia during her teething period. The mother, an expert knitter
(she knitted calmly during the entire conference), had sup-
ported herself and her precocious baby by supplying several
local knitting goods counters with a steady line of sweaters and
socks. The mother's name was Lillian Egelhofer. Daisy
Marcher was a *nom de plume*. The child was nine years old
and had always been called Mildred. There was no question of
the authenticity of *A Woman of Sin*. Mrs. Egelhofer had seen
her child put the story down page by page and had not added
or removed a word—only corrected the spelling.

"The child will simply not learn to spell," the mother
explained with a martyrish sigh, "although I've told her it
would be a great help to her career. Haven't I, darling?"

"Oh, mother! For Heaven's sake!" said the child, doubling up as if with a cramp.

Mrs. Egelhofer fed herself a large chocolate cream out of
a half-emptied box and settled her billowy figure more comfortably into the chair.

"Sugar deficiency," she explained in a sad voice. "The
doctor says I must watch out for it." She munched the choco-

late cream like a Spartan. "Well," she resumed, her needles flying, "those are all the facts I can think of about little Mildred. Unless you care to have me tell you about her aura. I'm very susceptible to auras and have made quite a study of them. Hers changes from a delicate yellow to a sort of magenta."

Little Mildred made a noise in the back of her throat like a tiger on the flanks of a bullock.

"Come here, darling," said Mrs. Egelhofer, "and let me fix your hair ribbon. These gentlemen will think you're a little street Arab."

"Mother!" Daisy exploded. "This is too much!" Her little face could not do justice to the look of murder in her eyes.

"Why, babykins," Mrs. Egelhofer extended a plump hand full of knitting needles, "where are your manners?" She looked at her child with a reproving but tender smile and in her distraction connected with another chocolate cream.

"Stop it! Stop it! Stop it!" Daisy cried through clenched teeth and threw herself face downward on the couch. It appeared for the moment that the child had burst into tears. But this was erroneous. Daisy wasn't crying. She was biting the cushion under her face.

"An uncontrollable temper," said Mrs. Egelhofer. "Her father, you know, was just like that. Dark purple, most of the time. I always felt that it was his aura that killed him. Not pneumonia at all."

"Flannigan," said Orlando, watching the child tearing the pillow with her teeth, "take Daisy into the other room. She's only disturbing her mother."

"Oh, thank you," said Mrs. Egelhofer, "but I'm used to her."

She bit into the medicinal chocolate cream.

"I want to talk business," Orlando said confidentially. Daisy sat up.

"Oh, no you don't," she cried. "Oh, I should say not. I

don't leave my mother alone with you. You'll cheat her."

"Do what the gentleman says." Mrs. Egelhofer smiled archly at her little girl.

"Go on, get out!" Orlando stood up and mopped his neck.

"Don't strike her," said Mrs. Egelhofer faintly.

"I'm not going to strike her," said Orlando peevishly. "I'm going to take her and throw her into that other room—from here."

Daisy got to her feet and looked up at him thoughtfully . . . Then, holding her head high, she walked proudly and slowly out of the room.

"Get in there with her, Flannigan," Orlando ordered, "and keep the door bolted."

"She needs a firm hand," Mrs. Egelhofer sighed and continued her knitting. "Would you be kind enough to bring me a glass of water? These scenes are really bad for me. My heart, you know." She smiled sadly.

I fetched the water. Orlando outlined his plan. It was very simple. It involved the mother giving him power of attorney for herself and the guardianship of Mildred Egelhofer alias Daisy Marcher for one year. In return she would receive $125,000 minus the ten per cent commission. Orlando paused a moment and then added that there would be another ten per cent reduction to cover the expenses of the baby's keep. Mrs. Egelhofer continued knitting calmly.

"Oh, I don't know, really, if it will do any good," she sighed. "You know, I've worked so hard."

"It will be roughly a hundred thousand dollars," said Orlando soothingly, "after the necessary deductions."

Mrs. Egelhofer nodded. There seemed to be little difference to her between $100,000 and $125,000.

"Oh, I'm not thinking of that," she said. "I was just worrying about little Mildred. After all, she's my first concern. And all that money going to her. It may spoil her character

[101]

entirely. She's so simple and unassuming now."

"The money is not going to her," Orlando said firmly. "It's going to you. It's your money to do what you want with. It would be criminal to hand over that money to a crack-brained infant like that."

"Poor babykins," Mrs. Egelhofer sighed. "I hate to deprive her of it. But I'll be able to do so much for her. After all, she needs an older head."

"Done and done," Orlando snapped and then explained the second phase of the situation. This was the need for complete secrecy. No one must find out that a child of nine was the author of *A Woman of Sin*.

"You see it's this way," Orlando said candidly. "Empire is going to sink two million dollars into this picture. Maybe more before they're through. And they're going to advertise it as the most sophisticated sex drama ever filmed. That's the angle they bought it on. In fact"—a hysterical light came into Orlando's eyes for a moment—"Mr. Cobb himself told me he considered it the most penetrating study of human passions ever attempted on the screen."

Mrs. Egelhofer nodded over her knitting with motherly pride.

"And if it was found out," continued Orlando, "that a child of nine—a mere baby—had written it, by God it would not only ruin Empire but give the whole movie industry a black eye. Oh, boy!" he added and looked mistily out of the window.

"Oh, yes, I know," said Mrs. Egelhofer. "The public is very fickle."

"That's right," said Orlando. "In putting over this deal for you I'm taking a terrific gamble. Do you know, for instance, what would happen to me if Empire found out about her?" He pointed to the bolted door. "I'd be lynched. I mean it. Lynched, by God!"

Orlando drew a deep breath and went on brightly. "The only way to avoid that sort of thing is to have Daisy put in my charge. I'll provide a fine home for her—and keep her locked in it—till after the picture is released. Of course, you can come to visit her whenever you want."

"Well," said Mrs. Egelhofer with a sigh, "I've got a bad back." She groaned by way of illustration. "It's very difficult for me to get around."

"You mean you won't let her go?" Orlando demanded.

"Oh, no," Mrs. Egelhofer sighed again, "you can have Mildred. I wouldn't think of standing in her way. And I know you'll be sweet to her. But couldn't we arrange it so that if the child gets lonely for her mother you can bring her to me at the seashore? You see, I want to go away and try to recover. I've been through a lot, you know."

"Will do!" Orlando snapped. "It's a deal!"

He walked to the bedroom door.

"O.K., Flannigan," he called, "you can let her out."

The door opened. Daisy was sitting in a large chair with her nude legs thrust rigidly in front of her.

"I heard every word you said," she announced.

"That's a lie," said Miss Flannigan, "we couldn't hear a thing."

"*You* couldn't," Daisy sneered, "but I heard him cheating my mother plain as anything."

"Come on, we're going," said Orlando happily. "Never mind taking any of her clothes along. We don't want her looking like a circus freak."

"Yep," said Orlando.

The child dropped to her hands and knees and removed a pile of True Confession and True Love Stories magazines from under the bed.

"Let's hurry up," she said.

*　　*　　*　　*　　*　　*

There were a score of telephone messages waiting in the office, most of them from Jerome B. Cobb.

"Get J. B.," Orlando ordered, "and then lock her up in the conference room. Go on, baby," he beamed on the authoress.

"I don't have to go home any more?" Daisy asked slowly.

"Not for a whole year," said Orlando.

With a cry of joy the child went skipping after Miss Flannigan toward the conference room.

"I want you to be a witness to this conversation," Orlando grinned at me as he held the phone. "You'd better take notes. Because it may be very important—afterwards."

"Hello, J. B.," he said heartily into the instrument. "Well, it's in the bag. All settled. Yep. Yep. Nope. No royalties. I put it over for you. I had to practically blackjack her. Just a hundred and twenty-five thousand flat, payable on signing the contract."

There was a slight rumble over the wire.

"Can't help it, J. B.," Orlando spoke up firmly, "she won't consider taking it in three payments. And, by the way, I'm signing the contracts for her. She's given me power of attorney."

There was a larger rumble over the wire.

"Listen," said Orlando, "I can't perform miracles. She simply refuses to see you or any other movie executives. Even talk to them on the phone. It's got something to do with psychoanalysis . . . Oh, didn't I tell you before? she's going to one. She's suffering from some kind of a shock, I guess . . . Yep. Yep. That's what makes her a genius."

Orlando listened and yepped happily for several minutes.

"That's fine," he resumed. "And now that you've agreed on the deal and everything's settled I want to go on record with something, J.B. And please don't interrupt me. I want to say frankly to you that I've read that script and I think it's pure rubbish. Worst I ever sold you. It could only have been

[104]

written by a half-wit or some child of nine."

Orlando listened to Mr. Cobb's shout with a happy smile.

"I'm not trying to double-cross you, J. B.," he resumed. "I'm just trying to be honest, for once in my life."

The Cobb roars crackled out of the instrument.

"All right, I'm crazy," Orlando agreed cheerily. "But I just want to go on record that in my opinion *A Woman of Sin* is a piece of unadulterated childish rubbish and should never be made by a grown-up company."

Orlando jerked his ear from the receiver and sat staring blandly at the instrument as it threatened to explode in his hand.

"O. K.," he resumed in a contrite voice, "maybe I'm wrong. No, I don't pretend to know as much as you, J. B. And if I haven't convinced you that only a child could have written that script, I'm willing to take your money. No, I'm not against your making great pictures. . . . No, J. B., I gotta be honest, it didn't make me cry when I read it . . . It did, eh? How about Mike Devlin, did he cry too? Is that so? Well, maybe I'm wrong . . . Listen, I'm an agent, not a genius."

His voice grew crisp.

"Yep. Tomorrow morning at ten. Bring all the contracts over. Yep. Okeydoke. Ten o'clock. *Be* there. Right. Will do! Call you back."

Orlando hung up the phone and, leaning back in his papal chair, laughed until the tears came from his eyes.

"The picture of Jerome B. Cobb crying over that brat's script is worth anything that happens," he said. "God, I love this town."

II

Considering that Orlando Higgens, Inc., was less than two miles removed from the Empire Studios and that some thirty Higgens employees were more or less involved in the

Daisy Marcher secret, you would naturally conclude that the whole thing would be out of the bag in a day or two. This is a conclusion, however, based on logic and rationality, neither of which attitudes will get you far as a Hollywood historian. For the cinema capital has a psychology of its own—as illusive as a frog's dream and as capricious as a June bride.

I will not go into the matter further than to explain how so elephantine a conspiracy as launched by Orlando Higgens could thrive undetected practically in the open. The basic reason is that nobody believes anything in Hollywood. The rest of the world may be sceptical about Hollywood stories, but Hollywood itself is far beyond that. It unblushingly knows itself for a liar and behaves accordingly, ignoring anything short of murder, open rape or other well-proved major world events.

Scandal and fantasy are not cake in movieland but daily bread. The place is a wilderness of tall tales and Sinbad anecdotes. A hundred publicity departments work twenty-four hours a day pumping insanities out of the industry for world consumption. Thousands of eccentric movie artists are continually engaged in eccentric marriages and divorces, feuds and public fandangos. Cyrano, Munchausen and Prester John —Cagliostro, Aladdin and the Mad Mullah—were they all to drive into Hollywood at once, would soon be lost in the shuffle. In a week the gossips would be wondering whatever had become of them. And in two weeks they would have formed themselves into a little foreign colony to which no one paid any attention.

There was a second factor that helped keep Orlando's secret hidden practically under everybody's nose. In Hollywood the Pharaohs and their Nobles are a sacred institution. They do not mingle except among themselves. They will unbend on occasions to listen to flattery from lowly sources but the discourse of such fortunate satellites must be brief and ecstatic. There are no hardy couriers to bear evil tidings to the royal ears. They live and thrive, incommunicado, like the happy Kings in Mother Goose.

It was thus that Orlando was able to become the guardian of Daisy Marcher, to board and room her in his hotel, to ride her to his office every morning (as befell later) and to continue in his desperate deception of Jerome B. Cobb and his myrmidons without discovery.

I was myself amazed.

Daisy remained in the hotel only for a brief time. Three nurses, hired by Orlando to watch his little client when he was too busy with other business, resigned in the first three days. Daisy refused to be treated as a parasite. She insisted on continuing with her literary career.

"Well, you can do your writing in this hotel suite," said Orlando. "It's a beautiful place. And when you get tired you can use the pool and learn how to swim."

"I don't want to swim," said Daisy, "and I can't write in a place like this. I want to write in your office."

Orlando was eating ice cream with his little client during this discussion.

"Okeydoke," he beamed at her. "I'll have everything fixed up for you in the conference room."

"And nobody can come in except me," said Daisy.

"Nobody," Orlando nodded, "unless you want them. It'll be your studio. But you've got to stay there. No monkey business."

After this Daisy rode to work with Orlando every morning and locked herself away in the conference room for the rest of the day. Within two weeks the whole thing had become a matter of routine to the Higgens organization.

The contracts were signed and Mr. Cobb, laying aside his Pharaoh mantle, busied himself personally with his chef d'oeuvre. His work consisted of hourly conferences with the heads of his publicity department, for Mr. Cobb felt that his moods as an artist were a matter of great public interest. The great Empire studios buzzed with the magnitude of the event and the Nobles sweated loyally to make certain that Mr. Cobb's achievement would be worthy of his position.

There was only one disturbing element for Mr. Cobb. This was the continued absence of Daisy Marcher from the arena of his labours. J. B., who had never felt the existence, let alone the need, of an author conceived an odd longing for Miss Marcher. He spoke of her frequently and it was obvious that her indifference to his favours had impressed him as much as her great work.

"She's an unusual type for a writer," he explained to his publicity heads, "the kind that you read about. She lives in her dreams and refuses to come out into the world. I understand that—and respect it."

And Mr. Cobb wooed this fellow dreamer daily in the press. His publicity department filled the movie columns with copy relating the depth and beauty of Daisy Marcher's mind. She was—one columnist friend of Mr. Cobb informed seven million readers of her syndicated articles—the first great dramatic talent to write directly for the motion pictures. Another proclaimed her as the greatest sex psychologist since Havelock Ellis. A number of literary figures, expensively employed by Mr. Cobb, read her screen play and likened it in print to Dostoevsky and Joseph Conrad and some of the more sophisticated ones to Balzac and Bernard Shaw. I am not being redundant. This is actually what happened, for literary figures in Hollywood (as literary figures everywhere else, for that matter) are unselfish in their admiration of the Boss's Mind.

Mr. Cobb's hopes of endearing himself to the exclusive Daisy Marcher by allowing her to share his press campaign had an unhappy effect on Orlando. He was reminded every

morning of the volcano on which he was sitting and his diges-
tion suffered—for part of the day. But Orlando found a use
for the Empire fanfare of Marcher publicity. He was able to
keep his child authoress reasonably contented by reading the
stories to her at night.

I was busy for two weeks attending a life-and-death re-
write matter on location. The new ending I had written for our
picture had necessitated a new beginning. I called on Orlando
immediately on my return. He was bland and untroubled. He
assured me that everything was hunky-dory and that Daisy
was an interesting child and was getting along nicely.

"I've changed her a little," he said, "so she don't look so
much like a baby cooch dancer. We've had a barrel of fun."

Daisy came out of her atelier holding some newspapers in
her hands. She *was* somewhat changed. The hair ribbon was
gone and the hair itself had been reasonably cut. Her dress
came below the knees and she had on long stockings.

"Looks a little older and a little fatter, don't you think?"
Orlando chuckled.

"I'd still take her for about nine," I said.

"Yes," said Orlando, "but not a young nine."

Daisy greeted me happily.

"What do you want now?" Orlando glowered at her but
there was a chumminess in his voice.

"I want to know," said Daisy, "who puts all these things
in the papers about me."

"Why, I do, honey." said Orlando tenderly. Daisy climbed
up on his lap and kissed him.

"You're wonderful," she said.

"How about my red-rimmed eyes," Orlando asked,
"huh?"

"Oh, those," said Daisy, "they're getting better."

I was impressed by the fact that in some curious way the
mastermind of Higgens, Inc., and Daisy Marcher seemed

[109]

twins, mentally and spritually.

"I would like you to put something else in the papers," Daisy pursued.

"A real ham," Orlando chuckled proudly. "What's biting you now?"

"I'm tired of reading about *A Woman of Sin*," Daisy pouted. "I would like to read about *The Sea of Blood*."

"What the hell is that?" Orlando's eyes widened.

"Oh, for heaven's sake," Daisy scowled. "I've told you and told you a hundred times. That's the screen drama I'm writing about those pirates I told you about. And it's half finished, too."

A phone rang. Miss Flannigan announced, "There's a Mr. Moriarity to see you."

Daisy slipped to the floor and ogled the door excitedly.

"Oh, he's come!" she panted. "Oh, goody, goody! Oh, isn't that wonderful?"

"Who the hell is Moriarity?" Orlando demanded.

"You'll see. Just wait." The little authoress started jumping up and down. "Tell him to come in right away, Miss Flannigan. Oh dear, this is very nice. Now I can finish *The Sea of Blood*. He knows all about pirates."

"He's on his way," said Miss Flannigan coolly.

The door opened slowly as it had done on a certain afternoon some weeks ago and there appeared on the threshold a figure almost as startling as had presented itself on that other time. It was a small fat boy in tight knee pants with legs protruding at a remarkable angle like a pair of props. He was wearing a sort of pancake hat and holding a large ice cream cone in his hand.

"Is this Moriarity?" Orlando asked. Daisy was too blissful to speak. She nodded.

"Yet, I'm Moriarity," the fat boy squeaked.

"Come on in," said Orlando and Moriarity advanced two

paces before his valour gave out. He covered his confusion by concentrating on the ice cream cone.

"What's your first name?" Orlando asked.

"They call me Captain," said Moriarity. "Hello, Daisy. I got your letter and I come over soon as I can. First I come over to your mother and she told me here."

"How is her mother?" Orlando asked.

"Knittin'," said Moriarity.

"Come on in here," said Daisy. She had skipped over and seized Moriarity's unoccupied hand. "We're going to work in here. And you can bring your boats. There's plenty of room and a sink even."

"I can only stay a couple of hours," said Moriarity, "then I gotta go home. But I'll come back and bring my boats."

The two children vanished into the conference room.

"Kind o' cute," said Orlando, beaming.

A phone rang.

"It's Mr. Cobb," said Miss Flannigan; "the white one."

"Hello, J. B.," Orlando greeted him, "how's everything coming along? . . . Oh, is that so? Start Wednesday, eh? Well, here's hoping." Orlando nodded and yepped for several minutes. He resumed suddenly, "Listen, J. B., you know I'm on your side. I've been breaking my neck to get Miss Marcher to see it your way. I told her straight I considered her absolutely psychopathic for behaving the way she is. She owes it to you to attend the studio party in her honour. Listen, we're absolutely together on that, J. B." There was a pause and more yepping. Orlando resumed, this time in a hurt voice, "I give you my word of honour I've done everything humanly possible. Do you know what happened? Last night I went so far as to threaten to kidnap her and drag her over to you by main force. She lit out and grabbed a midnight train . . . Oh, I don't know. She'll be back. Just one of her huffs. . . . Okey-doke. I'll keep plugging, J. B. Will do. And good luck to you."

[111]

Orlando hung up and shuddered.

"This is getting a little complicated," he said. "They start shooting Wednesday."

I asked him if he were worried. The larkish light returned to his eyes.

"Uh, uh," he said, "nothing will happen. These sort of things always blow over."

A Woman of Sin was finished on schedule. I sat with Orlando and a group of Empire Nobles in the projection room and watched a first rough cut run off. It was as daffy a piece of cinema claptrap as I had ever seen. It had cost two million and it was acted almost entirely by stars earning from $4 to $7 a minute. It related the woes of a beautiful Girl of the People who sought happiness through four different society men, all stars, and ended by dedicating her broken heart to the Red Cross. Here in the great struggle between Democracy and the Nazi philosophy she met a patriotic doctor—the only non-star in the picture—with whom at last she found true happiness as an ambulance driver.

When the lights went up, I beheld Jerome B. Cobb in a back seat. His eyes were streaming with tears. He was too overcome to speak but handed Orlando a sheaf of publicity matter. *A Woman of Sin* had been seen in its first rough cut by nine of the nation's leading cinema critics and acclaimed by all of them as Hollywood's finest and most sophisticated sex drama. These opinions were already in print awaiting the monster advertising campaign.

"The picture," said Mr. Cobb, who had finally stopped sobbing, "will be released in two months—just in time for Christmas week. It is my present to the thinking people of America."

"Great idea," said Orlando and then looked thoughtful. The Pharaoh's eyes were regarding him with the hunger of the artist before his wet canvas. Orlando was always at his worst in a projection room. "I can't help it," he had often apologized to his clients. "I guess I'm not a judge of movies. I hate 'em too much."

"Well, J.B.," he continued in a strained voice, "it's quite a picture. Lots of stuff in it. Ought to go big. But do you think you can get those sex scenes by the Hays office?"

"What sex scenes?" Mr. Cobb cried.

"Well, for instance, the one where she leaves her first husband's bed and rushes in her nightgown to the arms of her lover," said Orlando, "and gets into bed with him because it's raining."

"Only a pervert would notice that," said Mr. Cobb and stalked out. Seven train bearers followed him, all drying their eyes and all disdaining to say "good afternoon" to Orlando.

I was sound asleep a week later when my phone rang. It was almost noon and the caller was Orlando. He spoke in a throbbing sort of voice and said he had to see me at once. I asked, for what reason.

"I can't tell you over the phone," Orlando throbbed, "but you'd better shoot over right away. Don't stop for anything, for God's sake."

There were four people in the office when I got there. Two of them, Miss Flannigan and Daisy Marcher, were crying. Moriarity, the fat boy, was sitting in a chair, his hands folded in his lap like a neutral, and his splayed legs dangling. Orlando's face was mottled.

"There's hell to pay," he greeted me hoarsely.

"What's happened?" I asked.

"That big know-it-all, Flannigan." He glared at her.

"I tell you I didn't mail that script out," Miss Flannigan interrupted tearfully. "She mailed it herself."

Orlando continued in a relentless voice.

"Flannigan, that big know-it-all, mailed a copy of *The*

Sea of Blood to Jerome Cobb, personally. With Daisy Marcher's name on the envelope so he would be sure to open it and read it. His favourite writer, for God's sake."

"I didn't!" Miss Flannigan threw herself on the couch and wept.

"Who did then?" Orlando cried. "I've watched Daisy like a hawk. Ever since I read that pirate hog wash I've been worried something like this might happen. I haven't taken my eyes off her." His face grew redder. "The damnedest drivel I ever read," he went on as if fascinated by the horror of his tale. "A hundred and thirty duels to the death in the first twenty pages. And fifteen women have their heads cut off, including five harmless old ladies. And the hero, singlehanded, captures a whole fleet of ships. He stabs seventy-five sailors to death in the battle all alone. And for a finish, guess what? They hang a whole town. Two thousand men, women and children get hanged and then they set fire to them. Everybody gets hanged—God knows why!"

"Didn't Cobb like the script?" I asked.

"He threw a fit." Orlando glanced at the phone. "He hollered for two hours. I told him it was a practical joke— some sorehead writer trying to get back at Miss Marcher."

At this point Daisy flung herself to the floor and sobbed aloud.

"Go on, cry," Orlando sneered. "I ought to break your neck. Why didn't you stick to sex? Why'd you have to show what an ignoramus you are by writing about pirates?"

He had entered the conference room as he talked and started hurling various sailing-ship models across the office.

Moriarity slid from his chair and, still sobbing, started moving cautiously across the room.

"You little sneak!"—Light struck Orlando—"You did it! You sent that script out, didn't you?"

Moriarity made a bolt for it but Orlando thrust out a long

leg and tripped him. The fat boy sprawled on his face and let go an ear-splitting bellow.

"You've killed him," cried Miss Flannigan.

"Shut up," Orlando shouted, "or I will!" He lifted Moriarity to his feet. "Come on clean, you little tub-o'-guts, you sent it out, didn't you?" He shook the fat boy by his shoulders.

"Only a carbon copy," Moriarity wailed.

"That's right, that's right," Daisy screamed. She was crying savagely. "I never let anybody have the original one. I keep it myself. So there. You horrible monster, you!"

"You sex maniac!" Orlando glared at the smeared face of the little authoress. "Gimme that original, do you hear! And I want the original copy of A Woman of Sin or I'll break your neck."

"I'll break your neck, you!" Daisy jumped up and down and rushed for a lamp base. It was too heavy to lift. She continued screaming as she tugged at it, "You can't have it. You can't have A Woman of Sin either. I wrote it and it's mine. Nobody can have it. Stand back or I'll kill you."

This was evidently out of The Sea of Blood. Unable to take the lamp base with her, she rushed at Orlando unarmed and started kicking his shins and trying to bite him. There was a considerable racket in the room but the noise was not loud enough to mute the voice that spoke from the open doorway.

"What are you running here, a madhouse?" said Jerome B. Cobb. "What's the idea of beating up children in the middle of the day?"

Orlando turned but his eyes were not for Cobb. They rested on the persons of Freddie Blue and Mike Devlin who stood behind the Pharaoh and, staring at the scene, were ominously still.

"Come in, come right in," said Orlando and waved his arms at the bleating Moriarity and the attacking Daisy. "My

[115]

sister's kids. They've been raising hell."

He pulled himself out of range of Daisy's teeth and mopped the back of his neck.

"I came over," said Mr. Cobb, whose patriarchal soul appeared revolted by the scene, "because I want to track down personally the dirty crook who wrote this dreadful thing." He waved a manilla envelope in the air. "This thing called *The Sea of Blood.*"

"You give me that," cried Daisy and made a jump for the envelope.

"Go away, little girl," Mr. Cobb said sternly. "Go to your mother!"

"Gimmee that!" Daisy yelled again and kicked Mr. Cobb.

"Where are your manners?" Mr. Cobb shouted. He glared at Orlando. "For God's sake, get these children out of here. I want to talk to you."

"Hold it, chief," Freddie Blue broke his silence. "Let 'em stay."

"Don't be a stinker, Freddie," Orlando whispered desperately.

Freddie Blue, a dapper, lean-faced little man with cold grey eyes and a thin grey mouth, kneeled on one leg and confronted the little authoress.

"What's your name, little girl?" he asked soothingly.

"Daisy Marcher," she gurgled through her teeth, "and I want my story back from that fat man over there."

At the name, Jerome B. Cobb clapped his hand to the side of his head. He looked down at the disordered tot and asked in an abstracted voice, "What do you mean, your name is Daisy Marcher? What are you talking about?"

"Hold it, chief," Freddie fastened his eyes on Orlando. "There's something pretty fishy around here."

The blood was out of Mr. Cobb's face and with it the

organ-like voice of the Pharaoh ebbed to a whisper.

"What are you trying to tell me?" he inquired and his eyes rolled toward Orlando. He moved vaguely toward a chair and sat down. It was obvious his mind had stopped working for the moment.

"Little girl," Freddie Blue resumed in a seductive voice that seemed to fascinate Daisy, "did you really write *The Sea of Blood?*"

"Yes, I did," Daisy answered. "I did so, absolutely."

"I helped her," Moriarity spoke up with sudden pride. "But I got to go home now. My ma's waiting."

Mike Devlin, a stocky and powerful figure, closed the door and placed himself in front of it, barring the little fat boy's way like an ogre in a Walt Disney picture. Moriarity began to bellow. Mr. Cobb was wiping his grey face with a handkerchief that smelled of violets.

"Can you prove you wrote that story?" the unctuous Freddie Blue pursued and patted Daisy's head tenderly.

"What are ye askin' questions for?" Mike Devlin's gravelly voice sounded from the door. "You heard what she was sayin' when we came in. She's got the original copy. That one we got is only a carbon. I noticed that when I was reading it."

"Yes, I heard her," said Freddie Blue softly. "I also heard her say she had the original copy of something else."

He pursed his thin mouth. No one spoke.

"If you'll just let me handle this," Orlando finally said in a down-to-earth voice, "everything will be okeydoke. My word on it."

Mr. Cobb's eyes had been devouring Daisy for several minutes. He managed now to pull them away from her and look at Orlando. The sight of Orlando brought him roaring to his feet. He shook a finger wildly at Orlando.

"This man," he shouted, "is trying to put something

[117]

over. Something so dirty and cheap I refuse to believe it. I refuse to believe that any human being could sink so low as this man!"

"Hold it, chief," Freddie Blue said quietly. He was still kneeling in front of Daisy. Orlando frowned and kicked one of the sailing-ship models across the room.

"Is there any other Daisy Marcher besides you?" Freddie Blue asked.

"No, there is not," Daisy cried. "I'm the only one."

"Holy God!" Mr. Devlin growled from the door. "Go on, Freddie—ask her and get it over with."

"Have you ever written any other screen play than *The Sea of Blood?*" Freddie Blue pursued softly and patted the little golden head with a gentle hand.

"Yes, I did, I should say I did," Daisy answered.

"What was the name of that other screen play?" Freddie Blue continued his gentle quiz.

"*A Woman of Sin,*" said Daisy. "It's been in all the papers every day. *A Woman of Sin.* So there!"

Freddie Blue stood up and looked intently into Orlando's eyes.

"Is that true?" he asked.

"Listen, fellas." Orlando hopped to a seat on his table. "You come barging in here like a pack of hoodlums and frightening the wits out of that poor baby."

"You ain't said if it's true yet," Mike Devlin growled and his jaw muscles began working.

"For God's sake," Orlando yelled, "it isn't going to do any good to start getting tough about it! You'll spill *all* the beans then. I've broken my neck trying to protect you fellas from the beginning."

A cry came from Jerome B. Cobb but there were no words. His hand moved furtively to his bosom and rested over his heart. He closed his eyes and leaned back in his chair.

[118]

"Get Mr. Cobb some water," Mike Devlin growled.

Miss Flannigan hurried out.

"Never mind me," Mr. Cobb moaned. "The company... the company."

Orlando ignored this seeming deathbed interruption. "Listen, let's get everything straight," he said. "I begged J.B. not to buy that story. I pleaded with him. I told him it was pure childish tripe. But he wouldn't listen. I went on record that only a half-witted baby could have written it."

Miss Flannigan had returned with the water. Mr. Cobb pushed her aside and leaped to his feet like a Lazarus on springs.

"You scum!" His roar filled the room and he moved slowly toward Orlando. "You grave robber! Taking advantage of my friendship!"

"Nobody took advantage of you," Orlando shouted, "You took advantage of yourself like you always do, goddam it!"

"Shut up!" The Pharaoh's organ voice opened two more stops, "You have ruined me! For what? Why? Tell me why? Using a dirty child to make a dirty penny."

"Hold it, chief," Freddie Blue interrupted. "She's the author of our biggest epic. There's no sense in antagonizing her."

Mr. Cobb reeled. He clapped a hand against the side of his head again. His other hand reached out blindly for a chair.

"It's a lie! It's a rotten lie!" he shouted. "She never wrote it. I don't believe it! This innocent child write that thing! Never! Mike—call the police!"

Mr. Cobb had come close to Orlando but there were no blows struck. And Orlando at this time did a curious thing. He laughed—not hysterically nor mockingly. He laughed with a sound of honest if somewhat childish relief. And he sat down

[119]

calmly behind his fifteen-foot antique desk.

"Call the police," Orlando said aloofly. "Do anything you want. I'm washed up on this. You boys have got the ball."

The ironing out of the Daisy Marcher imbroglio took a full fifteen hours and was accomplished in Jerome B. Cobb's secret office, the one to be entered through a sliding panel. It was tastily furnished and had no telephones.

Until eleven that night there were present Mr. Cobb, his two Nobles, three lawyers from the legal department famed for their loyalty to the company, Orlando and myself. I had been invited as an accomplice. Daisy, under the guard of Mr. Cobb's sister-in-law—a Mrs. Sophia Cobb—was forced to cool her heels in one of the conference chambers adjoining the Pharaoh's main sanctum. Mrs. Sophia Cobb was a tall woman with a square face set in an expression of aversion, an expression she may well have caught from anyone around her. I felt sorry for Daisy as we left her to this monitor.

I also felt sorry for Mr. Cobb. The spectacle of a man face to face with the incontrovertible proofs of his own idiocy is never a pleasant one, however idiotic the victim. But my sorrow was more or less flitting. Mr. Cobb, confronted by the fact that he was an imbecile and that he had mistaken the droolings of a nine-year-old child for Art of the highest water, revealed himself a man of great resource. He pointed out in an oration lasting three hours that he had taken the cheap nonsense of this horrid child, Daisy Marcher, and converted it by his own genius into a powerful motion picture. He defied anyone to deny this. He defied anyone to deny the fact that he had been suspicious of that manuscript from the moment he clapped eyes on it. But somehow, by a miracle for which he was ready to thank God, this childish nonsense had struck a creative chord in his bosom. He had toiled—nobody would ever know how hard he had toiled—and created an adult Academy Award picture out of absolutely nothing.

These thumping lies were received with clucks of wonder by the three loyal barristers. Freddie Blue kept himself in a state of suspended animation during this rebuilding of the Pharaoh, by the Pharaoh for the Pharaoh. Mike Devlin scowled as if these revelations of human mendacity were too much for him. I felt he was thinking of happier days in the ring. As for Orlando, my friend conducted himself like a veritable craven. He bore out each and every one of the Pharaoh's idiotic statements and professed himself solemnly amazed at what J.B. had managed to make out of the sow's ear he had sold him.

"He turned a debacle into victory," said Orlando, beaming on everybody.

I decided that sorrow for Mr. Cobb was an emotion wasted.

After Jerome B. Cobb's summing up of his own genius the meeting took up more general topics. It was decided that the good of the industry required the suppression of the fact that a nine-year-old child had written Empire's two-million-dollar drama of human emotions—already advertised in all the magazines as Hollywood's Top Art Film.

"Exactly what I've been doing right along, hiding that fact," Orlando chirped. The group ignored him.

"We could explain to the public that I actually wrote it," said Mr. Cobb, "but I don't want to figure personally in the matter. It has always been my policy to work behind the scenes. I don't want to start hogging credit and setting a bad example for everybody."

He looked sternly at Freddie Blue and Mike Devlin.

"Well," said Freddie Blue, "it wouldn't help the situation to advertise you as Daisy Marcher's collaborator."

Mrs. Egelhofer, summoned from her seashore retreat, arrived at this point. She had left in a hurry and forgotten to bring her knitting, which seemed to rob her of her personality and her wits. She was touchingly pleased to see Orlando and hoped in a quavering voice that nothing had happened to her child. She was certain it had. She didn't want anyone to keep anything from her. The truth was better than the terrible suspense under which she had been labouring ever since the telephone had wakened her.

"There's nothing to worry about," Orlando assured her. "Daisy's in the next room and she's in fine health."

Mrs. Egelhofer trembled and sat down. Her mother's heart was not entirely convinced. It was explained to her that she would have to sign some papers transferring the guardianship of Daisy Marcher from Orlando Higgens to Jerome B. Cobb. Mrs. Egelhofer was unexpectedly stubborn.

"But I don't know any Mr. Cobb," she fluttered. "I can't just give my little girl away to anybody."

"For God's sake," Mike Devlin growled, "you gave the kid to that guy"—he pointed at Orlando—"and for all you knew he might have been a burglar."

"Oh, no," said Mrs. Egelhofer, "his aura was quite good. Very good. That gentleman's aura"—she looked critically at Mr. Cobb—"is quite something else. Dark green. I don't like it."

"Mr. Cobb's aura is all right when he's feeling better," said Mike Devlin, and it was explained to the perturbed mother just who Jerome B. Cobb was. The Pharaoh himself sat down next to her and took her plump hand in his.

"My dear young lady," he said soothingly, "I want to place the little girl in the best private school in southern California. And more than that. I am sending my own sister-in-law to live with her. She is a grand woman and understands children better than any of us. They're a hobby with her. In such a school, under the guidance of great teachers, who knows but what the child will have a chance to amount to something."

[122]

"I don't think any more fame would be good for her," Mrs. Egelhofer demurred. "At her age, too. She's had quite enough, don't you think?"

"I'm talking about real, human education," said Mr. Cobb, "something that will make a human being out of her and not just a—a movie writer."

Mrs. Egelhofer sighed.

"I don't know," she said. "It's all so queer and yet so heartbreaking. My little girl has been taken from me again."

Ten minutes later the papers were signed and Daisy was brought in. It was 1.0 A.M. but the little authoress was as alert as at any high noon.

"My poor darling," Mrs. Egelhofer said, holding out her arms.

"What are you doing here?" Daisy asked and backed away.

"I came here to rescue you," said Mrs. Egelhofer, putting a handkerchief to her eyes. She recovered a smile. "Let me be the one to break the news to her." She looked wistfully at the group. "Babykins, you are going to have a new father."

"Who?" said Daisy impassively.

"That gentleman over there." Mrs. Egelhofer indicated the Pharaoh. Daisy made a noise as of dice rattling in the back of her throat. The open-mouthed stares of the group in no way embarrassed her. She looked from one face to the other and said, "Why him?"

"Darling," said Mrs. Egelhofer, "Mother knows best."

Daisy turned and started for the door but Orlando grabbed her. He held her by the shoulder, pretending to pat it.

"Well, as I see it," said Orlando, "the whole thing depends on my little friend Daisy here. If she'll keep quiet, you're O.K. If she won't—well, that's another situation."

"Come here, little girl." Mr. Cobb smiled sourly at the child.

[123]

Daisy made no move.

"Of course she won't say anything," Mr. Cobb went on. "Why should she? She isn't a crook like you, Higgens. She's an honest, decent, sweet little girl."

Daisy was silent. Orlando shrugged his shoulders.

"O.K.," he said. "If you want to take a chance, that's all right with me. But I don't feel it's straight thinking."

Something seemed to give way in Mr. Cobb.

"Get out of here, you crook!" he shouted. "Get out of here and never darken this door again or I'll throw you out of the window with my own hands."

"Hold it, chief," said Freddie Blue. "Let's see what Higgens has to suggest."

"I don't give a damn what he's got to suggest," Mr. Cobb tried to scream but his voice broke and both his eyes appeared to fill with red tears.

"Take it easy, J.B.," Mike Devlin growled.

"I have this to suggest," said Orlando as if there had been no interruptions. "I suggest that you buy *The Sea of Blood* and produce it. With a few rewrites, of course. And also that you take an option on any other works from Miss Marcher's pen. She's going to be a great name in pictures after *A Woman of Sin* and all the ballyhoo you've given her. The critics are nuts about her. I think you're damned short-sighted if you don't cash in on all this."

He turned amiably to his little client.

"How about it, honey?" he asked. "You'll keep quiet if they do that, won't you?" He looked happily at Mr. Cobb. "Frankly, I wouldn't blame her if she blabbed her head off if you let her down now."

The room was silent.

"A Daisy Marcher picture every year," Orlando continued, beaming at his little client. "Each one a super-special. And your name in lights—same billing as the star or director.

What do you say, Daisy?"

"Oh, yes," said Daisy, "I would like that very much. If I can work with the Captain."

"Who's that?" Freddie Blue asked softly.

"Moriarity," said Orlando. "You met him in my office."

"Holy God!" Mike Devlin groaned. "Did he help her write *A Woman of Sin?*"

"No, he did not," said Daisy. "I wrote that all by myself."

Mike Devlin sighed with relief.

"Well, gentlemen," said Orlando, a jolly note in his voice, "is it a deal? Same price as *A Woman of Sin* for the next two. And a slight increase on the two thereafter. We can figure all that out later."

Mr. Cobb said nothing. His eyes were closed. Freddie Blue was likewise silent. Mike Devlin alone spoke. A faint grin was around his fighter's mouth. I could see he admired Orlando Higgens almost as much as I did.

"It's a deal," said Mr. Devlin.

It thus befell that Daisy Marcher was whisked off to a private school in southern California, her little arms loaded with papers, among them contracts for *The Sea of Blood* and for her next four pictures. Mrs. Sophia Cobb sat in the drawing room facing her, but all the distaste that lady could summon into her square face was not enough to flicker one of Daisy's eyelids.

No sooner had the train started than Daisy had asked for a table. When they were passing the town of Azusa the little authoress was already sitting hunched over it, her tongue protruding from the corner of her mouth, and a fierce light in her eyes. She was writing Picture Number Three.

Mr. Cobb, accompanied by his entire court, several nurses and a special osteopath, rushed off to the mud baths at

Arrowhead Lake. Here the Pharaoh and his Nobles lay basking for several weeks. They took short walks and discussed the state of J.B.'s health. It did not seem to be improving. The Pharaoh lay on his sun porch and grew greyer. He complained of pains around the heart. Mike Devlin summoned a specialist from Hollywood. The Empire publicity department sent three movie columnists down with the doctor. The specialist was glum. J.B. had been doing too much. He couldn't say what might happen.

His face gaunt, with the marks of dissolution plainly on him and a tall glass of milk at his side, Jerome B. Cobb unbosomed himself to the movie columnists in what he termed his first personal interview. "And maybe my last," he smiled wanly.

"Movie-making is more than a job," he said slowly. "It's a man's whole life. It's not earning money or fame that counts. It's bringing beauty and pleasure to a sorely troubled world.

"We who make movies"—the Pharaoh's eyes brightened for a moment with memories—"are on a battle front day and night. Sometimes we fall—and others take our place and carry on. And we are forgotten. But as long as there is life left in us—we must keep the show going with everything we've got."

Jerome B. Cobb closed his eyes. The movie columnists were deeply moved. They rose and tiptoed out of the sun room.

Mr. Cobb's recovery amazed his Nobles. The very next morning he was up at dawn packing his own suitcase and touching his toes fifteen times. He tarried only long enough for a final massage and then, gathering his court about him, whizzed back to Hollywood, refreshed for the great problem of movie-making.

A *Woman of Sin*, written by Daisy Marcher, the new Balzac of the screen was released the week before Christmas. It grossed four and a half million dollars.

Crazy Sunday

By F. SCOTT FITZGERALD

Fitzgerald is one of the writers of whom it is said that "they go to Hollywood to die". But though he was tired and sick, with his best work all behind him, Fitzgerald found it possible to become fascinated with the town and the industry. In addition to his filmscript work with Metro, he wrote some twenty workmanlike Hollywood short stories; and *The Last Tycoon*, though left unfinished at his death in 1940, is one of the classic Hollywood novels.

It was Sunday—not a day, but rather a gap between two other days. Behind, for all of them, lay sets and sequences, the long waits under the crane that swung the microphone, the hundred miles a day by automobiles to and fro across a county, the struggles of rival ingenuities in the conference rooms, the ceaseless compromise, the clash and strain of many personalities fighting for their lives. And now Sunday, with individual life starting up again, with a glow kindling in eyes that had been glazed with monotony the afternoon before. Slowly as the hours waned they came awake like "Puppenfeen" in a toy shop: an intense colloquy in a corner, lovers disappearing to neck in a hall. And the feeling of "Hurry, it's not too late, but for God's sake hurry before the blessed forty hours of leisure are over."

Joel Coles was writing continuity. He was twenty-eight and not yet broken by Hollywood. He had had what were considered nice assignments since his arrival six months before and he submitted his scenes and sequences with enthusiasm. He referred to himself modestly as a hack but really did not think of it that way. His mother had been a successful actress; Joel had spent his childhood between London and New York trying to separate the real from the unreal, or at least to keep one guess ahead. He was a handsome man with the pleasant

[127]

cow-brown eyes that in 1913 had gazed out at Broadway audiences from his mother's face.

When the invitation came it made him sure that he was getting somewhere. Ordinarily he did not go out on Sundays but stayed sober and took work home with him. Recently they had given him a Eugene O'Neill play destined for a very important lady indeed. Everything he had done so far had pleased Miles Calman, and Miles Calman was the only director on the lot who did not work under a supervisor and was responsible to the money men alone. Everything was clicking into place in Joel's career. ("This is Mr. Calman's secretary. Will you come to tea from four to six Sunday—he lives in Beverly Hills, number—.")

Joel was flattered. It would be a party out of the top-drawer. It was a tribute to himself as a young man of promise. The Marion Davies crowd, the high-hats, the big currency numbers, perhaps even Dietrich and Garbo and the Marquise, people who were not seen everywhere, would probably be at Calman's.

"I won't take anything to drink," he assured himself. Calman was audibly tired of rummies, and thought it was a pity the industry could not get along without them.

Joel agreed that writers drank too much—he did himself, but he wouldn't this afternoon. He wished Miles would be within hearing when the cocktails were passed to hear his succinct, unobtrusive, "No, thank you."

Miles Calman's house was built for great emotional moments—there was an air of listening, as if the far silences of its vistas hid an audience, but this afternoon it was thronged, as though people had been bidden rather than asked. Joel noted with pride that only two other writers from the studio were in the crowd, an ennobled limey and, somewhat to his surprise, Nat Keogh, who had evoked Calman's impatient comment on drunks.

Stella Calman (Stella Walker, of course) did not move on to her guests after she spoke to Joel. She lingered—she looked at him with the sort of beautiful look that demands some sort of acknowledgment and Joel drew quickly on the dramatic adequacy inherited from his mother:

"Well, you look about sixteen! Where's your kiddy car?"

She was visibly pleased; she lingered. He felt that he should say something more, something confident and easy—he had first met her when she was struggling for bits in New York. At the moment a tray slid up and Stella put a cocktail glass into his hand.

"Everybody's afraid, aren't they?" he said, looking at it absently. "Everybody watches for everybody else's blunders, or tries to make sure they're with people that'll do them credit. Of course that's not true in your house," he covered himself hastily. "I just meant generally in Hollywood."

Stella agreed. She presented several people to Joel as if he were very important. Reassuring himself that Miles was at the other side of the room, Joel drank the cocktail.

"So you have a baby?" he said. "That's the time to look out. After a pretty woman has had her first child, she's very vulnerable, because she wants to be reassured about her own charm. She's got to have some new man's unqualified devotion to prove to herself she hasn't lost anything."

"I never get anybody's unqualified devotion," Stella said rather resentfully.

"They're afraid of your husband."

"You think that's it?" She wrinkled her brow over the idea; then the conversation was interrupted at the exact moment Joel would have chosen.

Her attentions had given him confidence. Not for him to join safe groups, to slink to refuge under the wings of such acquaintances as he saw about the room. He walked to the window and looked out toward the Pacific, colorless under its

[129]

sluggish sunset. It was good here—the American Riviera and all that, if there were ever time to enjoy it. The handsome, well-dressed people in the room, the lovely girls, and the— well, the lovely girls. You couldn't have everything.

He saw Stella's fresh boyish face, with the tired eyelid that always drooped a little over one eye, moving about among her guests and he wanted to sit with her and talk a long time as if she were a girl instead of a name; he followed her to see if she paid anyone as much attention as she had paid him. He took another cocktail—not because he needed confidence but because she had given him so much of it. Then he sat down beside the director's mother.

"Your son's gotten to be a legend, Mrs. Calman—Oracle and a Man of Destiny and all that. Personally, I'm against him but I'm in a minority. What do you think of him? Are you impressed? Are you surprised how far he's gone?"

"No, I'm not surprised," she said calmly. "We always expected a lot from Miles."

"Well now, that's unusual," remarked Joel. "I always think all mothers are like Napoleon's mother. My mother didn't want me to have anything to do with the entertainment business. She wanted me to go to West Point and be safe."

"We always had every confidence in Miles." . . .

He stood by the built-in bar of the dining room with the good-humored, heavy-drinking, highly paid Nat Keogh.

"—I made a hundred grand during the year and lost forty grand gambling, so now I've hired a manager."

"You mean an agent," suggested Joel.

"No, I've got that too. I mean a manager. I make over everything to my wife and then he and my wife get together and hand me out the money. I pay him five thousand a year to hand me out my money."

"You mean your agent."

"No, I mean my manager, and I'm not the only one—a lot

of other irresponsible people have him."

"Well, if you're irresponsible why are you responsible enough to hire a manager?"

"I'm just irresponsible about gambling. Look here—"

A singer performed; Joel and Nat went forward with the others to listen.

II

The singing reached Joel vaguely; he felt happy and friendly toward all the people gathered there, people of bravery and industry, superior to a bourgeoisie that outdid them in ignorance and loose living, risen to a position of the highest prominence in a nation that for a decade had wanted only to be entertained. He liked them—he loved them. Great waves of good feeling flowed through him.

As the singer finished his number and there was a drift toward the hostess to say good-by, Joel had an idea. He would give them "Building It Up," his own composition. It was his only parlor trick, it had amused several parties and it might please Stella Walker. Possessed by the hunch, his blood throbbing with the scarlet corpuscles of exhibitionism, he sought her.

"Of course," she cried. "Please! Do you need anything?"

"Someone has to be the secretary that I'm supposed to be dictating to."

"I'll be her."

As the word spread, the guests in the hall, already putting on their coats to leave, drifted back and Joel faced the eyes of many strangers. He had a dim foreboding, realizing that the man who had just performed was a famous radio entertainer. Then someone said "Sh!" and he was alone with Stella, the center of a sinister Indian-like half-circle. Stella smiled up at him expectantly—he began.

His burlesque was based upon the cultural limitations of Mr. Dave Silverstein, an independent producer; Silverstein was presumed to be dictating a letter outlining a treatment of a story he had bought.

"—a story of divorce, the younger generators and the Foreign Legion," he heard his voice saying, with the intonations of Mr. Silverstein. "But we got to build it up, see?"

A sharp pang of doubt struck through him. The faces surrounding him in the gently molded light were intent and curious, but there was no ghost of a smile anywhere; directly in front the Great Lover of the screen glared at him with an eye as keen as the eye of a potato. Only Stella Walker looked up at him with a radiant, never faltering smile.

"If we make him a Menjou type, then we get a sort of Michael Arlen only with a Honolulu atmosphere."

Still not a ripple in front, but in the rear a rustling, a perceptible shift toward the left, toward the front door.

"—then she says she feels this sex appil for him and he burns out and says 'Oh, go on destroy yourself—'"

At some point he heard Nat Keogh snicker and here and there were a few encouraging faces, but as he finished he had the sickening realization that he had made a fool of himself in view of an important section of the picture world, upon whose favor depended his career.

For a moment he existed in the midst of a confused silence, broken by a general trek for the door. He felt the undercurrent of derision that rolled through the gossip; then— all this was in the space of ten seconds—the Great Lover, his eye hard and empty as the eye of a needle, shouted "Boo! Boo!" voicing in an overtone what he felt was the mood of the crowd. It was the resentment of the professional toward the amateur, of the community toward the stranger, the thumbs-down of the clan.

Only Stella Walker was still standing near and thanking him as if he had been an unparalleled success, as if it hadn't occurred to her that anyone hadn't like it. As Nat Keogh helped him into his overcoat, a great wave of self-disgust swept over him and he clung desperately to his rule of never betraying an inferior emotion until he no longer felt it.

"I was a flop," he said lightly, to Stella. "Never mind, it's a good number when appreciated. Thanks for your coôperation."

The smile did not leave her face—he bowed rather drunkenly and Nat drew him toward the door. . . .

The arrival of his breakfast awakened him into a broken and ruined world. Yesterday he was himself, a point of fire against an industry, today he felt that he was pitted under an enormous disadvantage, against those faces, against individual contempt and collective sneer. Worse than that, to Miles Calman he was become one of those rummies, stripped of dignity, whom Calman regretted he was compelled to use. To Stella Walker on whom he had forced a martyrdom to preserve the courtesy of her house—her opinion he did not dare to guess. His gastric juices ceased to flow and he set his poached eggs back on the telephone table. He wrote:

"Dear Miles: You can imagine my profound self-disgust. I confess to a taint of exhibitionism, but at six o'clock in the afternoon, in broad daylight! Good God! My apologies to your wife.

"Yours ever,

"Joel Coles."

Joel emerged from his office on the lot only to slink like a malefactor to the tobacco store. So suspicious was his manner that one of the studio police asked to see his admission card. He had decided to eat lunch outside when Nat Keogh, confident and cheerful, overtook him.

"What do you mean you're in permanent retirement? What if that Three-Piece Suit did boo you?

"Why, listen," he continued, drawing Joel into the studio restaurant. "The night of one of his premières at Grauman's,

[133]

Joe Squires kicked his tail while he was bowing to the crowd. The ham said Joe'd hear from him later but when Joe called him up at eight o'clock next day and said, 'I thought I was going to hear from you,' he hung up the phone."

The preposterous story cheered Joel, and he found a gloomy consolation in staring at the group at the next table, the sad, lovely Siamese twins, the mean dwarfs, the proud giant from the circus picture. But looking beyond at the yellow-stained faces of pretty women, their eyes all melancholy and startling with mascara, their ball gowns garish in full day, he saw a group who had been at Calman's and winced.

"Never again," he exclaimed aloud, "absolutely my last social appearance in Hollywood!"

The following morning a telegram was waiting for him at his office:

"You were one of the most agreeable people at our party. Expect you at my sister June's buffet supper next Sunday.
"STELLA WALKER CALMAN."

The blood rushed fast through his veins for a feverish minute. Incredulously he read the telegram over.

"Well, that's the sweetest thing I ever heard of in my life!"

III

Crazy Sunday again. Joel slept until eleven, then he read a newspaper to catch up with the past week. He lunched in his room on trout, avocado salad and a pint of California wine. Dressing for the tea, he selected a pin-check suit, a blue shirt, a burnt orange tie. There were dark circles of fatigue under his eyes. In his second-hand car he drove to the Riviera apartments. As he was introducing himself to Stella's sister, Miles and Stella arrived in riding clothes—they had been quarreling fiercely most of the afternoon on all the dirt roads back of Beverly Hills.

Miles Calman, tall, nervous, with a desperate humor and the unhappiest eyes Joel ever saw, was an artist from the top of his curiously shaped head to his niggerish feet. Upon these last he stood firmly—he had never made a cheap picture though he had sometimes paid heavily for the luxury of making experimental flops. In spite of his excellent company, one could not be with him long without realizing that he was not a well man.

From the moment of their entrance Joel's day bound itself up inextricably with theirs. As he joined the group around them Stella turned away from it with an impatient little tongue click—and Miles Calman said to the man who happened to be next to him:

"Go easy on Eva Goebel. There's hell to pay about her at home." Miles turned to Joel, "I'm sorry I missed you at the office yesterday. I spent the afternoon at the analyst's."

"You being psychoanalyzed?"

"I have been for months. First I went for claustrophobia, now I'm trying to get my whole life cleared up. They say it'll take over a year."

"There's nothing the matter with your life," Joel assured him.

"Oh, no? Well, Stella seems to think so. Ask anybody—they can all tell you about it," he said bitterly.

A girl perched herself on the arm of Miles' chair; Joel crossed to Stella, who stood disconsolately by the fire.

"Thank you for your telegram," he said. "It was darn sweet. I can't imagine anybody as good-looking as you are being so good-humored."

She was a little lovelier than he had ever seen her and perhaps the unstinted admiration in his eyes prompted her to unload on him—it did not take long, for she was obviously at

[135]

the emotional bursting point.

"—and Miles has been carrying on this thing for two years, and I never knew. Why, she was one of my best friends, always in the house. Finally when people began to come to me, Miles had to admit it."

She sat down vehemently on the arm of Joel's chair. Her riding breeches were the color of the chair and Joel saw that the mass of her hair was made up of some strands of red gold and some of pale gold, so that it could not be dyed, and that she had on no make-up. She was that good-looking—

Still quivering with the shock of her discovery, Stella found unbearable the spectacle of a new girl hovering over Miles; she led Joel into a bedroom, and seated at either end of a big bed they went on talking. People on their way to the washroom glanced in and made wisecracks, but Stella, emptying out her story, paid no attention. After a while Miles stuck his head in the door and said, "There's no use trying to explain something to Joel in half an hour that I don't understand myself and the psychoanalyst says will take a whole year to understand."

She talked on as if Miles were not there. She loved Miles, she said—under considerable difficulties she had always been faithful to him.

"The psychoanalyst told Miles that he had a mother complex. In his first marriage he transferred his mother complex to his wife, you see—and then his sex turned to me. But when we married the thing repeated itself—he transferred his mother complex to me and all his libido turned toward this other woman."

Joel knew that this probably wasn't gibberish—yet it sounded like gibberish. He knew Eva Goebel; she was a motherly person, older and probably wiser than Stella, who was a golden child.

Miles now suggested impatiently that Joel come back

with them since Stella had so much to say, so they drove out to the mansion in Beverly Hills. Under the high ceilings the situation seemed more dignified and tragic. It was an eerie bright night with the dark very clear outside of all the windows and Stella all rose-gold raging and crying around the room. Joel did not quite believe in picture actresses' grief. They have other preoccupations—they are beautiful rose-gold figures blown full of life by writers and directors, and after hours they sit around and talk in whispers and giggle innuendoes, and the ends of many adventures flow through them.

Sometimes he pretended to listen and instead thought how well she was got up—sleek breeches with a matched set of legs in them, an Italian-colored sweater with a little high neck, and a short brown chamois coat. He couldn't decide whether she was an imitation of an English lady or an English lady was an imitation of her. She hovered somewhere between the realest of realities and the most blatant of impersonations.

"Miles is so jealous of me that he questions everything I do," she cried scornfully. "When I was in New York I wrote him that I'd been to the theater with Eddie Baker. Miles was so jealous he phoned me ten times in one day."

"I was wild," Miles snuffled sharply, a habit he had in times of stress. "The analyst couldn't get any results for a week."

Stella shook her head despairingly. "Did you expect me just to sit in the hotel for three weeks?"

"I don't expect anything. I admit that I'm jealous. I try not to be. I worked on that with Dr. Bridgebane, but it didn't do any good. I was jealous of Joel this afternoon when you sat on the arm of his chair."

"You were?" she started up. "You were! Wasn't there somebody on the arm of your chair? And did you speak to me for two hours?"

"You were telling your troubles to Joel in the bedroom."

[137]

"When I think that that woman"—she seemed to believe that to omit Eva Goebel's name would be to lessen her reality—"used to come here—"

"All right—all right," said Miles wearily. "I've admitted everything and I feel as bad about it as you do." Turning to Joel he began talking about pictures, while Stella moved restlessly along the far walls, her hands in her breeches pockets.

"They've treated Miles terribly," she said, coming suddenly back into the conversation as if they'd never discussed her personal affairs. "Dear, tell him about old Beltzer trying to change your picture."

As she stood hovering protectively over Miles, her eyes flashing with indignation in his behalf, Joel realized that he was in love with her. Stifled with excitement he got up to say good night.

With Monday the week resumed its workaday rhythm, in sharp contrast to the theoretical discussions, the gossip and scandal of Sunday; there was the endless detail of script revision—"Instead of a lousy dissolve, we can leave her voice on the sound track and cut to a medium shot of the taxi from Bell's angle or we can simply pull the camera back to include the station, hold it a minute and then pan to the row of taxis"—by Monday afternoon Joel had again forgotten that people whose business was to provide entertainment were ever privileged to be entertained. In the evening he phoned Miles' house. He asked for Miles but Stella came to the phone.

"Do things seem better?"

"Not particularly. What are you doing next Saturday evening?"

"Nothing."

"The Perrys are giving a dinner and theater party and Miles won't be here—he's flying to South Bend to see the Notre Dame-California game. I thought you might go with me in his place."

[138]

After a long moment Joel said, "Why—surely. If there's a conference I can't make dinner but I can get to the theater."

"Then I'll say we can come."

Joel walked his office. In view of the strained relations of the Calmans, would Miles be pleased, or did she intend that Miles shouldn't know of it? That would be out of the question—if Miles didn't mention it Joel would. But it was an hour or more before he could get down to work again.

Wednesday there was a four-hour wrangle in a conference room crowded with planets and nebula of cigarette smoke. Three men and a woman paced the carpet in turn, suggesting or condemning, speaking sharply or persuasively, confidently or despairingly. At the end Joel lingered to talk to Miles.

The man was tired—not with the exaltation of fatigue but life-tired, with his lids sagging and his beard prominent over the blue shadows near his mouth.

"I hear you're flying to the Notre Dame game."

Miles looked beyond him and shook his head.

"I've given up the idea."

"Why?"

"On account of you." Still he did not look at Joel.

"What the hell, Miles?"

"That's why I've given it up." He broke into a perfunctory laugh at himself. "I can't tell what Stella might do just out of spite—she's invited you to take her to the Perrys', hasn't she? I wouldn't enjoy the game."

The fine instinct that moved swiftly and confidently on the set, muddled so weakly and helplessly through his personal life.

"Look, Miles," Joel said frowning. "I've never made any passes whatsoever at Stella. If you're really seriously canceling your trip on account of me, I won't go to the Perrys' with her. I won't see her. You can trust me absolutely."

Miles looked at him, carefully now.

[139]

"Maybe." He shrugged his shoulders. "Anyhow there'd just be somebody else. I wouldn't have any fun."

"You don't seem to have much confidence in Stella. She told me she'd always been true to you."

"Maybe she has." In the last few minutes several more muscles had sagged around Miles' mouth. "But how can I ask anything of her after what's happened? How can I expect her—" He broke off and his face grew harder as he said, "I'll tell you one thing, right or wrong and no matter what I've done, if I ever had anything on her I'd divorce her. I can't have my pride hurt—that would be the last straw."

His tone annoyed Joel, but he said:

"Hasn't she calmed down about the Eva Goebel thing?"

"No." Miles snuffled pessimistically. "I can't get over it either."

"I thought it was finished."

"I'm trying not to see Eva again, but you know it isn't easy just to drop something like that—it isn't some girl I kissed last night in a taxi. The psychoanalyst says—"

"I know," Joel interrupted. "Stella told me." This was depressing. "Well, as far as I'm concerned if you go to the game I won't see Stella. And I'm sure Stella has nothing on her conscience about anybody."

"Maybe not," Miles repeated listlessly. "Anyhow I'll stay and take her to the party. Say," he said suddenly, "I wish you'd come too. I've got to have somebody sympathetic to talk to. That's the trouble—I've influenced Stella in everything. Especially I've influenced her so that she likes all the men I like—it's very difficult."

"It must be," Joel agreed.

IV

Joel could not get to the dinner. Self-conscious in his silk hat against the unemployment, he waited for the others in front of the Hollywood Theater and watched the evening parade: obscure replicas of bright, particular picture stars, spavined men in polo coats, a stomping dervish with the beard and staff of an apostle, a pair of chic Filipinos in collegiate clothes, reminder that this corner of the Republic opened to the seven seas, a long fantastic carnival of young shouts which proved to be a fraternity initiation. The line split to pass two smart limousines that stopped at the curb.

There she was, in a dress like ice-water, made in a thousand pale-blue pieces, with icicles trickling at the throat. He started forward.

"So you like my dress?"

"Where's Miles?"

"He flew to the game after all. He left yesterday morning—at least I think—" She broke off. "I just got a telegram from South Bend saying that he's starting back. I forgot—you know all these people?"

The party of eight moved into the theater.

Miles had gone after all and Joel wondered if he should have come. But during the performance, with Stella a profile under the pure grain of light hair, he thought no more about Miles. Once he turned and looked at her and she looked back at him, smiling and meeting his eyes for as long as he wanted. Between the acts they smoked in the lobby and she whispered:

"They're all going to the opening of Jack Johnson's night club—I don't want to go, do you?"

"Do we have to?"

"I suppose not." She hesitated. "I'd like to talk to you. I suppose we could go to our house—if I were only sure—"

Again she hesitated and Joel asked:

"Sure of what?"

"Sure that—oh, I'm haywire I know, but how can I be sure Miles went to the game?"

"You mean you think he's with Eva Goebel?"

[141]

"No, not so much that—but supposing he was here watching everything I do. You know Miles does odd things sometimes. Once he wanted a man with a long beard to drink tea with him and he sent down to the casting agency for one, and drank tea with him all afternoon."

"That's different. He sent you a wire from South Bend— that proves he's at the game."

After the play they said good night to the others at the curb and were answered by looks of amusement. They slid off along the golden garish thoroughfare through the crowd that had gathered around Stella.

"You see he could arrange the telegrams," Stella said, "very easily."

That was true. And with the idea that perhaps her uneasiness was justified, Joel grew angry: if Miles had trained a camera on them he felt no obligations toward Miles. Aloud he said:

"That's nonsense."

There were Christmas trees already in the shop windows and the full moon over the boulevard was only a prop, as scenic as the giant boudoir lamps of the corners. On into the dark foliage of Beverly Hills that flamed as eucalyptus by day, Joel saw only the flash of a white face under his own, the arc of her shoulder. She pulled away suddenly and looked up at him.

"Your eyes are like your mother's," she said. "I used to have a scrap book full of pictures of her."

"Your eyes are like your own and not a bit like any other eyes," he answered.

Something made Joel look out into the grounds as they went into the house, as if Miles were lurking in the shrubbery. A telegram waited on the Hall table. She read aloud:

"CHICAGO.
"Home tomorrow night. Thinking of you. Love.
"MILES."

"You see," she said, throwing the slip back on the table, "he could easily have faked that." She asked the butler for drinks and sandwiches and ran upstairs, while Joel walked into the empty reception rooms. Strolling about he wandered to the piano where he had stood in disgrace two Sundays before.

"Then we could put over," he said aloud, "a story of divorce, the younger generation and the Foreign Legion."

His thoughts jumped to another telegram.

"You were one of the most agreeable people at our party—"

An idea occurred to him. If Stella's telegram had been purely a gesture of courtesy then it was likely that Miles had inspired it, for it was Miles who had invited him. Probably Miles had said:

"Send him a wire—he's miserable—he thinks he's queered himself."

It fitted in with "I've influenced Stella in everything. Especially I've influenced her so that she likes all the men I like." A woman would do a thing like that because she felt sympathetic—only a man would do it because he felt responsible.

When Stella came back into the room he took both her hands.

"I have a strange feeling that I'm a sort of pawn in a spite game you're playing against Miles," he said.

"Help yourself to a drink."

And the odd thing is that I'm in love with you anyhow."

The telephone rang and she freed herself to answer it.

"Another wire from Miles," she announced. "He dropped it, or it says he dropped it, from the airplane at Kansas City."

"I suppose he asked to be remembered to me."

"No, he just said he loved me. I believe he does. He's so very weak."

"Come sit beside me," Joel urged her.

It was early. And it was still a few minutes short of midnight a half-hour later, when Joel walked to the cold hearth, and said tersely:

"Meaning that you haven't any curiosity about me?"

"Not at all. You attract me a lot and you know it. The point is that I suppose I really do love Miles."

"Obviously."

"And tonight I feel uneasy about everything."

He wasn't angry—he was even faintly relieved that a possible entanglement was avoided. Still as he looked at her, the warmth and softness of her body thawing her cold blue costume, he knew she was one of the things he would always regret.

"I've got to go," he said. "I'll phone a taxi."

"Nonsense—there's a chauffeur on duty."

He winced at her readiness to have him go, and seeing this she kissed him lightly and said, "You're sweet, Joel." Then suddenly three things happened: he took down his drink at a gulp, the phone rang loud through the house and a clock in the hall struck in trumpet notes.

Nine—ten—eleven—twelve—

V

It was Sunday again. Joel realized that he had come to the theater this evening with the work of the week still hanging about him like cerements. He had made love to Stella as he might attack some matter to be cleaned up hurriedly before the day's end. But this was Sunday—the lovely, lazy perspective of the next twenty-four hours unrolled before him—every minute was something to be approached with lulling indirection, every moment held the germ of innumerable possibilities. Nothing was impossible—everything was just beginning. He poured himself another drink.

With a sharp moan, Stella slipped forward inertly by the

telephone. Joel picked her up and laid her on the sofa. He squirted soda-water on a handkerchief and slapped it over her face. The telephone mouthpiece was still grinding and he put it to his ear.

"—the plane fell just this side of Kansas City. The body of Miles Calman has been identified and—"

He hung up the receiver.

"Lie still," he said, stalling, as Stella opened her eyes.

"Oh, what's happened?" she whispered. "Call them back. Oh, what's happened?"

"I'll call them right away. What's your doctor's name?"

"Did they say Miles was dead?"

"Lie quiet—is there a servant still up?"

"Hold me—I'm frightened."

He put his arm around her.

"I want the name of your doctor," he said sternly. "It may be a mistake but I want someone here."

"It's Doctor—Oh, God, is Miles dead?"

Joel ran upstairs and searched through strange medicine cabinets for spirits of ammonia. When he came down Stella cried:

"He isn't dead—I know he isn't. This is part of his scheme. He's torturing me. I know he's alive. I can feel he's alive."

"I want to get hold of some close friend of yours, Stella. You can't stay here alone tonight."

"Oh, no," she cried. "I can't see anybody. You stay. I haven't got any friend." She got up, tears streaming down her face. "Oh, Miles is my only friend. He's not dead—he can't be dead. I'm going there right away and see. Get a train. You'll have to come with me."

"You can't. There's nothing to do tonight. I want you to tell me the name of some woman I can call: Lois? Joan? Carmel? Isn't there somebody?"

Stella stared at him blindly.

"Eva Goebel was my best friend," she said.

Joel thought of Miles, his sad and desperate face in the office two days before. In the awful silence of his death all was clear about him. He was the only American-born director with both an interesting temperament and an artistic conscience. Meshed in an industry, he had paid with his ruined nerves for having no resilience, no healthy cynicism, no refuge—only a pitiful and precarious escape.

There was a sound at the outer door—it opened suddenly, and there were footsteps in the hall.

"Miles!" Stella screamed. "Is it you, Miles? Oh, it's Miles."

A telegraph boy appeared in the doorway.

"I couldn't find the bell. I heard you talking inside."

The telegram was a duplicate of the one that had been phoned. While Stella read it over and over, as though it were a black lie, Joel telephoned. It was still early and he had difficulty getting anyone; when finally he succeeded in finding some friends he made Stella take a stiff drink.

"You'll stay here, Joel," she whispered, as though she were half-asleep. "You won't go away. Miles liked you—he said you—" She shivered violently, "Oh, my God, you don't know how alone I feel." Her eyes closed, "Put your arms around me. Miles had a suit like that." She started bolt upright. "Think of what he must have felt. He was afraid of almost everything, anyhow."

She shook her head dazedly. Suddenly she seized Joel's face and held it close to hers.

"You won't go. You like me—you love me, don't you? Don't call up anybody. Tomorrow's time enough. You stay here with me tonight."

He stared at her, at first incredulously, and then with shocked understanding. In her dark groping Stella was trying to keep Miles alive by sustaining a situation in which he had

figured—as if Miles' mind could not die so long as the possibilities that had worried him still existed. It was a distraught
and tortured effort to stave off the realization that he was
dead.

Resolutely Joel went to the phone and called a doctor.

"Don't, oh, don't call anybody!" Stella cried. "Come
back here and put your arms around me."

"Is Doctor Bales in?"

"Joel," Stella cried. "I thought I could count on you.
Miles liked you. He was jealous of you—Joel, come here."

Ah then—if she betrayed Miles she would be keeping him
alive—for if he were really dead how could he be betrayed?

"—has just had a very severe shock. Can you come at
once, and get hold of a nurse?"

"Joel!"

Now the door-bell and the telephone began to ring inter-
mittently, and automobiles were stopping in front of the door.

"But you're not going," Stella begged him. "You're going
to stay, aren't you?"

"No," he answered. "But I'll be back, if you need me."

Standing on the steps of the house which now hummed
and palpitated with the life that flutters around death like
protective leaves, he began to sob a little in his throat.

"Everything he touched he did something magical to,"
he thought. "He even brought that little gamin alive and made
her a sort of masterpiece."

And then:

"What a hell of a hole he leaves in this damn wilderness
—already!"

And then with a certain bitterness, "Oh, yes, I'll be back
—I'll be back!"

Altagracia's Dying Party

By AMANDA M. CHASE

They fetched her from the hospital,
Ten, and carried her like a three-year-old.
Weazened face, shrunken body,
Great eyes pondering mysteries of pain;
Too busy with the labor of her breath
For much rejoicing in her pink silk robe;
Nor could blue slippers rouse her feet to dance.
The oldsters glided in and sat about
To watch her die. Children dashed in from play,
Grey shadows crept from murky corners
Enveloping the girl. She pushed aside
The little Jesus she was begged to kiss,
Put a chilling finger to her mother's cheek.
Tears! They flung her into fretful terror.
"Laugh!" she gasped, "Laugh! Laugh aloud!"
The mother laughed—a mirthless broken sound;
It might have been the cracking of a heart.
The daughter flashed an answering smile
Fading into gray. Her dying party
Had been to Altagracia's wish.

The Girl

By MERIDEL LE SUEUR

Miss LeSueur was born in Iowa in 1900 and has been a
reporter, teacher, lecturer, and theater director as well as
a writer. Her books include *North Star Country* (1945)
and *Salute to Spring* (1940), a collection of her masterly
short stories.

She was going the inland route because she had been
twice on the coast route. She had asked three times at the automobile club how far it was through the Tehachapi Mountains,
and she had the route marked on the map in red pencil. The car
was running like a T, the garage man told her. All her dresses
were back from the cleaners, and there remained only the lace
collar to sew on her black crepe so that they would be all ready
when she got to San Francisco. She had read up on the history
of the mountains and listed all the Indian tribes and marked
the route of the Friars from the Sacramento Valley. She was
glad now that Clara Robbins, the "Math." teacher, was not
going with her. She liked to be alone, to have everything just
the way she wanted it, exactly.

There was nothing she wanted changed. It was a remarkable pleasure to have everything just right, to get into her
neat fine-looking little roadster, start out in the fine morning,
with her map tucked into the seat, every road marked. She was
lucky too, how lucky she was. She had her place secure at
Central "High," teaching history. On September 18, she
knew she would be coming back to the same room, to teach
the same course in history. It was a great pleasure. Driving
along, she could see her lean face in the windshield. She
couldn't help but think that she had no double chin, and her
pride rose in her, a lean thing. She saw herself erect, a little
caustic and severe, and the neat turn-over collar of her little

blue suit. Her real lone self. This was what she wanted. Nothing messy. She had got herself up in the world. This was the first summer she had not taken a summer course, and she felt a little guilty; but she had had a good summer just being lazy, and now she was going to San Francisco to see her sister and would come back two days before school opened. She had thought in the spring that her skin was getting that papyrus look so many teachers had, and she had a little tired droop to her shoulders and was a little bit too thin. It was fine to be thin but not too thin. Now she looked better, brown, and she had got the habit of a little eye shadow, a little dry rouge, and just a touch of lipstick. It was really becoming.

Yes, everything was ideal.

But before long she was sorry she had come through the Tehachapi Mountains. Why hadn't someone told her they were like that? They did her in. Frightening. Mile after mile in the intense September heat, through fierce mountains of sand, and bare gleaming rock faces jutting sheer from the road. Her eyes burned, her throat was parched, and there was mile after mile of lonely road without a service station and not a soul passing. She wished, after all, that Miss Robbins had come with her. It would have been nice to be able to say, "What an interesting formation, Miss Robbins! We really should make sketches of it, so we could look up the geological facts when we get back." Everything would have seemed normal then.

She drove slowly through the hot yellow swells, around the firm curves; and the yellow light shone far off in the tawny valleys, where black mares, delicate haunched, grazed, flesh shining as the sun struck off them. The sun beat down like a golden body about to take form on the road ahead of her. She drove very slowly, and something began to loosen in her, and her eyes seemed to dilate and darken as she looked into the fold upon fold of earth flesh lying clear to the horizon. She saw she was not making what is called "good time." In fact, she was making very bad time.

She had been driving five hours. She looked at her wrist watch and decided she would stop, even if it was only eleven-thirty, and have lunch. So when she saw a little service station far down, tucked into the great folds of dun hill, she was glad. Her car crept closer circling out of sight of it and then circling back until her aching eyes could read the sign—Half Way Station—and she drew up to the side and stopped. Her skin felt as if it were shrivelling on her bone. She saw a man—or was it a boy?—with a pack, standing by the gas pump proba-bly waiting to catch a ride; she wouldn't pick him up, that was certain. These hills were certainly forsaken.

She went in at the door marked Ladies. The tiny cubicle comforted her. She opened her vanity case and took out some tissue, made little pads and put them over her eyes. But still all she could see was those terrifying great mounds of the earth and the sun thrusting down like arrows. What a ghastly country! Why hadn't someone told her? It was barbarous of the automobile club to let her come through this country. She couldn't think of one tribe of Indians.

She really felt a kind of fright and stayed there a long time, and then she got a fright for fear she had left her keys in the car and with that boy out there—she could see his sharp piercing glance out of his brown face—and she had to go pouncing all through her bag, and at last she found them, of all places, in her coin purse and she always put them into the breast pocket of her suit. She did think people were nuisances who had to go looking in all their pockets for keys. Habit was an excellent thing and saved nobody knew how much time.

But at last she drew a deep breath, opened the door onto the vast terrible bright needles of light, and there she saw through the heavy down pouring curtain the boy still standing there exactly as he had been standing before, half leaning,

[151]

looking from under his black brows. He looked like a dark stroke in the terrible light, and he seemed to be still looking at her. She fumbled the collar at her throat, brushed off the front of her skirt, and went into the lunch room.

"My, it's certainly hot," she said to the thin man behind the counter. She felt strange hearing her voice issue from her.

"It is," said the proprietor, "but a little cooler in here." He was a thin shrewd man.

She sat down in the booth. "Yes," she said, and saw that the boy had followed her in and sat down on the stool at the lunch counter, but he seemed to still be looking at her. He looked as if he had been roasted, slowly turned on a spit until he seemed glowing, like phosphorus, as if the sun were in him, and his black eyes were a little bloodshot as if the whites had been burned, and his broad chest fell down easily to his hips as he ground out a cigarette with his heel. The thin man brought her a glass of water. "What will you have, ma'am?" he said with respect. "I'll have a lettuce sandwich," she said. "I'm afraid we ain't got any proper lettuce ma'am," he said bowing a little. "We can't get it fresh out here. We have peanut butter, sliced tongue—" "All right," she said quickly, "peanut butter and, well, a glass of beer." She felt that the boy was somehow laughing at her. She felt angry.

"This the first time you been in these parts?" called out the thin man from behind the counter. "Yes," she said, and her own voice sounded small to her. "It is." The boy at the counter turned his head, still with it lowered, so that his eyes looked up at her even though she was sitting down in the booth, and a soft charge went through her, frightening. She felt herself bridling, and she said in a loud cool voice: "This is a very interesting country. Do you know anything about the formation of these curious rocks that jut out of the hills?— they are so bare and then suddenly this rock—"

Was she imagining it only, that the boy seemed to smile

and shifted his weight?

"No'm," said the thin man, drawing the beer, "I can't say I ever thought about it." She felt as if something passed between the two men, and it made her angry, as if they were subtly laughing at her. "I know it's hard to grow anything here, unless you got a deep well," he said.

"Oh, I can imagine," she sang out too loud; she felt her voice ringing like metal. The boy seemed not to be touched by what she was saying, but he attended curiously to every word, standing silent but alert like a horse standing at a fence waiting for something. So she began to tell the lunch room proprietor the history of the country, and he seemed amazed but not impressed. It made her feel vindicated somehow. Still the boy drooped alert on the stool, his half face turned towards her, his huge burned ear springing from his head. She stayed half an hour and so cut her time still further, but she felt much better and thought she would make up for it. She got up and paid her bill. "I'll send you a book about the Indians," she said to the thin man.

He smiled, "That will be very nice," he said. "Thank you, I'm sure," and the two men looked at each other again, and she was amazed at the anger that gushed like a sudden fountain in her breast. She sailed out and got into the car. The thin man came after her. "Oh, by the way," he said, "the lad in there has had an awful time this morning catching a ride. He's got to get up to the bridge, about fifty miles." She felt they were putting something over on her. "I'll vouch for him," the thin man said. "He lives here, and I know his folks now for eighteen years. He's been to the harvest fields, and it would be something for him to ride with an educated lady like you," he added cunningly. The boy came out and was smiling at her now very eagerly. "Now they want something," she thought, and she was suddenly amazed to find out that she despised men and always had.

[153]

"I don't like to drive with a strange man," she said, stubborn.

"Oh, this boy is harmless," the thin man said, and that look passed between the two of them again. "I can vouch for him—good as gold his family is. I thought maybe anyhow you might give him a mite of education on the way." A pure glint of malice came into the thin man's eyes that frightened her. He hates me, too, she thought. Men like that hate women with brains.

"All right," she said, "get in."

"Get right in there," the thin man said. "It's only a piece."

The boy rose towards her, and she drew away, and he sat down in a great odor of milk and hay, right beside her, stifling. Without speaking she threw the car in, and they plunged up the bald brow of the hill and began to climb slowly. The sun was in the central sky, and the heat fell vertically. She wouldn't look at him and wished she could get out her hand-kerchief—such a nauseating odor of sweat and something like buttermilk. She couldn't help but be conscious of the side of his overall leg beside her and his big shoes, and she felt he never took his eyes off her, like some awful bird—and that curious little smile on his mouth as if he knew something about her that she didn't know herself. She knew without looking that he was bending his head towards her with that curious awful little glimmer of a smile.

He said in a soft cajoling voice, "It's pretty hot, and it's nice of you to take me. I had a hard time."

It disarmed her. She felt sorry for him, wanting to be helpful. She always wanted to help men, do something for them, and then really underneath she could hate them. "Oh," she said, "that was all right. You know one hates to pick up just anyone."

"Sure enough," he said. "I heard in Colorado a fellow got killed."

[154]

"Yes," she said, but she was on her guard. His words seemed to mean nothing to him. He was like the heat, in a drowse. "My, you must have been in the sun," she said.

"Yes," he said, "I've been as far as Kansas—looking for work."

"The conditions are pretty bad," she said.

"There ain't no work," he said simply.

"Oh," she said, "that's too bad," and felt awkward and inane. He seemed in such a sun-warmed ease, his legs stretching down. He had his coat in his arms and his shirtsleeves were torn off, showing his huge roasted arms. She could see the huge turn of the muscles of his arms, out of the corner of her eye.

They went climbing in gear up that naked mountain, and it began to affect her curiously. The earth seemed to turn on the bone rich and shining, the great mounds burning in the sun, the great golden body, hard and robust, and the sun striking hot and dazzling.

"These mountains," she began to tell him, "are thousands of years old."

"Yeah," he said looking at her sharply, "I'll bet." He lounged down beside her. "I'm sleepy," he said. "I slept on a bench in L.A. las' night." She felt he was moving slowly towards her as if about to touch her leg. She sat as far over as she could, but she felt him looking at her, taking something for granted.

"Yes," she said, "it would be an interesting study, these mountains."

He didn't answer and threw her into confusion. He lounged down, looking up at her. She drew her skirt sharply down over her leg. Something became very alert in her, and she could tell what he was doing without looking at him.

They didn't stop again. The country looked the same every minute. They rose on that vast naked curve into the

[155]

blue sky, and dropped into the crevasse and rose again on the same curve. Lines and angles, and bare earth curves, tawny and rolling in the heat. She thought she was going a little mad and longed to see a tree or a house.

"I could go on to San Francisco with you," he said and she could feel her heart suddenly in her.

"Why would you do that?" she said drawing away, one hand at her throat.

"Why shouldn't I?" he said insolently. "It would be kind of nice for both of us," he was smiling that insolent knowing smile. She didn't know how to answer. If she took him seriously it would implicate her, and if she didn't it might also. "It would be kind of nice now, wouldn't it?" he said again with his curious soft impudence. "Wouldn't it?"

"Why, of course, I'm going to San Francisco anyway," she said evasively.

"Oh sure," he said, "I know that. But it isn't so hot going alone. And we get along, don't we?" He didn't move, but his voice drove into her.

"Why, I don't know," she said coldly, "I'm only taking you to the bridge."

He gave a little grunt and put his cap on his head, pulling the beak over his eyes which only concentrated his awful power. She pulled her blouse up over her shoulders. She had never noticed before that it fell so low in front. She felt terribly. And to her horror he went on talking to her softly.

"You wouldn't kid me, would you? You know I like you, I like you. You're pretty."

She couldn't say a word. She felt her throat beating. He was making love to her just as if she was any common slut. She felt her throat beating and swelling.

He kept on his soft drowsy talk, "The times is sure hard." His words seemed to be very tiny falling from the enormous glow of his presence, wonderful, as if he had been turned

[156]

naked, roasted in the sun. You could smell his sunburnt flesh. And you could smell the earth turning on its spit under the mighty sun. If only he were not so near; the car threw them close together, and she tried to go easy around the curves so that his big body would not lounge down upon her like a mountain. She couldn't remember when she had been so close to a man. It was as frightening as some great earth cataclysm. She prided herself on knowing men. She was their equal in every way, she knew that.

If only she could see something familiar, then she could get back her normal feelings about men. She felt as if she were in a nightmare.

"I worked when I was twenty," he went on softly. "Made good money, blew it in on Saturday night. Made big money when I was twenty—Jesus, I've got something to look forward to, haven't I."

She sat over as far as she could. "Where did you work?" she managed to say. She prided herself on always getting information about people. They talked about Roosevelt and the New Deal. She always had strong views, but for the first time in her life she felt as if what she was saying was no good, like talking when some gigantic happening is silently going on. She didn't know what was happening, but she felt that every moment he won, was slowly overcoming her, and that her talk gave him a chance silently to overcome her. She was frightened as if they were about to crack up in a fearful accident. She relaxed on the seat, and the heat stroked down her body. She wished she wasn't driving a car. The great body of the earth seemed to touch her, and she began looking where the shadows were beginning to stroke down the sides of the mounds as if she might sleep there for a little while. An awful desire to sleep drugged her, as if she hadn't slept for years and years. She felt warm and furred and dangerously drugged.

It was as if a little rocket exploded in front of her face

[157]

when he said, "Let's don't talk about that," and he leaned closer than he had. "Let's talk about you." She could see suddenly his whole face thrust to her, the gleaming strong teeth, the roasted young cheeks, and he had long single whiskers growing out like a mandarin. She laughed a little. "Who do you think I am?" she asked nervously. "Why, I guess you're a pretty good-looking girl," he said. "You look pretty good to me." She bridled at this common language, as if she were nothing but any girl you pick up anywhere.

"Why, I'm a school teacher," she cried.

He didn't seem surprised. "O.K.," he said, laughing into her face.

"Why, I could almost be your mother," she cried.

"Aw, that's a new one," he said, and he put his great hand straight on her arm. "Never heard of a girl wanting to make out she was old before."

She had an awful desire to make him say more; she was frightened. Swift thoughts, habitual thoughts, came into her head, and they seemed like frail things that the heat pounded down. Was it because they were so far out in these strange, rising, mounded hills?

"Are those cigarettes?" he said pointing to the pocket beside her. "Let's stop and have a smoke."

"Oh no," she cried, "I haven't time. I'm behind now. I've got to make up a lot of time."

"O.K.," he said. "We can smoke here."

"All right," she said, handing him the package. "You keep the package."

"All right," he said and took one out and put the package into his pocket.

The sun moved to her side and fell on her shoulder and breast and arm. It was as if all her blood sprang warm out of her. The sun moved slowly and fell along her whole side.

"Oh," he said, "I know you like me."

"How do you know?" she said offended, trying to see the road. She felt fatuous indulging in this adolescent conversation. She let her skirt slip up a little. She knew she had good legs, tapering down swiftly to her ankles. But he didn't seem actually to be looking at her; a heat came out of his great lax body and enveloped her. He seemed warmly to include her, close to himself.

"What kind of a wheel is that?" he said and put his large thick hand beside her own small one on the wheel. "Oh, it turns easy," he said. "I haven't driven a car since I left home. A good car is a pretty sweet thing," he said, and leaned over and began to fondle the gadgets on the front, and she looked fascinated at his huge wrist joint covered with golden hair bleached in the sun. She had to look and saw that his hair was black on his skull but also burnt around the edges. Looking at him she met his gaze and felt her face flush.

They fell down the valley, yellow as a dream. The hills lifted themselves out on the edge of the light. The great animal flesh jointed mountains wrought a craving in her. There was not a tree, not a growth, just the bare swelling rondures of the mountains, the yellow hot swells, as if they were lifting and being driven through an ossified torrent.

The Tehachapis rolled before them, with only their sharp primeval glint, warm and fierce. They didn't say anything about that in the books. She felt suddenly as if she had missed everything. She should say something more to her classes. Suppose she should say—"The Tehachapi Mountains have warmed and bloomed for a thousand years." After all, why not? This was the true information.

She stopped the car. She turned and looked directly at him. "What is you name?" she asked.

Puzzled, he leaned towards her, that tender warm glint on his face. "Thom Beason," he said. The hot light seemed to fall around them like rain.

[159]

"Listen," he said gripping her hands, twisting them a little, "Let's get out. Wouldn't it be swell to lie down over there in the hills. Look there's a shadow just over there. It's cool in those shadows if you dig down a little—"

She saw his wrists, his giant breast, his knees, and behind him the tawny form and heat of the great earth woman, basking yellow and plump in the sun, her cliffs, her joints gleaming yellow rock, her ribs, her sides warm and full. The rocks that skirted the road glistened like bone, a sheer precipice and dazzle of rock, frightening and splendid, like the sheer precipice of his breast looming towards her so that she could feel the heat come from him and envelop her like fire, and she felt she was falling swiftly down the sides of him, and for the first time in her life she felt the sheer sides of her own body dropping swift and fleet down to her dreaming feet, and an ache, like lightning piercing stone, struck into her between the breasts.

She let her head fall over their hands and pulled back from him in hard resistance. She could not go to his breast that welcomed her—All my delicacy, my purity, she thought. He will not see me. I must not change. I must not change. The tears came to her eyes, and at the same time a canker of self-loathing, terrible, festered in her.

The moment had passed. He withdrew from her. "O.K.," he said.

"You don't need to be scared. Only if you wanted to. O.K. Let's go. You can make up your time. We're only about a half hour from the bridge where I blow."

She began driving very fast, very well. He withdrew completely from her, just waiting to get out. It hurt her, as if there had been before her some sumptuous feast she had been unable to partake of, the lush passional day, the wheaty boy, some wonderful, wonderful fruit.

"I'll swan," he said. "There's old Magill going with a

load of melons. Hi!" he shouted.

She wished he was gone already. She wildly began thinking what she could say to him. She thought she would say, casually—"Well, good luck." She felt easier knowing what she was going to say. She stopped the car. He got out and stood by the car. She wanted to do something for him. She really would have liked to give him something. She thought she would buy him a melon. "How much are they?" she said nodding towards the melons and hunting for her pocketbook. He ran over. "You pick out a good one," she called after him.

He came back with a large one with yellow crevasses. His strong talons curved around it, and he kept pressing it, leaving a dent which swelled out after his fingers. He held up the great melon with its half-moon partitions, grading golden towards the sun. She fumbled with her purse to pay for it, and suddenly she saw that he was holding it towards her, that he was giving it to her, and she was ashamed and held the quarter she had taken out, in her hand. He was smiling at her as if he felt sad for her. She smiled foolishly and sat pressing her wet hands together.

"Well, good-bye," he said. "And good luck."

"Good-bye," she said. Now she could not say good luck. He had beat her to it. Why should he wish her good luck when she had it? . . .

He turned and ran towards the wagon, climbed in and did not look back. She drove around the curve, stopped, turned down the mirror and looked at her face. She felt like a stick and looked like a witch. Now she was safe—safe. She would never never change, pure and inviolate forever; and she began to cry.

After five minutes she saw a car rounding the mountain to her right. It would pass her soon. She got out her whiskbroom, brushed her suit, brushed off the seat where he had sat, opened the back window to air out the smell of buttermilk and hay, started the car and drove to San Francisco because that was where she was going.

Modoc County Cowboy

Modoc is a large and beautiful but virtually uninhabited county in the extreme northeast corner of the state. The ballad-maker is anonymous.

Used to be a ranch hand, I could rope or ride;
Here in Modoc County I'm just froze or fried.

Went to Steelswamp City, hunting me a date.
All closed up at nine oclock, called it very late.

Rode to Alturas County Seat, went down the line.
One old Siwash squaw there, sick and halfway blind.

Came from Carson City, had a girl and a job.
Here in Modoc County even a sheep would starve.

God damn Modoc County! I am going away
Just as soon as I can draw just a little pay.

Galvez got me drunk, or I would of never come.
Rather sell my saddle and hike off on the bum.

Johnny Bear

By JOHN STEINBECK

Steinbeck is preeminently the California novelist. His *Grapes of Wrath* (1939) ranks with Helen Hunt Jackson's *Ramona* and Frank Norris's *Octopus* as a classic statement of California's hazy conscience about the distribution of wealth; and such other novels as *Tortilla Flat* (1935), *In Dubious Battle* (1936), and *East of Eden* (1952), are required reading for the California reader. Steinbeck's short stories, among them "Johnny Bear", are collected in *The Pastures of Heaven* (1932) and *The Long Valley* (1938). Steinbeck's themes are almost invariably rural or rural-proletarian. Steinbeck (born 1902) was raised in the Salinas Valley east of Monterey, and it was a matter of course that he ran cultivators, bucked grain bags, and worked around cattle. He attended Stanford off and on in the twenties, and has left it on record that this was the least useful part of his education. "Johnny Bear," is set in the familiar Salinas Valley, also called The Steinbeck Country.

The village of Loma is built, as its name implies, on a low round hill that rises like an island out of the flat mouth of the Salinas Valley in central California. To the north and east of the town a black tule swamp stretches for miles, but to the south the marsh has been drained. Rich vegetable land has been the result of the draining, land so black with wealth that the lettuce and cauliflowers grow to giants.

The owners of the swamp to the north of the village began to covet the black land. They banded together and formed a reclamation district. I work for the company which took the contract to put a ditch through. The floating clamshell digger arrived, was put together and started eating a ditch of open water through the swamp.

[163]

I tried living in the floating bunkhouse with the crew for a while, but the mosquitoes that hung in banks over the dredger and the heavy pestilential mist that sneaked out of the swamp every night and slid near to the ground drove me into the village of Loma, where I took a furnished room, the most dismal I have ever seen, in the house of Mrs. Ratz. I might have looked farther, but the idea of having my mail come in care of Mrs. Ratz decided me. After all, I only slept in the bare cold room. I ate my meals in the galley of the floating bunkhouse.

There aren't more than two hundred people in Loma. The Methodist church has the highest place on the hill; its spire is visible for miles. Two groceries, a hardware store, an ancient Masonic Hall and the Buffalo Bar comprise the public buildings. On the side of the hills are the small wooden houses of the population, and on the rich southern flats are the houses of the landowners, small yards usually enclosed by high walls of clipped cypress to keep out the driving afternoon winds.

There was nothing to do in Loma in the evening except to go to the saloon, an old board building with swinging doors and a wooden sidewalk awning. Neither prohibition nor repeal had changed its business, its clientele, or the quality of its whiskey. In the course of an evening every male inhabitant of Loma over fifteen years old came at least once to the Buffalo Bar, had a drink, talked a while and went home.

Fat Carl, the owner and bartender, greeted every new-comer with a phlegmatic sullenness which nevertheless inspired familiarity and affection. His face was sour, his tone downright unfriendly, and yet—I don't know how he did it. I know I felt gratified and warm when Fat Carl knew me well enough to turn his sour pig face to me and say with some impatience, "Well, what's it going to be?" He always asked that although he served only whiskey, and only one kind of whiskey. I have seen him flatly refuse to squeeze some lemon juice into it for a stranger. Fat Carl didn't like fumadiddles. He wore a big towel tied about his middle and he polished the glasses on it as he moved about. The floor was bare wood sprinkled with sawdust, the bar an old store counter, the chairs were hard and straight; the only decorations were the posters and cards and pictures stuck to the wall by candidates for county elections, salesmen and auctioneers. Some of these were many years old. The card of Sheriff Rittal still begged for re-election although Rittal had been dead for seven years.

The Buffalo Bar sounds, even to me, like a terrible place, but when you walked down the night street, over the wooden sidewalks, when the long streamers of swamp fog, like waving, dirty bunting, flapped in your face, when finally you pushed open the swinging doors of Fat Carl's and saw men sitting around talking and drinking, and Fat Carl coming along toward you, it seemed pretty nice. You couldn't get away from it.

There would be a game of the mildest kind of poker going on. Timothy Ratz, the husband of my landlady, would be playing solitaire, cheating pretty badly because he took a drink only when he got it out. I've seen him get it out five times in a row. When he won he piled the cards neatly, stood up and walked with great dignity to the bar. Fat Carl, with a glass half filled before he arrived, asked, "What'll it be?"

"Whiskey," said Timothy gravely.

In the long room, men from the farms and the town sat in the straight hard chairs or stood against the old counter. A soft, monotonous rattle of conversation went on except at times of elections or big prize fights, when there might be orations or loud opinions.

I hated to go out into the damp night, and to hear far off in the swamp the chuttering of the Diesel engine on the dredger and the clang of the bucket, and then to go to my own dismal room at Mrs. Ratz'.

Soon after my arrival in Loma I scraped an acquaintance with Mae Romero, a pretty half-Mexican girl. Sometimes in the evenings I walked with her down the south side of the hill, until the nasty fog drove us back into town. After I escorted her home I dropped in at the bar for a while.

I was sitting in the bar one night talking to Alex Hartnell, who owned a nice little farm. We were talking about black bass fishing, when the front doors opened and swung closed. A hush fell on the men in the room. Alex nudged me and said, "It's Johnny Bear." I looked around.

His name described him better than I can. He looked like a great, stupid, smiling bear. His black matted head bobbed forward and his long arms hung out as though he should have been on all fours and was only standing upright as a trick. His legs were short and bowed, ending with strange, square feet. He was dressed in dark blue denim, but his feet were bare; they didn't seem to be crippled or deformed in any way, but they were square, just as wide as they were long. He stood in the doorway, swinging his arms jerkily the way half-wits do. On his face there was a foolish happy smile. He moved forward and for all his bulk and clumsiness, he seemed to creep. He didn't move like a man, but like some prowling night animal. At the bar he stopped, his little bright eyes went about from face to face expectantly, and he asked, "Whiskey?"

Loma was not a treating town. A man might buy a drink for another if he were pretty sure the other would immediately buy one for him. I was surprised when one of the quiet men laid a coin on the counter. Fat Carl filled the glass. The monster took it and gulped the whiskey.

"What the devil——" I began. But Alex nudged me and said, "Sh."

There began a curious pantomime. Johnny Bear moved to the door and then he came creeping back. The foolish smile

[166]

never left his face. In the middle of the room he crouched down on his stomach. A voice came from his throat, a voice that seemed familiar to me.

"But you are too beautiful to live in a dirty little town like this."

The voice rose to a soft throaty tone, with just a trace of accent in the words. "You just tell me that."

I'm sure I nearly fainted. The blood pounded in my ears. I flushed. It was my voice coming out of the throat of Johnny Bear, my words, my intonation. And then it was the voice of Mae Romero—exact. If I had not seen the crouching man on the floor I would have called to her. The dialogue went on. Such things sound silly when someone else says them. Johnny Bear went right on, or rather I should say I went right on. He said things and made sounds. Gradually the faces of the men turned from Johnny Bear, turned toward me, and they grinned at me. I could do nothing. I knew that if I tried to stop him I would have a fight on my hands, and so the scene went on, to a finish. When it was over I was cravenly glad Mae Romero had no brothers. What obvious, forced, ridiculous words had come from Johnny Bear. Finally he stood up, still smiling the foolish smile, and he asked again, "Whiskey?"

I think the men in the bar were sorry for me. They looked away from me and talked elaborately to one another. Johnny Bear went to the back of the room, crawled under a round cardtable, curled up like a dog and went to sleep.

Alex Hartnell was regarding me with compassion. "First time you ever heard him?"

"Yes, what in hell is he?"

Alex ignored my question for a moment. "If you're worrying about Mae's reputation, don't. Johnny Bear has followed Mae before."

"But how did he hear us? I didn't see him."

"No one sees or hears Johnny Bear when he's on business.

He can move like no movement at all. Know what our young men do when they go out with girls? They take a dog along. Dogs are afraid of Johnny and they can smell him coming."

"But good God! Those voices———"

Alex nodded. "I know. Some of us wrote up to the university about Johnny, and a young man came down. He took a look at him and then he told us about Blind Tom. Ever hear of Blind Tom?"

"You mean the Negro piano player? Yes, I've heard of him."

"Well, Blind Tom was a half-wit. He could hardly talk, but he could imitate anything he heard on the piano, long pieces. They tried him with fine musicians and he reproduced not only the music but every little personal emphasis. To catch him they made little mistakes, and he played the mistakes. He photographed the playing in the tiniest detail. The man says Johnny Bear is the same, only he can photograph words and voices. He tested Johnny with a long passage in Greek and Johnny did it exactly. He doesn't know the words he's saying, he just says them. He hasn't brains enough to make anything up, so you know that what he says is what he heard."

"But why does he do it? Why is he interested in listening if he doesn't understand?"

Alex rolled a cigarette and lighted it. "He isn't, but he loves whiskey. He knows if he listens in windows and comes here and repeats what he hears, someone will give him whiskey. He tries to palm off Mrs. Ratz' conversation in the store, or Jerry Noland arguing with his mother, but he can't get whiskey for such things."

I said, "It's funny somebody hasn't shot him while he was peeking in windows."

Alex picked at his cigarette. "Lots of people have tried, but you just don't see Johnny Bear, and you don't catch him. You keep your windows closed, and even then you talk in a whisper if you don't want to be repeated. You were lucky it was dark tonight. If he had seen you, he might have gone through the action too. You should see Johnny Bear screw up his face to look like a young girl. It's pretty awful."

Johnny Bear's back was turned to the room. The light fell on his black matted hair. I saw a big fly land on his head, and then I swear I saw the whole scalp shiver the way the skin of a horse shivers under flies. The fly landed again and the moving scalp shook it off. I shuddered too, all over.

Conversation in the room had settled to the bored monotone again. Fat Carl had been polishing a glass on his apron towel for the last ten minutes. A little group of men near me was discussing fighting dogs and fighting cocks, and they switched gradually to bullfighting.

Alex, beside me, said, "Come have a drink."

We walked to the counter. Fat Carl put out two glasses. "What'll it be?"

Neither of us answered. Carl poured out the brown whiskey. He looked sullenly at me and one of his thick, meaty eyelids winked at me solemnly. I don't know why, but I felt flattered. Carl's head twitched back toward the card table. "Got you, didn't he?"

I winked back at him. "Take a dog next time." I imitated his clipped sentences. We drank our whiskey and went back to our chairs. Timothy Ratz won a game of solitaire and piled his cards and moved up on the bar.

I looked back at the table under which Johnny Bear lay. He had rolled over on his stomach. His foolish, smiling face looked out at the room. His head moved and he peered all about, like an animal about to leave its den. And then he came sliding out and stood up. There was a paradox about his movement. He looked twisted and shapeless, and yet he moved with complete lack of effort.

Johnny Bear crept up the room toward the bar, smiling

about at the men he passed. In front of the bar his insistent question arose. "Whiskey? Whiskey?" It was like a bird call. I don't know what kind of bird, but I've heard it—two notes on a rising scale, asking a question over and over, "Whiskey? Whiskey?"

The conversation in the room stopped, but no one came forward to lay money on the counter. Johnny smiled plaintively. "Whiskey?"

Then he tried to cozen them. Out of his throat an angry woman's voice issued. "I tell you it was all bone. Twenty cents a pound, and half bone." And then a man, "Yes, ma'am. I didn't know it. I'll give you some sausage to make it up."

Johnny Bear looked around expectantly. "Whiskey?" Still none of the men offered to come forward. Johnny crept to the front of the room and crouched. I whispered, "What's he doing?"

Alex said, "Sh. Looking through a window. Listen!"

A woman's voice came, a cold, sure voice, the words clipped. "I can't quite understand it. Are you some kind of monster? I wouldn't have believed it if I hadn't seen you."

Another woman's voice answered her, a voice low and hoarse with misery. "Maybe I am a monster. I can't help it. I can't help it."

"You *must* help it," the cold voice broke in. "Why you'd be better dead."

I heard a soft sobbing coming from the thick smiling lips of Johnny Bear. The sobbing of a woman in hopelessness. I looked around at Alex. He was sitting stiffly, his eyes wide open and unblinking. I opened my mouth to whisper a question, but he waved me silent. I glanced about the room. All the men were stiff and listening. The sobbing stopped. "Haven't you ever felt that way, Emalin?"

Alex caught his breath sharply at the name. The cold voice announced, "Certainly not."

[170]

"Never in the night? Not ever—ever in your life?"

"If I had," the cold voice said, "if ever I had, I would cut that part of me away. Now stop your whining, Amy. I won't stand for it. If you don't get control of your nerves I'll see about having some medical treatment for you. Now go to your prayers."

Johnny Bear smiled on. "Whiskey?"

Two men advanced without a word and put down coins. Fat Carl filled two glasses and, when Johnny Bear tossed off one after the other, Carl filled one again. Everyone knew by that how moved he was. There were no drinks on the house at the Buffalo Bar. Johnny Bear smiled about the room and then he went out with that creeping gait of his. The doors folded together after him, slowly and without a sound.

Conversation did not spring up again. Everyone in the room seemed to have a problem to settle in his own mind. One by one they drifted out and the back-swing of the doors brought in little puffs of tule fog. Alex got up and walked out and I followed him.

The night was nasty with the evil-smelling fog. It seemed to cling to the buildings and to reach out with free arms into the air. I doubled my pace and caught up with Alex. "What was it?" I demanded. "What was it all about?"

For a moment I thought he wouldn't answer. But then he stopped and turned to me. "Oh, damn it. Listen! Every town has its aristocrats, its family above reproach. Emalin and Amy Hawkins are our aristocrats, maiden ladies, kind people. Their father was a congressman. I don't like this. Johnny Bear shouldn't do it. Why! they feed him. Those men shouldn't give him whiskey. He'll haunt that house now....Now he knows he can get whiskey for it."

I asked, "Are they relatives of yours?"

"No, but they're—why, they aren't like other people. They have the farm next to mine. Some Chinese farm it on

[171]

shares. You see, it's hard to explain. The Hawkins women, they're symbols. They're what we tell our kids when we want to—well, to describe good people."

"Well," I protested, "Nothing Johnny Bear said would hurt them, would it?"

"I don't know. I don't know what it means. I mean, I kind of know. Oh! Go on to bed. I didn't bring the Ford. I'm going to walk out home." He turned and hurried into that slow squirming mist.

I walked along to Mrs. Ratz' boarding house. I could hear the chuttering of the Diesel engine off in the swamp and the clang of the big steel mouth that ate its way through the ground. It was Saturday night. The dredger would stop at seven Sunday morning and rest until midnight Sunday. I could tell by the sound that everything was all right. I climbed the narrow stairs to my room. Once in bed I left the light burning for a while and stared at the pale insipid flowers on the wallpaper. I thought of those two voices speaking out of Johnny Bear's mouth. They were authentic voices, not reproductions. Remembering the tones, I could see the women who had spoken, the chill-voiced Emalin, and the loose, misery-broken face of Amy. I wondered what caused the misery. Was it just the lonely suffering of a middle-aged woman? It hardly seemed so to me, for there was too much fear in the voice. I went to sleep with the light on and had to get up later and turn it off.

About eight the next morning I walked down across the swamp to the dredger. The crew was busy bending some new wire to the drums and coiling the worn cable for removal. I looked over the job and at about eleven o'clock walked back to Loma. In front of Mrs. Ratz' boarding house Alex Hartnell sat in a model T Ford touring car. He called to me, "I was just going to the dredger to get you. I knocked off a couple of chickens this morning. Thought you might like to come out and help with them."

I accepted joyfully. Our cook was a good cook, a big pasty man; but lately I had found a dislike for him arising in me. He smoked Cuban cigarettes in a bamboo holder. I didn't like the way his fingers twitched in the morning. His hands were clean—floury like a miller's hands. I never knew before why they called them moth millers, those little flying bugs. Anyway I climbed into the Ford beside Alex and we drove down the hill to the rich land of the southwest. The sun shone brilliantly on the black earth. When I was little, a Catholic boy told me that the sun always shone on Sunday, if only for a moment, because it was God's day. I always meant to keep track to see if it were true. We rattled down to the level plain.

Alex shouted, "Remember about the Hawkinses?"

"Of course I remember."

He pointed ahead. "That's the house."

Little of the house could be seen, for a high thick hedge of cypress surrounded it. There must be a small garden inside the square too. Only the roof and the tops of the windows showed over the hedge. I could see that the house was painted tan, trimmed with dark brown, a combination favored for railroad stations and schools in California. There were two wicket gates in the front and side of the hedge. The barn was outside the green barrier to the rear of the house. The hedge was clipped square. It looked incredibly thick and strong.

"The hedge keeps the wind out," Alex shouted above the roar of the Ford.

"It doesn't keep Johnny Bear out," I said.

A shadow crossed his face. He waved at a whitewashed square building standing out in the field. "That's where the Chink share-croppers live. Good workers. I wish I had some like them."

At that moment from behind the corner of the hedge a horse and buggy appeared and turned into the road. The grey horse was old but well groomed, the buggy shiny and the harness polished. There was a big silver H on the outside of each blinder. It seemed to me that the check-rein was too short for such an old horse.

Alex cried, "There they are now, on their way to church."

We took off our hats and bowed to the women as they went by, and they nodded formally to us. I had a good look at them. It was a shock to me. They looked almost exactly as I thought they would. Johnny Bear was more monstrous even than I had known, if by the tone of voice he could describe the features of his people. I didn't have to ask which was Emalin and which was Amy. The clear straight eyes, the sharp sure chin, the mouth cut with the precision of a diamond, the stiff, curveless figure, that was Emalin. Amy was very like her, but so unlike. Her edges were soft. Her eyes were warm, her mouth full. There was a swell to her breast, and yet she did look like Emalin. But whereas Emalin's mouth was straight by nature, Amy *held* her mouth straight. Emalin must have been fifty or fifty-five and Amy about ten years younger. I had only a moment to look at them, and I never saw them again. It seems strange that I don't know anyone in the world better than those two women.

Alex was shouting, "You see what I meant about aristocrats?"

I nodded. It was easy to see. A community would feel kind of—safe, having women like that about. A place like Loma with its fogs, with its great swamp like a hideous sin, needed, really needed, the Hawkins women. A few years there might do things to a man's mind if those women weren't there to balance matters.

It was a good dinner. Alex's sister fried the chicken in butter and did everything else right. I grew more suspicious and uncharitable toward our cook. We sat around in the dining-room and drank really good brandy.

I said, "I can't see why you ever go into the Buffalo. That whiskey is——"

"I know," said Alex. "But the Buffalo is the mind of Loma. It's our newspaper, our theatre and our club."

This was so true that when Alex started the Ford and prepared to take me back I knew, and he knew, we would go for an hour or two to the Buffalo Bar.

We were nearly into town. The feeble lights of the car splashed about on the road. Another car rattled toward us. Alex swung across the road and stopped. "It's the doctor, Doctor Holmes," he explained. The oncoming car pulled up because it couldn't get around us. Alex called, "Say, Doc, I was going to ask you to take a look at my sister. She's got a swelling on her throat."

Doctor Holmes called back, "All right, Alex, I'll take a look. Pull out, will you? I'm in a hurry."

Alex was deliberate. "Who's sick, Doc?"

"Why, Miss Amy had a little spell. Miss Emalin phoned in and asked me to hurry. Get out of the way, will you?"

Alex squawked his car back and let the doctor by. We drove on. I was about to remark that the night was clear when, looking ahead, I saw the rags of fog creeping around the hill from the swamp side and climbing like slow snakes on the top of Loma. The Ford shuddered to a stop in front of the Buffalo. We went in.

Fat Carl moved toward us, wiping a glass on his apron. He reached under the bar for the nearby bottle. "What'll it be?"

"Whiskey."

For a moment a faint smile seemed to flit over the fat sullen face. The room was full. My dredger crew was there, all except the cook. He was probably on the scow, smoking his Cuban cigarettes in a bamboo holder. He didn't drink. That was enough to make me suspicious of him. Two deck hands and an engineer and three levermen were there. The levermen were arguing about a cutting. The old lumber adage certainly held for them: "Women in the woods and logging in the honkytonk."

[175]

That was the quietest bar I ever saw. There weren't any fights, not much singing and no tricks. Somehow the sullen baleful eyes of Fat Carl made drinking a quiet, efficient business rather than a noisy game. Timothy Ratz was playing solitaire at one of the round tables. Alex and I drank our whiskey. No chairs were available, so we just stayed leaning against the bar, talking about sports and markets and adventures we had had or pretended we had—just a casual barroom conversation. Now and then we bought another drink. I guess we hung around for a couple of hours. Alex had already said he was going home, and I felt like it. The dredger crew trooped out, for they had to start to work at midnight.

The doors unfolded silently, and Johnny Bear crept into the room, swinging his long arms, nodding his big hairy head and smiling foolishly about. His square feet were like cats' feet.

"Whiskey?" he chirruped. No one encouraged him. He got out his wares. He was down on his stomach the way he had been when he got me. Sing-song nasal words came out, Chinese I thought. And then it seemed to me that the same words were repeated in another voice, slower and not nasally. Johnny Bear raised his shaggy head and asked, "Whiskey?" He got to his feet with effortless ease. I was interested. I wanted to see him perform. I slid a quarter along the bar. Johnny gulped his drink. A moment later I wished I hadn't. I was afraid to look at Alex; for Johnny Bear crept to the middle of the room and took that window pose of his.

The chill voice of Emalin said, "She's in here, doctor." I closed my eyes against the looks of Johnny Bear, and the moment I did he went out. It was Emalin Hawkins who had spoken.

I had heard the doctor's voice in the road, and it was his veritable voice that replied, "Ah—you said a fainting fit?"

"Yes, doctor."

[176]

There was a little pause, and then the doctor's voice again, very softly, "Why did she do it, Emalin?"

"Why did she do what?" There was almost a threat in the question.

"I'm your doctor, Emalin. I was your father's doctor. You've got to tell me things. Don't you think I've seen that kind of a mark on the neck before? How long was she hanging before you got her down?"

There was a longer pause then. The chill left the woman's voice. It was soft, almost a whisper. "Two or three minutes. Will she be all right, doctor?"

"Oh, yes, she'll come around. She's not badly hurt. Why did she do it?"

The answering voice was even colder than it had been at first. It was frozen. "I don't know, sir."

"You mean you won't tell me?"

"I mean what I say."

Then the doctor's voice went on giving directions for treatment, rest, milk and a little whiskey. "Above all, be gentle," he said. "Above everything, be gentle with her."

Emalin's voice trembled a little. "You would never—tell, doctor?"

"I'm your doctor," he said softly. "Of course I won't tell. I'll send down some sedatives tonight."

"Whiskey?" My eyes jerked open. There was the horrible Johnny Bear smiling around the room.

The men were silent, ashamed. Fat Carl looked at the floor. I turned apologetically to Alex, for I was really responsible. "I didn't know he'd do that," I said. "I'm sorry."

I walked out the door and went to the dismal room at Mrs. Ratz'. I opened the window and looked out into that coiling, pulsing fog. Far off in the marsh I heard the Diesel engine start slowly and warm up. And after a while I heard the clang of the big bucket as it went to work on the ditch.

The next morning one of those series of accidents so common in construction landed on us. One of the new wires parted on the in-swing and dropped the bucket on one of the pontoons, sinking it and the works in eight feet of ditch water. When we sunk a dead man and got a line out to it to pull us from the water, the line parted and clipped the legs neatly off one of the deck hands. We bound the stumps and rushed him to Salinas. And then little accidents happened. A leverman developed blood poisoning from a wire scratch. The cook finally justified my opinion by trying to sell a little can of marijuana to the engineer. Altogether there wasn't much peace in the outfit. It was two weeks before we were going again with a new pontoon, a new deck hand and a new cook.

The new cook was a sly, dark, little long-nosed man, with a gift for subtle flattery.

My contact with the social life of Loma had gone to pot, but when the bucket was clanging into the mud again and the big old Diesel was chuttering away in the swamp I walked out to Alex Hartnell's farm one night. Passing the Hawkins place, I peered in through one of the little wicket gates in the cypress hedge. The house was dark, more than dark because a low light glowed in one window. There was a gentle wind that night, blowing balls of fog like tumbleweeds along the ground. I walked in the clear a moment, and then was swallowed in a thick mist, and then was in the clear again. In the starlight I could see those big silver fog balls moving like elementals across the fields. I thought I heard a soft moaning in the Hawkins yard behind the hedge, and once when I came suddenly out of the fog I saw a dark figure hurrying along in the field, and I knew from the dragging footsteps that it was one of the Chinese field hands walking in sandals. The Chinese eat a great many things that have to be caught at night.

Alex came to the door when I knocked. He seemed glad to see me. His sister was away. I sat down by his stove and he

[178]

brought out a bottle of that nice brandy. "I heard you were having some trouble," he said.

I explained the difficulty. "It seems to come in series. The men have it figured out that accidents come in groups of three, five, seven and nine."

Alex nodded. "I kind of feel that way myself."

"How are the Hawkins sisters?" I asked. "I thought I heard someone crying as I went by."

Alex seemed reluctant to talk about them, and at the same time eager to talk about them. "I stopped over about a week ago. Miss Amy isn't feeling very well. I didn't see her. I only saw Miss Emalin." Then Alex broke out, "There's something hanging over those people, something—"

"You almost seem to be related to them," I said.

"Well, their father and my father were friends. We called the girls Aunt Amy and Aunt Emalin. They can't do anything bad. It wouldn't be good for any of us if the Hawkins sisters weren't the Hawkins sisters."

"The community conscience?" I asked.

"The safe thing," he cried. "The place where a kid can get gingerbread. The place where a girl can get reassurance. They're proud, but they believe in things we hope are true. And they live as though—well, as though honesty really is the best policy and charity really is its own reward. We need them."

"I see."

"But Miss Emalin is fighting something terrible and—I I don't think she's going to win."

"What do you mean?"

"I don't know what I mean. But I've thought I should shoot Johnny Bear and throw him the swamp. I've really thought about doing it."

"It's not his fault," I agreed. "He's just a kind of recording and reproducing device, only you use a glass of whiskey instead of a nickel."

We talked of some other things then, and after a while I walked back to Loma. It seemed to me that that fog was clinging to the cypress hedge of the Hawkins house, and it seemed to me that a lot of the fog balls were clustered about it and others were slowly moving in. I smiled as I walked along at the way a man's thought can rearrange nature to fit his thoughts. There was no light in the house as I went by.

A nice steady routine settled on my work. The big bucket cut out the ditch ahead of it. The crew felt the trouble was over too, and that helped, and the new cook flattered the men so successfully that they would have eaten fried cement. The personality of a cook has a lot more to do with the happiness of a dredger crew than his cooking has.

In the evening of the second day after my visit to Alex I walked down the wooden sidewalk trailing a streamer of fog behind me and went into the Buffalo Bar. Fat Carl moved toward me polishing the whiskey glass. I cried, "Whiskey," before he had a chance to ask what it would be. I took my glass and went to one of the straight chairs. Alex was not there. Timothy Ratz was playing solitaire and having a phenomenal run of luck. He got it out four times in a row and had a drink each time. More and more men arrived. I don't know what we would have done without the Buffalo Bar.

At about ten o'clock the news came. Thinking about such things afterwards, you never can remember quite what transpired. Someone comes in; a whisper starts; suddenly everyone knows what has happened, knows details. Miss Amy had committed suicide. Who brought in the story? I don't know. She had hanged herself. There wasn't much talk in the barroom about it. I could see the men were trying to get straight on it. It was a thing that didn't fit into their schemes. They stood in groups, talking softly.

The swinging doors opened slowly and Johnny Bear crept

in, his great hairy head rolling, and that idiot smile on his face. His square feet slid quietly over the floor. He looked about and chirruped, "Whiskey? Whiskey for Johnny?"

Now those men really wanted to know. They were ashamed of wanting to know, but their whole mental system required the knowledge. Fat Carl poured out a drink. Timothy Ratz put down his cards and stood up. Johnny Bear gulped the whiskey. I closed my eyes.

The doctor's tone was harsh. "Where is she, Emalin?"

I've never heard a voice like that one that answered, cold control, layer and layer of control, but cold penetrated by the most awful heartbreak. It was a monotonous tone, emotionless, and yet the heartbreak got into the vibrations. "She's in here, doctor."

"H-m-m." A long pause. "She was hanging a long time."

"I don't know how long, doctor."

"Why did she do it, Emalin?"

The monotone again. "I don't—know, doctor."

A longer pause, and then, "H-m-m. Emalin, did you know she was going to have a baby?"

The chill voice cracked and a sigh came through. "Yes, doctor," very softly.

"If that was why you didn't find her for so long—No, Emalin, I didn't mean that, poor dear."

The control was back in Emalin's voice. "Can you make out the certificate without mentioning—"

"Of course I can, sure I can. And I'll speak to the undertaker, too. You needn't worry."

"Thank you, doctor."

"I'll go and telephone now. I won't leave you here alone. Come into the other room, Emalin. I'm going to fix you a sedative. . . ."

"Whiskey? Whiskey for Johnny?" I saw the smile and the rolling hairy head. Fat Carl poured out another glass. Johnny

[181]

Bear drank it and then crept to the back of the room and crawled under a table and went to sleep.

No one spoke. Then men moved up to the bar and laid down their coins silently. They looked bewildered, for a system had fallen. A few minutes later Alex came into the silent room. He walked quickly over to me. "You've heard?" he asked softly.

"Yes."

"I've been afraid," he cried. "I told you a couple of nights ago. I've been afraid."

I said, "Did you know she was pregnant?"

Alex stiffened. He looked around the room and then back at me. "Johnny Bear?" he asked.

I nodded.

Alex ran his palm over his eyes. "I don't believe it." I was about to answer when I heard a little scuffle and looked to the back of the room. Johnny Bear crawled like a badger out of his hole and stood up and crept toward the bar.

"Whiskey?" He smiled expectantly at Fat Carl.

Then Alex stepped out and addressed the room. "Now you guys listen! This has gone far enough. I don't want any more of it." If he had expected opposition he was disappointed. I saw the men nodding to one another.

"Whiskey for Johnny?"

Alex turned on the idiot. "You ought to be ashamed. Miss Amy gave you food, and she gave you all the clothes you ever had."

Johnny smiled at him. "Whiskey?"

He got out his tricks. I heard the sing-song nasal language that sounded like Chinese. Alex looked relieved.

And then the other voice, slow, hesitant, repeating the words without the nasal quality.

Alex sprang so quickly that I didn't see him move. His fist splattered into Johnny Bear's smiling mouth. "I told you there was enough of it," he shouted.

Johnny Bear recovered his balance. His lips were split and bleeding, but the smile was still there. He moved slowly and without effort. His arms enfolded Alex as the tentacles of an anemone enfold a crab. Alex bent backward. Then I jumped and grabbed one of the arms and wrenched at it, and could not tear it loose. Fat Carl came rolling over the counter with a bung-starter in his hand. And he beat the matted head until the arms relaxed and Johnny Bear crumpled. I caught Alex and helped him to a chair. "Are you hurt?"

He tried to get his breath. "My back's wrenched, I guess," he said. "I'll be all right."

"Got your Ford outside? I'll drive you home."

Neither of us looked at the Hawkins place as we went by. I didn't lift my eyes off the road. I got Alex to his own dark house and helped him to bed and poured a hot brandy into him. He hadn't spoken all the way home. But after he was propped in the bed he demanded, "You don't think anyone noticed, do you? I caught him in time, didn't I?"

"What are you talking about? I don't know yet why you hit him."

"Well, listen," he said. "I'll have to stay close for a little while with this back. If you hear anyone say anything, you stop it, won't you? Don't let them say it."

"I don't know what you're talking about."

He looked into my eyes for a moment. "I guess I can trust you," he said. "That second voice—that was Miss Amy."

Helen, Thy Beauty is to Me—

By JOHN FANTE

> Born in Denver in 1911, Fante began his California career
> in 1930 by working in canneries, in hotels, and as a
> grocery clerk. After his expulsion from Long Beach Junior
> College he began writing short stories. Among his subse-
> quent works are several novels, many filmscripts, and the
> semi-autobiographical *Full of Life* (1952).

When love came to Julio Sal, he was not prepared. Julio
Sal, Filipino boy, forty cents an hour, Tokyo Fish Company,
Wilmington. Her name was Helen, she wore a smooth red
dress and she worked at the Angels' Ballroom, in Los Angeles.
Five feet, four inches was the height of Julio Sal, but when
that Helen's golden head lay on his shoulder, strength and
grandeur filled his body. A dream shaped itself in his Malay
brain. She sensed it too. She always sensed that sort of thing
in the Filipino customers. A gallant flame possessed them, and
they bought more tickets. The dances were ten cents apiece;
she got half of it.

Towering over the golden hair, Julio Sal saw half a
hundred of his countrymen gazing after him, watching the
serpentine undulations beneath the red dress, watching the
fast-diminishing roll of tickets in Helen's left hand. The dances
were one minute long. Somewhere behind the four-piece
colored band, a bell clanged the end of each number. Since ten
o'clock Julio Sal had danced continuously.

Now it was almost midnight. Already he had spent twelve
dollars. Forty cents remained in his pocket. It meant four more
minutes with the golden hair, and it meant his fare back to the
canneries.

The bell clanged, the dance ended, another dance began.
In the best alligator style, Julio jittered the dream toward the

glass ticket box. Her hand over his shoulder tore a stub from the string and dropped it into the slot.

"Only one left," the girl panted as Julio bounced her in the corner. It was her first word in an hour. Sweat oozed from the dark face of Julio Sal. Again he gazed across the floor at the group of his countrymen.

Ten of them strained against the railing, each clutching at a fat roll of tickets, ready to rush upon the golden girl the moment Julio's last ticket disappeared inside the glass box. Despair clutched the heart of Julio Sal. Resolution showed in his brown eyes.

"I get some more," he said.

The bell clanged, the dance ended, another dance began. There was a smile on the girl's white, hot face as she dropped the last ticket into the slot. This time it was a waltz, a breathing spell. Julio Sal nodded to the ticket man, who made his way through the couples, coins jingling in his money apron. Dismay seeped into the faces of the Penoys pressed against the rail. Julio's fingers dug into his watch pocket. Surprise widened the blue eyes of Helen when she saw forty cents— nickel, dime and quarter pinched between Julio Sal's thumb and forefinger.

"Four tickets," said Julio Sal.

The ticket vender rolled a cigar through his teeth. "Only four?"

"Please."

The bell clanged, the dance ended, another dance began. Out of the corner of his eye Julio Sal saw the dismay leave the faces of his little brown brothers. Their smiles mocked him. They had waited so long; they would gladly wait another four dances. The bell clanged, the dance ended, another dance began; again the bell clanged.

"Helen," said Julio Sal. "Helen, I love you, Helen."

"That's nice," she said, because all the Filipinos loved

[185]

Helen, because all the Filipinos managed to say it when they got down to their last two or three.

"I write you a letter," said Julio Sal.

"Please do." Because she always said that; because letters meant that they would be coming back on payday. "Please write."

"You write me too?"

But the bell clanged, the dance ended and he had no more tickets. She slipped from his arms. The wicker gate opened and he was lost in an avalanche of little brown men fighting for the golden girl. Smiling weakly, he stood at the rail and watched her settle her child's face against the chest of Johnny Dellarosa, label machine, Van Camp's, San Pedro. A wave of tenderness suffocated Julio Sal. A small white doll— that was his Helen. The blissful future revealed itself in a reverie that shut out the boogy-woogy and the clanging bell—she was frying his bacon and eggs in a blue-tinted kitchen like in the movie pitch, and he came grinning from the bedroom in a green robe with a yellow sash, like in the movie pitch. "Ah, Helen," he was saying to her, "you are most wonderful cook in whole California. Pretty soon we take boat back to Luzon to meet my mamma and papa."

The reverie endured through twenty-five clangs of the bell before he remembered that his pockets were empty and that it was eighteen miles to Wilmington.

On his way out, buttoning his square-cut, shoulder-padded, tight overcoat, Julio Sal paused before a huge photograph of the Angels' Ballroom Staff; forty beautiful girls, forty. She was there, his Helen, her lovely face and slim-hipped figure third from the left, front row.

"Helen, Helen, I love you."

He descended the stairs to Main Street, saw the fog flowing north like a white river. Julio Sal, well-dressed Filipino boy—black serge suit, hand-tailored overcoat, black patent-leather shoes, snappy, short-brimmed hat. Breasting the white river, he walked south on Main Street. Eighteen miles to the harbor. Good. It had been worth while. He breathed fog and cigarette smoke and smiled for his love. Mamma, this is Helen; papa, this is Helen, my wife. The dream held. He couldn't marry her in California. The law said no. They would go to Reno. Or Tijuana. Or Seattle. Work a while up north. Then home to the Philippines. Mamma, this is Helen. Papa, this is Helen.

Eighteen miles to Wilmington.

II

He arrived at six o'clock, his patent-leather shoes in ruins. Behind the cannery, in the duplexes, the five Japanese families were already up, lights from their windows a dull gold in the deep fog.

He smelled the fertilizer vats, the tar, the oil, the copra, the bananas and oranges, the bilge, the old rope, the decaying anchovies, the lumber, the rubber, the salt—the vast bouquet of the harbor. This, too, was part of the dream. While working here at this spot, I met my love. I, Julio Sal.

Like one barefoot, he walked down the long veranda of the flat, salt-blackened building. They were single apartments set like cell blocks—one door, one window; one door, one window. A board creaked beneath his step, a baby wakened and cried. Babies, ah, babies. A little girl, he hoped, with the face and eyes of Mamma Helen.

He lived in the last apartment; he and Silvio Lazada, Pacito Celestino, Manuel Bartolome, Delfin Denisio, Vivente Macario, Johnny Andrino and Fred Bunda, all young men who had come to America as boys in the late 20's.

They were asleep now, the cramped room reeking with the odor of fish, bodies, burned rice and salt air. Bunda, Lazada and Celestino were in the wall bed; Andrino lay on the davenport; Bartolome, Macario and Denisio on the floor. Good boys. Loyal countrymen; though he had been gone all night, none had taken his bed in the bathtub.

On tiptoe he made his way over the sleepers to the bathroom. Through the gray fog-swept light he saw that someone was in the bathtub after all. The sleeper lay deep in blankets, old linen and soiled clothing, his head under the water spouts, his feet on the tub incline. Julio Sal bent down and smiled: it was Antonio Repollo. He had not seen Antonio in two years, not since the Seattle and Alaska canneries. Julio Sal whistled with pleasure. Now his letter-writing problem was solved. Antonio Repollo was a graduate of the University of Washington; he could write beautiful letters. Antonio Repollo was not only a university graduate, he also wrote poetry for El Grafico in Manila.

Julio Sal bent over and shook him awake.

"Antonio, my friend. Welcome."

Repollo turned over, a laundry bag in his arms.

"Antonio, is me. Julio Sal. I have girl."

"Is American?" asked Repollo.

"Is blonde," said Julio Sal. "Is wonderful."

"Is bad," said Antonio.

"No," said Julio Sal. "Is good, very good."

"Is very bad," said Repollo. "Is worst thing possible."

"No," said Julio Sal. "Is best thing possible."

He slipped into his greasy dungarees, found a clean shirt behind the kitchen door, and put that on too. It was Vivente Macario's turn to cook breakfast. Since 1926, at the asparagus fields, the celery fields, the canneries from Alaska to San Diego, Vivente Macario always prepared the same breakfast when his turn came—warmed-over rice, three cans of sardines stolen from the cannery, a hunk of bread and tea. They sat around the knife-scarred breakfast nook and ate quietly over a table whose surface was a mass of initials and dates of the hundreds of Filipino cannery workers who had come and gone throughout the years.

His brown face glowing from cold water, Antonio Repollo came into the kitchen. The poet, the college man. He was here, in their house, and they were honored; had even provided him with a bathtub in which to sleep. They made a place for him at the table, watched his long beautiful fingers remove sardines from the can.

"Julio Sal," he said, "what is the name of the woman?"

"Is Helen."

"Helen? No more? No Anderson, no Smith, Brown?"

"No more. Helen, all the same. Helen."

"He has girl," explained Repollo. "Name of Helen. He wish to marry this girl. American girl."

"No good," said Fred Bunda.

"Crazy," said Delfin Denisio.

"Too much trouble"—Johnny Andrino.

"Helen?" Manuel Bartolome talking. "Is not same Helen for to work Angels' Ballroom, taxi dance?"

"Ya, ya," said Julio Sal. "She is him, all the same."

Bartolome sucked his big lips tight. "Is no good, this woman. Cannot be. For to marry, I try myself. She damn liar. You give money, she take. Give you nothing."

"No, no," smiled Julio Sal. "Is another Helen. This one, she is good. This one love. She like me. She say 'write letter.' This I am do tonight."

"Gnah," said Bartolome, coughing an evil memory from his mouth. "For why you believe that? Is applesauce. I am write letter, too—six times. She take my money, give nothing. She no love you, Julio Sal. She no marry Filipino. She take his money, but she no marry. Is not love. Is business."

The strong fist of Julio Sal whacked the table. "I make her love me. You wait. You see. Pretty soon, three months, cannery close down. I have money. We go get married. Reno, Seattle."

[189]

"Is bad," said Pacito Celestino.
"Crazy," said Vivente Macario.
"Is terrible," said Delfin Denisio. "Is awful."
"Is love," said Julio Sal. "Is wonderful!"

III

Said Julio Sal to Antonio Repollo, "You will write letter for me tonight, yes?"

Said Antonio Repollo, "No."

It was evening. The poet, Antonio Repollo, sat before his portable typewriter, line upon line of typescript rattling across the page. The fog had cleared. The moon showed big and yellow, rising over the American-Hawaiian docks.

"I am disappoint," said Julio Sal. "I write letter myself."

He asked for paper, and Repollo gave it to him. He asked for a fountain pen, and got that too. He sat across from the poet, his tongue making a bulge against his cheek. A half hour passed. Sweat broke out upon the brow of Julio Sal; the paper before him was white and untouched. Pleading eyes observed the dancing fingers of Antonio Repollo.

Said Julio Sal, pushing the paper away, "I cannot do. Is too hard to write."

Said Repollo, "You are a fool, Julio Sal. Sixteen years ago in Hawaii I say to you: 'Go to school, Julio Sal. Learn to read English, learn to write English; it come in handy someday.' But no, you work in the pineapple, you make money, you play Chinee lottery, you shoot crap, you lose the cockfights. You have no time for American school. Me, I am different. I have big education. I am graduate, University of Washington. Maybe next year we go to Pasadena for the Rose Bowl."

"Maybe I write the Spanish."

"This Helen, she is Spanish?"

"No. She is American."

"What for you write Spanish?"

"I cannot write the English. I write the Spanish. Maybe she have Spanish friend."

"Fool, Julio Sal. Fool you are."

Julio felt tears stinging his eyes. "Is true, Antonio. I am make big mistake. You write for me letter. Next year I go for the school."

"I work hard for education. For write, I get paid. El Grafico, she pay me, for poetry, ten cents a word. For prose, one cents. First-class rates."

"I pay you, Antonio. Write beautiful letter. I pay you first-class rates. How much for this, Antonio?"

"For letter, prose composition, is one cents a word. Same rates I get, El Grafico."

Antonio rolled a clean sheet of paper under the platen and began to write. Julio Sal stood behind him and watched the letters dance across the white background.

"Good," said Julio, "Is wonderful. Write whole lots, Antonio. I pay one penny for the word."

The creative instinct in Antonio Repollo at once grew cold. He swung around and shook his hand under the fine nose of Julio Sal. "How do you know is good or bad? You cannot read the English good. How you know this?"

"She look good, Antonio. Look fine."

"I read to you," said Antonio. "I wish to give satisfaction all the time." As though harking to a distant foghorn, Julio Sal looked out the window and listened as Antonio read:

"*Dear Miss Helen:* The Immortal Bard has said, 'What's in a name?' I concur. And though I know not how you are yclept for a surname, it matters little. Oh, Miss Helen! Lugubrious is often the way of amour; profound its interpretations; powerful its judgments. Oh, bright Diana of the Dance! My love for you is like a muted trumpet sobbing among the brasses. Destiny has brought us together, and the aroma of devotion rises from your Humble Servant—"

[191]

Julio Sal shook his head. "Is no good, Antonio. Is terrible. Steenk."

"Is wonderful!" shouted Repollo. "Better than my stuff for El Grafico!"

Julio Sal sighed at the moon. "Antonio, you write, I talk. You put 'em down what I say."

A haughty shrug from Antonio. He lifted his palms. "As you wish, Julio. Same price for dictation. One cents a word."

Julio Sal was not listening. Both hands were cupped at his heart as the moonlight bathed his brown eyes. "Oh, lovely Helen!" He spoke in his native Tagalog. "Oh, wonderful moon girl! Thy beams have filled my soul with wild pleasure. Could I but kneel at thy feet in worship, the hem of thy red gown in these unworthy hands, I should die for joy. Many there are who are worthier than Julio Sal, but no man can say he loves you more. My wish and my hope is that you will become my bride. Back to the beloved motherland we will go, there to live forever beneath the coconut palms of beautiful Luzon My wealthy father and mother shall welcome you to their plantation of fifteen thousand acres—rice, dates, pineapples and coconuts. Over it all you shall reign like a queen to the end of your days."

That was too much for Antonio Repollo. "You lie, Julio Sal. Your mamma and pappa are peasants. They are poor people, Julio Sal. You betray them with such lies. You make them capitalist dogs. Caciques."

"You write," said Julio Sal. "I am pay one penny for the word. You write 'em down."

Repollo wrote it down, wrote three hundred and fifty-six words in all. They counted them together—three dollars and fifty-six cents. Expensive. But Antonio made no charge for punctuation marks, for "a" and "an," nor for the envelope, or for addressing it to Miss Helen, in care of the Angels' Ballroom, Los Angeles. Julio Sal was pleased with the cool, clean type-

script and the boldness of his signature at the bottom, under-
scored three times, with a whirlwind flourish of curlicues.

"I pay," said Julio Sal, "come payday."

It came six days later, and Julio Sal paid thirteen dollars
and eighty cents for that letter and three more. Even so, he
managed to save another fifteen, for it had been a big week,
with overtime. She did not answer his letters. But he could
understand that; the life of a taxi dancer was not an easy one—
to dance by night, to sleep by day, with never a moment to
herself. All that was going to be changed someday. Pretty
soon—after the tuna.

He saved his money. Was Betty Grable playing at The
Harbor? All the little brown men loved Betty Grable; her autographed photograph hung over the kitchen sink; en masse they
went to see her picture. All but Julio Sal. Seated on a piling at
Dock 158, he smoked a cheap cigar and watched the steve-
dores load the President Hoover, bound for Hawaii and the
Philippines. Came Madeleine Carroll, Virginia Bruce, Carole
Lombard, Anita Louise—big favorites with the Penoys. But
Julio Sal stayed home. There was the night Sixto Escobar
fought Baby Pacito at the Hollywood Legion. And the night
the bolo-punching Ceferino Garcia flattened Art Gonzales to
the cries of "Boola, boola!" from his countrymen in the gal-
lery. Where was Julio Sal? At home, saving his money.

IV

In September the tuna disappeared. And where does the
tuna go, when he goes? No one can say. Overnight the roaring
canneries shut down. No fish, no work. If wise, the Filipino
boy had saved his money. Maybe he had three hundred,
maybe five.

Home now? Back to Luzon and Ilocos Norte? No, not yet.
Big money up north in the crops—lettuce, prunes, hops,

olives, grapes, asparagus, walnuts, melons. Take rest, few days. Go to Los Angeles, see some girls, buy some clothes, chip in together and buy big car, ride down Hollywood Boulevard, maybe see Carole Lombard, maybe Anita Louise, can't tell. Then to the great agricultural centers of the north. Merced, Stockton, Salinas, Marysville, Woodland, Watsonville. Good-by to friends and fellow workers—to Celestino, Bartolome, Bunda, Denisio, Lazada, Marcario. See you up north.

Said Antonio Repollo to Julio Sal that last day, "The prunes, she is good in Santa Clara County. You come with me?"

Said Julio Sal, "No. I go to Los Angeles for to get Helen. We go to Reno, maybe. For to get married."

Said Repollo, "You have letter then? She say yes?"

"No letter. Just the same, we get married."

"Maybe," said Repollo, not meaning it.

"No maybe. Is truth. You wait. You see. Pretty soon Mrs. Julio Sal, with ring."

"You have money, Julio Sal? Costa plenty for to have American wife."

"Three hundred fifty, I have."

"Is very small amount."

"Is plenty. I get some more in the crops."

Repollo took out his wallet. "I loan you twenty buck. After asparagus you pay me back."

"Is plenty, three hundred fifty."

Repollo held out a five-dollar bill. "This, for a wedding present. Some chocolate. Compliments, Antonio Repollo."

Mist welled up in the eyes of Julio Sal. He folded the green-back and wet his lips. "You are good Filipino, Repollo. Smart man. I tell Helen. Maybe someday I tell her you write letter on the machine—someday, maybe. *Gracias*, my friend."

"Is nothing," said Repollo. "For that I am A. B., University of Washington. Pretty soon we play Minnesota; we win maybe."

When he left the apartment that last time, a grip in each hand, his topcoat over his shoulder, he smelled sweet and clean, did Julio Sal, and he knew that, according to the pictures in Esquire, he was sartorially correct, even to the tan golf sweater that matched his light brown tie. There was one slight imperfection in his ensemble—his brown shoes. They had been half-soled.

It was forty minutes to town by way of the big red cars. At a quarter to one Julio Sal was on Hill Street. On the corner, there in the window, a pair of shoes caught his eye. They were light brown, a pock-marked pigskin, moccasin type, light soles, box toes. Fifteen dollars was the price beneath the velvet stand. Julio Sal bit his lips and tried to hold down his Spanish-Malay passion for bright leather. But it was a losing battle. Relishing his own weakness, he walked through the glass doors and stepped into a fragrant, cool world of leather and worsteds, silks and cashmere.

At two-thirty the new Julio Sal strutted up Hill Street with the grandeur of a bantam cock. The new shoes made him taller; the new gabardine slacks gave him a sense of long, virile steps; the new sport coat, belted and pleated in back, built him into a wedge-shaped athlete; the soft wool sweater scarcely existed, it was so soft, so tender. That new hat! Dark green, with a lighter band, high crown, short brim, pulled over one eye. At every window Julio Sal watched himself passing by. The transformation had cost him a hundred and twenty-five. No matter.

Said Julio Sal to the handsome Filipino flashing past the shop windows, "Is better first to become engaged. Wait few months. Hops in Marysville. Asparagus in Stockton. Big money. After asparagus we get married."

The idea came to him suddenly, giving warmth to his

[195]

conscience. But the coldness of guilt made him shudder. The first jewelry store in sight swallowed him up. An engagement ring. He was not happy when he walked into the hot street again, his purse thinner by seventy-five dollars. He felt himself falling to pieces with a suddenness that left him breathing through his mouth. Crossing to Pershing Square, he got no pleasure from his new clothes as he sat in the sun. A deep loneliness held him. What was the matter with Julio Sal? This Helen—not once had she answered his letter. He was a fool. Bartolome had warned him. But what was Filipino boy to do? For every Filipino girl in California there were twenty-two Filipino boys. The law made it so, and the law said Filipino boy could not marry white girl. What was Filipino boy to do? But Helen was different. Helen was taxi-dance girl. Working girl. Big difference. At once he felt better. He got up and walked toward Main Street, proud of his new clothes again.

V

First at the ticket window of the Angels' Ballroom that night was Julio Sal. It was a few minutes before seven. He bought a hundred tickets. On the stand, the four-piece colored band was tuning up. As yet, the girls had not come out of the dressing rooms. Julio Sal followed the wicker fence down to the bandstand, six feet from the dressing-room door. Then the band began to play the blatant hotcha wired down to a loud-speaker that spewed it in all directions out on the street.

By seven-fifteen the noise had lured five Filipinos, three Mexicans, two sailors and an Army private. The dressing-room door opened and the girls began to appear. Among the first was Helen.

Said Julio Sal, waving his tickets, "Hello."

"Be right with you," she said.

He watched her walk to the bandstand and say some-

[196]

thing to the trumpet player. She had changed in three months
—changed a great deal. The memory he retained was of a girl
in red. Tonight she wore a blue pleated chiffon that spilled
lightly to her shoes. Something else—her hair. It had been a
golden blond; now it was platinum. He had not time to decide
whether or not he liked the changes, for now she was coming
toward him.

"Hi. Wanna dance?"

The bell clanged and she did not hear him. Hurrying to
the gate, he felt his legs trembling. She met him there, flowed
into his arms professionally, yet like a warm wind. It was a
waltz. She danced easily, methodically, with a freshness that
made him feel she enjoyed it. But she did not remember him—
he was sure of it. He was about to speak his own name when
she looked up and smiled. It was friendly, but there was some
peculiarity about it, an iciness in her blue eyes that made him
suddenly conscious of his race, and he was glad she did not
remember Julio Sal.

"You been here before?"

"First time," he said.

"Seems like I seen you someplace."

"No, no. First time here."

Gradually the place filled. They were mostly Filipinos.
For an hour they danced, until he began to tire. Beyond the
wicker fence were a bar and tables. He felt the pinch of his
new shoes and longed to sit down. It made no difference. Dancing or sitting with her, the price was the same—ten cents a
minute.

"I buy you a drink," he said.

They walked off the floor to the tables. Each was marked
with a Reserved card. The waiter standing at the end of the
bar dashed forward and yanked the card from the table where
they sat. The bell clanged. The girl tore a ticket from the roll
and stuffed it into a blue purse that matched her dress. Her

[197]

small fingers tightened at his wrist.

"What's your name?"

"Tony," he said. "Is Tony Garcia."

"I like Tony. It's a swell name."

The waiter was tall, Kansas-like, tough, impersonal.

"Something to drink?" said Julio Sal. "What you like?"

She lowered her face, then looked up with blue, clean eyes. "Could I have something nice, Tony? Champagne?" She took his head in her hands, pulled it against her lips and whispered into his ear, "I get a percentage." He already knew that, but the touch of her lips, the warmth of her breath at his neck, the scent of her perfume, left him deliriously weak. The bell clanged and she tore away another ticket.

"Champagne," said Julio Sal.

"It's seven bucks," the waiter said.

"Seven?" Julio rubbed his jaw, felt soft, cool fingers under the table, squeezing his knee. He looked at the girl. Her face and eyes were downcast, her lips smiling impishly.

"Champagne."

They waited in silence. Four times the bell sounded and four times Helen's crimson nails tore at the thinning roll of tickets. The waiter came back with two glasses and a bottle on a tray. He gave Julio Sal a slip of paper.

"Nine?" said Julio Sal. "But you say seven."

"Cover charge."

"Is too much for to pay, only little bottle wine."

The waiter picked up the tray and started back to the bar. Julio called to him. "I pay," he said.

After he paid, the cork popped. Julio lifted his glass, touched hers. "For you, for prettiest girl in whole California."

"You're sweet," she said, drinking.

Julio tested the wine with his teeth and tongue. Only fair. He had tasted better in San Jose, and for a third of the price. The bell clanged, the red nails nibbled, a new dance began. It was a waltz, Blue Hawaii.

Helen's eyes closed; she sighed and swayed to the music. "My favorite number. Dance with me, Tony."

They walked to the floor and she pressed herself hard against his body. The bell clanged as they reached the orchestra. She tore away another ticket and spoke to the trumpet player. The next three numbers were repeats of Blue Hawaii. Julio Sal was very pleased. She liked the music of the islands. She would like the music of the Philippines better.

She clung to his arm as they walked back to the table. The wine glasses and champagne were gone. Once more the table was marked Reserved. Julio Sal called the waiter.

"I thought you beat it," the waiter said.

"No. no. Only to dance a little bit."

"That's tough."

"But she was whole bottle. Only little bit, we drink."

"Sorry."

"Bring 'nother bottle," demanded Julio Sal.

They sat down, Helen holding the few remaining tickets like beads.

"It's a shame," she said. "We hardly tasted it."

"No shame. We get more."

The waiter brought another bottle and two glasses. He handed Julio Sal another piece of paper, but Julio wouldn't accept it; he pushed it away, he shook his head. "I already pay. This one for nothing."

"Gotta pay."

"No. You cheat me. Nine dollars, not one drink."

The waiter leaned across the table and the waiter's thick hand clutched the throat of Julio Sal, pushed back his head. "I don't have to take that kind of talk from a Filipino. Take it or leave it."

Nausea flowed up and down the bones of Julio Sal— shame and helplessness. He smoothed back his ruffled hair and

[199]

kept his wild eyes away from Helen, and when the bell clanged he was glad she busied herself tearing off another ticket.

The waiter cursed and walked away. Julio Sal panted and stared into his calloused hands. It wasn't the waiter and it wasn't the nine dollars, but why had she tricked him with three encores of Blue Hawaii? Julio Sal wanted to cry. Then there were cool fingers on the back of his hand, and he saw her sweet face.

"Forget it," she said. "I can do without, if I have to."

But Julio Sal no longer cared, not even for himself.

"Waiter," he said.

That night Julio Sal drank five botles of champagne, drank most of it himself, yet the bitterness within him remained dry and aching, and drunkenness did not come. There was only thirst and desire, and a salty satisfaction in playing the fool. At midnight he stared in fascination as the red nails clawed at the three hundredth ticket. Sometimes she said, "Wanna dance?" And sometimes he asked, "Drink" Sometimes she squeezed his hand and asked, "Having a good time?" And always he answered, "Very good time."

Searching for a match, his fingers touched something hard and square in his pocket.

He brought out the jewel box that held the engagement ring. It was a single diamond set in white gold. He held it under her eyes.

"You like?"

"Beautiful."

"I buy for girl. She die."

"Automobile accident?"

"Just die. Sick. You want ring, you keep."

"I couldn't."

He slipped it on her finger. She tilted it to and from the light, laughing as it sparkled.

Three times the bell clanged, but she forgot the roll of

tickets. Then she looked at him again, studied his delicate nose, his fine lips. She lifted his hand and pressed a kiss into the calloused palm.

"You can take me home. That is, if you want to."

He stared into his empty glass, twirled it around and smiled at the memory of the little speech he had prepared that afternoon, the words he planned to say when he slipped the ring on her finger.

"Don't you want to?"

"I like, very much."

"Do you have a car?"

"We take taxi."

She pushed her chair closer to him, so that they sat crowded side by side. She held his hand in both of hers, pressed it, played absently with his fingers.

When he suggested one more bottle of champagne, she frowned. "It's for suckers."

"I am sucker."

"You're not either. You're nice," she said.

"I have friend," he said. "Name Julio Sal. He know you."

"The guy that writes all them crazy letters? He must be nuts."

"Ya. He nuts."

He looked at the clock over the bar and wanted to sigh; instead a sob shook itself from his throat. It was twelve-thirty. The dream was dead.

"I wait for you at door downstairs," he said.

He got up and left her sitting there. It was warm in the street. He walked a few doors north to a small, hole-in-the-wall, all-night grocery store. Boxes of figs and grapes were tilted toward the street. The sight of them increased the acrid, cigarette-and-champagne dryness of his mouth. He bought a bunch of grapes for a nickel, waved the clerk aside about a paper sack. The grapes were Black Princes, big and meaty.

[201]

He put one of them into his mouth, felt it burst between his teeth, tasted the sweet juice that filled his mouth. A grape from Sonoma County, from the vineyards around Santa Rosa. He had picked grapes in Sonoma—who could say, perhaps from the very vine upon which this bunch had grown.

Eating grapes, Julio Sal walked a block to the Terminal Building, took his overcoat and grips from the ten-cent lockers, went down the stairs to Los Angeles Street and the bus depot. The ticket agent nodded.

"One-way ticket, Santa Rosa," said Julio Sal.

No More Sad Thoughts

By GEORGE MARDIKIAN

> Mardikian, an Armenian by birth, supplies his dates and
> provenance as part of the recipe which follows. The pas-
> sage is from *Dinner at Omar Khayyam's* (1944), his own
> account of his own famous San Francisco restaurant.

When I first came to America as a young man of twenty-
two, fresh from the horrible wars in the Near East, from
murder and torture, I knew what it meant at first hand to be
starved and frozen and left for dead in the snows of winter.
And when I escaped these tortures and came to America, it
was like coming to Heaven. As a child I remember my first
glimpse of Mt. Ararat, which is the most majestic sight to
every Armenian. Across a hot valley and far up into the sky
this snow-covered mountain rises nearly 17,000 feet, with two
peaks. This mountain was the legendary resting place for
Noah's Ark. I shall never forget it. But there are also bitter
memories of Armenia, and I shall never forget the new thrill I
had when, as an immigrant boy, I saw the Statue of Liberty as
we came into New York Harbor. Here was relief from torture
and heartbreak, and I felt it with all my heart. At that moment,
I decided to leave all hatred and bitterness behind and begin
life anew; like the many wonderful things we had heard about
America in Armenia, the Statue of Liberty seemed to sym-
bolize them all that day.

When we arrived at Ellis Island, immigration officers inspected us, gave us a shower and changed our clothes. That
shower seemed to wash all the ugliness of the world away
forever. My brother Arshag had wired from San Francisco to
tell us he had my railroad tickets, and so I set out to cross the
United States. Since I could not speak a word of English or
understand anything that was said to me, my ticket was

pinned to the lapel of my coat; this had my name and destination on it. People were kind and smiled at me; the contrast was so great, it was hard to believe that people could be as happy and cheerful as I saw them that day on the train. Everything I saw inspired me with an ambition to be one of them. I thought of the many things and decided I should go to school immediately, study English and learn how to be a good American.

The cross-country trip was not without momentary excitement and misgivings. Coming into Kansas City, the Traveler's Aid Society took charge of me. During the stopover I looked out into a street and saw thousands of men wearing fezzes and marching toward the depot. My God, I thought, are there Turks over here too? And I reached instinctively into my pocket for the rock I invariably carried at home as protection against them. When they came closer, I realized they were not dressed quite right and they seemed too happy to be Turks. I believe the first thing I asked my sister when I reached San Francisco was who these people were. She told me they were Shriners who had been to a convention.

The following day was Sunday. My family took me on a tour of San Francisco, and we went to the beach. It was a bright clear day and it was a marvelous sight to see thousands of people playing in the sand, laughing and having a hilarious time. Women and children were swimming and riding the Chutes, and even old men with whiskers were throwing balls and playing leapfrog. I couldn't understand it.

Are these people crazy? I asked myself. In our country when people grow up they are solemn and have dignity. For years I had not seen them laugh and play. What is the matter with these people? I thought.

This bothered me. That night I couldn't eat or sleep thinking about my first day here. I remember my sister and brother talking about me and wondering what was wrong. The next morning I decided to see the city by myself and walked many blocks until I was exhausted. However, I remained on the same street so I wouldn't get lost. What I saw was amazing. I saw men with pails going to work. They were whistling. Milkmen were humming quietly as they left bottles on the doorsteps. The motorman on the cable car was whistling merrily as he pulled on the brakes. Even the street-sweeper smiled at me as he cheerily called, "Good morning." He didn't even know me. But I smiled back.

Suddenly I had it! I rushed home to my sister, and ran into the kitchen yelling, "These San Francisco people are not crazy. They are right. We are wrong. It is right to be happy. You feel better. You make the other fellow feel better. I am going to be a happy American; no more thinking sad thoughts, making sad music, and dwelling on the woes of our people."

But to get to the subject of food, and one food in particular. I had arrived in New York in the month of July, in 1922, and got on one of those trains that took eight days to get to San Francisco. People could see that I couldn't speak English because I was labeled with a tag showing my name and destination. Fortunately, my brother had sent me money enough so that I could well afford to eat in the dining car, but the trouble was that I couldn't order in English. Being able to read French, I could make out potato salad on the menu. It is practically the same in my language, so I took a chance and ordered it for my first dinner. The next day I was presented with an identical menu. Again I ordered potato salad. This went on for eight days, and it was *bad* potato salad—really terrible potato salad.

Right then and there I resolved that some day when I got the opportunity I was going to serve to Americans the best potato salad in the world. And that is the reason why, in my sandwich shops today, I serve more than a thousand orders of potato salad a day. It is the same potato salad that I serve at outstanding functions. I use it not only as a fine delicacy, but

[205]

for buffet luncheons I use a large plateful as the table center-
piece, with the message of the day written on it in colored
mayonnaise.

Potato Salad

1 pound firm, fresh potatoes
2 hardboiled eggs
1 teaspoonful salt
white pepper to taste
¼ cupful vinegar
1 pimiento (chopped fine)
⅔ cupful mayonnaise
1 small onion sliced
2 tablespoonfuls chopped parsley

Boil potatoes in skins. When cool, peel and cut in quarters. Then slice or dice. Add vinegar, mix well, and let
soak. Slice onion and pour salt over it. Then squeeze
out all the juice, and wash salt away with cold water.
Mix onion with potatoes; add pimiento, eggs, salt and
pepper, parsley and mayonnaise. Mix well and let stand in
refrigerator for some time before serving.

ROBINSON JEFFERS

Robinson Jeffers was born in Pittsburg in 1887, and studied in Pittsburg, Zurich, U.C.L.A., and the University of Washington, seeking a destiny in pedagogy, medicine, forestry, and other crafts. In 1912 he turned to poetry, married, and built a house ("Tor House") on a cliff near Carmel, partly carving it from the native stone with his own hand. From that place came the many volumes of verse in which he considered the fate of earlier settlers (as in the great *Roan Stallion*, 1925), the weakness and sorrow of the human fate (*Women at Point Sur*, 1927, and *Thurso's Landing*, 1932), and—a constant theme with him—the impermanence of man's hopes and man's civilizations.

Shine, Perishing Republic

While this America settles in the mould of its vulgarity,
    heavily thickening to empire,
And protest, only a bubble in the molten mass, pops and sighs
    out, and the mass hardens,

I sadly smiling remember that the flower fades to make fruit,
    the fruit rots to make earth.
Out of the mother; and through the spring exultances, ripeness
    and decadence; and home to the mother.

You making haste haste on decay; not blameworthy; life is
    good, be it stubbornly long or suddenly
A mortal splendor: meteors are not needed less than
    Mountains: shine, perishing republic.

But for my children, I would have them keep their distance
    from the thickening center; corruption
Never has been compulsory, when the cities lie at the
    monster's feet there are left the mountains.

[207]

And boys, be in nothing so moderate as in love of man, a clever
    servant, insufferable master.
There is the trap that catches noblest spirits, that caught—
    they say—God, when he walked on earth.

Clouds of Evening

Enormous cloud-mountains that form over Point Lobos and
    into the sunset,
Figures of fire on the walls of tonight's storm,
Foam of gold in gorges of fire, and the great file of warrior
    angels:
Dreams gathering in the curdled brain of the earth—
The sky the brain-vault—on the threshold of sleep: poor
    earth; you, like your children
By inordinate desires tortured, make dreams?
Storms more enormous, wars nobler, more toppling mountains,
    more jeweled waters, more free
Fires on impossible headlands . . . as a poor girl
Wishing her lover taller and more desirous, and herself maned
    with gold,
Dreams the world right, in the cold bed, about dawn.
Dreams are beautiful; the slaves of form are beautiful also;
    I have grown to believe
A stone is a better pillow than many visions.

Hurt Hawks

I

The broken pillar of the wing jags from the clotted shoulder,
The wing trails like a banner in defeat,
No more to use the sky forever but live with famine
And pain a few days: cat nor coyote

[208]

Will shorten the week of waiting for death, there is game
    without talons.
He stands under the oak-bush and waits
The lame feet of salvation; at night he remembers freedom
And flies in a dream, the dawns ruin it.
He is strong and pain is worse to the strong, incapacity is
    worse.
The curs of the day come and torment him
At distance, no one but death the redeemer will humble
    that head,
The intrepid readiness, the terrible eyes.
The wild God of the world is sometimes merciful to those
That ask mercy, not often to the arrogant.
You do not know him, you communal people, or you have
    forgotten him;
Intemperate and savage, the hawk remembers him;
Beautiful and wild, the hawks, and men that are dying,
    remember him.

II

I'd sooner, except the penalties, kill a man than a hawk,
    but the great redtail
Had nothing left but unbearable misery
From the bone too shattered for mending, the wing that
    trailed under his talons when he moved.
We had fed him six weeks, I gave him freedom,
He wandered over the foreland hill and returned in the
    evening, asking for death,
Not like a beggar, still eyed with the old
Implacable arrogance. I gave him the lead gift in the
    twilight. What fell was relaxed,
Owl-downy, soft feminine feathers; but what
Soared: the fierce rush: the night-herons by the flooded
    river cried fear at its rising
Before it was quite unsheathed from reality.

[209]

Post Mortem

Happy people die whole, they are all dissolved in a moment,
  they have had what they wanted,
No hard gifts; the unhappy
Linger a space, but pain is a thing that is glad to be forgotten;
  but one who has given
His heart to a cause or a country,
His ghost may spaniel it a while, disconsolate to watch it. I
  was wondering how long the spirit
That sheds this verse will remain
When the nostrils are nipped, when the brain rots in its vault
  or bubbles in the violence of fire
To be ash in metal. I was thinking
Some stalks of the wood whose roots I married to the earth of
  this place will stand five centuries;
I held the roots in my hand,
The stems of the trees between two fingers; how many remote
  generations of women
Will drink joy from men's loins,
And dragged from between the thighs of what mothers will
  giggle at my ghost when it curses the axmen,
Gray impotent voice on the sea-wind,
When the last trunk falls? The women's abundance will have
  built roofs over all this foreland;
Will have buried the rock foundations
I laid here: the women's exuberance will canker and fail in its
  time and like clouds the houses
Unframe, the granite of the prime
Stand from the heaps: come storm and wash clean: the plaster
  is all run to the sea and the steel
All rusted; the foreland resumes
The form we loved when we saw it. Though one at the end of
  the age and far off from this place

Should meet my presence in a poem,
The ghost would not care but be here, long sunset shadow in
    the seams of the granite, and forgotten
The flesh, a spirit for the stone.

Continent's End

At the equinox when the earth was veiled in a late rain,
    wreathed with wet poppies, waiting spring,
The ocean swelled for a far storm and beat its boundary, the
    ground-swell shook the beds of granite.

I gazing at the boundaries of granite and spray, the established
    sea-marks, felt behind me
Mountain and plain, the immense breadth of the continent,
    before me the mass and doubled stretch of water.

I said: You yoke the Aleutian seal-rocks with the lava and
    coral sowings that flower the south,
Over your flood the life that sought the sunrise faces ours that
    has followed the evening star.

The long migrations meet across you and it is nothing to you,
    you have forgotten us, mother.
You were much younger when we crawled out of the womb
    and lay in the sun's eye on the tideline.

It was long and long ago; we have grown proud since then and
    you have grown bitter; life retains
Your mobile soft unquiet strength; and envies hardness, the
    insolent quietness of stone.

[211]

The tides are in our veins, we still mirror the stars, life is your
    child, but there is in me
Older and harder than life and more impartial, the eye that
    watched before there was an ocean.

That watched you fill your beds out of the condensation of
    thin vapor and watched you change them,
That saw you soft and violent wear your boundaries down,
    eat rock, shift places with the continents.

Mother, though my song's measure is like your surf-beat's
    ancient rhythm I never learned it of you.
Before there was any water there were tides of fire, both our
    tones flow from the older fountain.

PART VII

The Adjustment of Images

The Adjustment of Images

LIKE THE UNTHINKING AMERICAN everywhere, the unthinking Californian was considerably shocked by the events of December 7, 1941. For the thinking Californian, including most of the state's serious writers, neither these events nor the wars that followed them came as a surprise. Keeping their Eastern watch for many years they had seen too many other countries shifting from economic to military enterprises. The Ethiopian war, the Spanish war, and the steady growth of fascism in Italy and Germany had hurt and disheartened them. So had the wars and conquests beyond their own Western gate: the organized blood-lusts in Japan, the agonies of a China constantly at war with itself or with others, and the throbbing overtures to anti-colonial wars in India, Indo-China, and all the islands of their familiar Pacific. Though suddenly louder the song was old.

It was the Pacific side of the great war itself that affected their lives most. Those who could add and subtract were able to laugh at the Government's dire warnings about Japanese air raids, invasions, infiltrations, and other deviltries. But the blackouts and practice air raids and overfilled barrooms were a

[215]

definite nuisance; and those who honored such abstractions as Truth and Justice were dismayed by such things as the concentration of their niesei neighbors in desert camps, the shutting off of some freedoms in speech and writing, and the institutionalized blatancy of the propaganda drummed against their resisting eyes and ears. James Leigh's description of wartime Los Angeles as seen by a sensitive California adolescent nicely illustrates these deep-grained though nearly bloodless effects of the war on the western slope.

As had happened before in California, business went on not as usual but much better than usual. There was an end to job-hunting and hunger; the whole nation seemed to be pouring its wealth into the state; ranchers, businessmen, manufacturers, and workers shared the wealth equally among them; the Californian had never had it so good. Immigration quickened as it had before, and, for the same geographic and economic reasons as before, a huge overplus of the new immigrants settled in the Los Angeles area. Prices and wages rose together, but rose with such miraculous swiftness that the old quarrel between labor and capital lost its relevance and meaning. Deprived of that quarrel, resisting the shrill clamors and vulgarities that accompanied the nation's high quarrels, disengaging themselves as best they could from the obvious, often ugly processes of boosterism and megopolis-building, disenchanted with the past and dubious about the future, California writers led all others in their discovery of sidesteps and realignments, shifts of their sympathies, a sweeping readjustment of images. It was the awful dullness and sameness of an institutionalized population that they chose for their enemy; for the object of their sympathies and loyalties they chose the individual, the One Lone Man who, caught up in the squeeze and suction of massed and impersonal social forces, fights to preserve his separate identity from a bland or comfortable absorption.

One need not praise or blame this change of direction, with its obvious advantages for literature and its equally obvious social debits. Nor may one call it a California development, though several of its features are recognisably Californian. But one or two of its effects belong strictly to the state. It was in the rebellious and isolative California literary scene, for example, that outside writers such as Jack Kerouac, Gregory Corso, and Allen Ginsberg developed the special characteristics of their thought and work. The San Francisco area spawned its eternal plethora of poets and novelists and lonely unpublishing inquirers, the "Subterraneans" as Kerouac calls them, "very quiet; they are very Christlike." Writers who used Hollywood for a setting concerned themselves as usual with the brutalities and inequities of the city, but shifted from thoughts of general evil and general unrest to the minute, singular evils that befall individuals, and the small page-four human-interest actions that follow them, the unrest of one man, the fights of a couple. The shift was a fast one, but complete. In 1940 the thinking Californian, writer or not, was still thinking in terms of large panaceas, reforms, some widespread fruits of a social victory. In 1950 the fate he cared for was that of the single separate person, isolated in a mortgaged but private tract-house, insulated even on public throughways by the steel and glass of his private automobile. When the Korean war in his own Pacific was over, he scarcely asked himself who had won it. He cared about brain-washing though, and the weakness and strength of those isolates who faced it; he wanted identity for himself and others, and sought it with his analyst or sometimes by writing.

KENNETH REXROTH

Kenneth Rexroth (b. 1906) left his Midwestern school "in a row over military training," traveled widely as an industrial and agricultural worker, and devoted his energies on the one hand to liberal and radical politics and on the other to verse. As a critic, editor, translator, lecturer, and playwright he has been near the center of San Francisco literary activity since his arrival in 1927, and is often called the "indispensable" writer of that city. His volumes of poetry include *In What Hour* (1940), *The Phoenix and the Tortoise* (1944), and *In Defense of the Earth* (1956).

Requiem for the Spanish Dead

The great geometrical winter constellations
Lift up over the Sierra Nevada,
I walk under the stars, my feet on the known round earth.
My eyes following the lights of an airplane,
Red and green, growling deep into the Hyades.
The note of the engine rises, shrill, faint,
Finally inaudible, and the lights go out
In the southeast haze beneath the feet of Orion.

As the sound departs I am chilled and grow sick
With the thought that has come over me. I see Spain
Under the black windy sky, the snow stirring faintly,
Glittering and moving over the pallid upland,
And men waiting, clutched with cold and huddled together,
As an unknown plane goes over them. It flies southeast
Into the haze above the lines of the enemy.
Sparks appear near the horizon under it.
After they have gone out the earth quivers
And the sound comes faintly. The men relax for a moment
And grow tense again as their own thoughts return to them.

[218]

I see the unwritten books, the unrecorded experiments,
The unpainted pictures, the interrupted lives,
Lowered into the graves with the red flags over them.
I see the quick gray brains broken and clotted with blood,
Lowered each in its own darkness, useless in the earth.
Alone on a hilltop in San Francisco suddenly
I am caught in a nightmare, the dead flesh
Mounting over half the world presses against me.

Then quietly at first and then rich and full-bodied,
I hear the voice of a young woman singing.
The emigrants on the corner are holding
A wake for their oldest child, a driverless truck
Broke away on the steep hill and killed him,
Voice after voice adds itself to the singing.
Orion moves westward across the meridian,
Rigel, Bellatrix, Betelgeuse, marching in order,
The great nebula glimmering in his loins.

At Lake Desolation

The sun is about to come up and the regiments lie
Scattered in the furrows, their large eyes
Wet in the pale light and their throats cut.
At noon the plow shearing the purple loam,
And the hands of the plowmen, the blood
Black on the knuckles. He has asked.
He has seen the naked virgins and matrons
Impaled and disembowled. He has asked.
He has seen water wafering
Over stones. He has asked. He has seen
The roan gelding break through the alkali crust,
Sink rampant in the fetid mud. He has asked.
Moving towards hot crepuscular horizons,
He has asked. He has seen the nude children

[219]

Run screaming. He has asked. Their eyes
Festering their nostrils scalded. He has asked.
The fermented pulp oozes through the rotting fruit skin,
The unborn phoenix screams within the breakfast eggs.
The horrible abundances, the little blind answers
Like maggots, the dukes on the towering moor
Benighted in their cardboard armor; and he,
Locked in the vertebrae of the Sierra, saw
The sharp alley of night, the trail
Glimmering and feet pausing and going
On beside him; and beyond the tangled
Thicket and the thorns saw
Hackeldama, the potter's field,
Full of dead strangers.

On What Planet

Uniformly over the whole countryside
The warm air flows imperceptibly seaward;
The autumn haze drifts in deep bands
Over the pale water;
White egrets stand in the blue marshes;
Tamalpais, Diablo, St. Helena
Float in the air.
Climbing on the cliffs of Hunter's Hill
We look out over fifty miles of sinuous
Interpenetration of mountains and sea.

Leading up a twisted chimney,
Just as my eyes rise to the level
Of a small cave, two white owls
Fly out, silent, close to my face.
They hover, confused in the sunlight,
And disappear into the recesses of the cliff.

All day I have been watching a new climber,
A young girl with ash blond hair
And gentle confident eyes.
She climbs slowly, precisely,
With unwasted grace.
While I am coiling the ropes,
Watching the spectacular sunset,
She turns to me and says, quietly,
"It must be very beautiful, the sunset,
On Saturn, with the rings and all the moons."

A Christmas Note for Geraldine Udell

Do the prairie flowers, the huge autumn
Moons, return in season?
Debs, Berkman, Larkin, Haywood, they are dead now.
All the girls are middle aged.
So much has escaped me, so much lies covert
In memory, and muffled
Like thunder muttering through sleep, that woke me,
To watch the city wink
Out in the violet light under the twisting rain.
Lightning storms are rare here,
In this statistically perfect climate.
The eucalyptus shed
Branches, doors banged, glass broke, the sea smashed its walls.
I, in my narrow bed,
Thought of other times, the hope filled post war years,
Exultant, dishevelled
Festivals, exultant eyes, dishevelled lips,
Eyes dulled now, and lips thinned,
Festivals that have betrayed their occasions.
I think of you in *Gas*,
The heroine on the eve of explosion;

[221]

Or angry, white, and still,
Arguing with me about Sasha's tragic book.
Here in the empty night,
I light the lamp and hunt for pad and pencil.
A million sleepers turn,
While bombs fall in their dreams. The storm goes away,
Muttering in the hills.
The veering wind brings the cold, organic smell
Of the flowing ocean.

Delia Rexroth

California rolls into
Sleepy summer, and the air
Is full of the bitter sweet
Smoke of the grass fires burning
On the San Francisco hills.
Flesh burns so, and the pyramids
Likewise, and the burning stars.
Tired tonight, in a city
Of parvenus, in the inhuman
West, in the most blood drenched year,
I took down a book of poems
That you used to like, that you
Used to sing to music I
Never found anywhere again—
Michael Field's book, *Long Ago.*
Indeed it's long ago now—
Your bronze hair and svelte body.
I guess you were a fierce lover,
A wild wife, an animal
Mother. And now life has cost
Me more years, though much less pain,
Than you had to pay for it.

[222]

And I have bought back, for and from
Myself, these poems and paintings,
Carved from the protesting bone,
The precious consequences
Of your torn and distraught life.

The Daughters

Strong ankled, sun burned, almost naked,
The daughters of California
Educate reluctant humanists;
Drive into their skulls with tennis balls
The unhappy realization
That nature is still stronger than man.
The special Hellenic privilege
Of the special intellect seeps out
At last in this irrigated soil.
Sweat of athletes and juice of lovers
Are stronger than Socrates' hemlock;
And the games of scrupulous Euclid
Vanish in the gymnopedia.

O. K., Baby, This is the World

By WILLIAM SAROYAN

Born of Armenian parents in Fresno (1908), Saroyan lost
his father very early and was raised partly in an orphan-
age and partly by his mother's profits as a cannery worker.
Saroyan himself worked at an amazing variety of jobs
until the time when, living in a San Francisco hotel, he
set himself the task of writing a story a day "forever."
Much of his work since then has taken the short-story
form, but he won the Pulitzer Prize for drama (*The Time
of Your Life*, 1940), both wrote and directed his unfor-
gettable movie *The Human Comedy* (1944), and is a pro-
lific poet and essayist.

One Saturday at noon I took a cab at Paramount and
rode to the Brown Derby on Vine Street and all the way down
I listened to the radio. There were two programs: a football
game in the Middle West, or maybe in the East, and music,
a song: *The World Is Mine Tonight.*

I wanted the music, and the driver wanted the game. He
asked if I would mind if we listened to the game, and I told
him I wouldn't mind at all.

I think Notre Dame lost. Navy won. It was an upset.
Notre Dame was supposed to win. Easy. I didn't win or lose
anything on the game. I didn't care one way or another who
won or lost. I didn't even listen to the winning and losing part
of the game. I listened only to a couple of mediocre plays.
Nobody got anywhere, although a half-back was injured.

I learned later that Navy won. Three to nothing, I think.
It was rather nice to know how the game turned out, but it
wasn't amazing.

I wouldn't have been amazed if Navy had won by a score
of six hundred and twelve to five hundred and ninety-seven,

[224]

and I don't believe I would have been amazed if Notre Dame had won by a score of twenty-one to nothing.

I believe I wouldn't have been amazed if Navy, fearing defeat, had sent in a new team armed with machine-guns, and destroyed the Notre Dame team, including substitutes, the coach, the assistant coach, and several innocent bystanders, making a score of sixty-one to nothing.

I wouldn't have been the least startled if the mob of one side of the stadium had met the mob of the other side of the stadium in the center of the field and fought it out hand to hand.

The song, *The World Is Mine Tonight*, is better than mediocre. In the song love wins, two to nothing. It's pleasant, but not amazing. I knew love would win before the song ended, before it began, before it was written. Love won in another song once, three million to nothing: *I Can't Give You Anything But Love, Baby.*

It was the same with Roosevelt, too. I knew Roosevelt would win, too. Navy, love, and Roosevelt are always good bets. I thought I would send Hearst a cablegram or a telegram, but I didn't know where to reach him. There would have been two words in the message: HA HA. The telegram would have cost me anywhere from sixty cents to two dollars, but I didn't send it. A lot of rich people in San Francisco were angry with me because I had told them Mr. Landon had no more chance than I had. They said if that was so, then goodby Democracy. I said, All right, good-by. Twenty years ago, when I was eight, I suppose I would have been horrified if there had been a threatening of good-by Democracy.

I got out of the cab, bought a paper, and walked into the Brown Derby for lunch. The headline said the rebels were near Madrid, but don't think for a moment that I was amazed. I just took the paper to the table and when the director came in and sat down I said, The Fascists are near Madrid.

[225]

We ordered lunch. I had cold meats and the director had cold meats. It was a good lunch and I daresay the Navy-Notre Dame game was a good game. The election was an excellent election. Mr. Landon telegraphed Mr. Roosevelt: *The nation has spoken.*

I never did find out what Mr. Hearst said. Bugs Baer said something about Maine.

If the N.R.A. Eagle comes back, he said, Maine will get a squab.

Ha ha.

What's wrong with Maine? In Frisco they put up a big sign before the election. It said: *Remember Spain and vote with Maine.*

They forgot.

It looks like we're going to have a solid Fascist Europe, I said to the director.

He didn't care. Maybe I didn't care, either. I hadn't bet a nickel on whether or not we were going to have a solid Fascist Europe.

A little girl came up to the director with a scratch pad and asked the director if he would sign his name on the blank page.

The little girl was thrilled and unconsciously I reached for my pencil. I would have been glad to sign my name seventeen times. She didn't ask me to, however. Most people under twelve don't know who I am, and people over twelve seldom, if ever, care to have my signature on a blank piece of paper.

The director laughed and said, Who *am* I?

I don't know, the little girl said. I know you're *somebody.*

Christ, I'm somebody myself. And even though she little suspects it, so is the little girl. Her name is probably Alice.

The director signed his name modestly, the little girl thanked him very much without pausing to read the name, returned to her table where her mother and her aunt welcomed her home after triumphs abroad, and the director said, What are you doing?

When? I said.

If he meant all the time, he had me.

When you work, he said.

I'm working on a movie about a young doctor, I said.

Is it any good? he said.

I don't know, I said.

What happens? he said.

Well, I said, he's a young doctor. A society girl is in love with him. He's in love with a nurse, only he doesn't know it.

Is that all? the director said.

Not exactly, I said. There are certain minor themes and complications.

For instance? the director said.

Well, there is a child prodigy, I said. He is a genius. He is expert on the violin, although only eight years old. Well, this boy, Michael Bartok, has a bad right arm. No, a bad left arm. We spent two days deciding which arm should be bad. We chose the left arm. The bad doctor who is the greatest surgeon in America abandons this boy on the operating table to go to a rich patient in Long Island. The boy's arm gets worse and worse, and it looks like he'll never be able to play again. His mother goes crazy and shoots the good young doctor, our hero.

Why? the director said.

I don't know, I said. I've given the matter a lot of thought, day and night, but I've never been able to find out. She just shoots him, that's all. It's very exciting, and she is an excellent shot. He doesn't die, though, because he likes the nurse. He starts to get well and the nurse comes in and takes the thermometer out of his mouth and kisses him.

Oh, boy, the director said. Did you make up the story?

No, I said, but I wouldn't be surprised if I could make up

[227]

one just like it.

Well, where do *you* come in on this thing? the director said. What are *you* doing?

I'm sort of bringing the dialogue to life, I said.

Oh, said the director. How?

I don't know *how*, I said.

We ate in silence for a while. Two famous actresses with two famous actors went down the aisle. They went down the aisle just like two famous actresses and two famous actors.

This town stinks, I said. In a way, though, it's the most magic place in the world.

It's impossible for a writer to write about this town or the people of this town, the director said.

I don't know, I said. I don't think it's impossible. It's not easy, but it's not easy to write about any town or any people. Especially, I said, if you can't write.

No, he said. A writer can write about San Francisco and the people of San Francisco, but nobody in the world can write about Hollywood and the people of Hollywood. All the actors and actresses are phony.

I believe that everybody in the world is partly phony and that nobody in the world is altogether phony and that a writer's job is to determine how much of anybody is phony and how much real and to make something of it, one way or another. I believe also that the phoniest people in the world are often the most real people in the world, and the most genuinely tragic people in the world.

I used to get sore, but I don't any more because I don't know who to get sore at. It's too easy to get sore at people you never meet like Hearst and Hitler and Mussolini. I don't believe I've ever been really sore at Hearst and Hitler and Mussolini. And I can't get sore at the people I know because I know them. God Almighty, they're all right, even if they're rats. Even if they're rats, they're not *always* rats. Sometimes

[228]

they're not even house mice.

Anyway, the director said, Everything is phony down here and no writer has ever come to this place and written anything about this place that was worth anything. Take the people from Ohio in this town, he said. Girls who've won beauty contests. Even they're phony, even when everything they do is tragic. They're phony because when they suffer, as they do, they suffer because they want to be actresses. Everything everybody wants down here is not worth suffering for.

I didn't agree, but I didn't say anything because I knew it would take me an hour to show why it is not possible for anything to be phony if one suffers for it. That isn't a very subtle thing to know, but it is a difficult thing to explain.

Do you like the work you're doing? the director said.

It's very interesting, I said. It's not exactly writing, but it's different, and interesting.

This doctor, the director said, is he a good character?

He isn't a character at all, I said. He's somebody in a white coat to be photographed. Everybody will believe he's a doctor because they want to believe.

Well, does he say anything worth hearing? the director said.

He says a couple of things here and there, I said.

All right, the director said. What does the young doctor say?

Well, I said, he greets a lot of people and says good-by to a lot of people in the picture.

Does he say anything special? the director said. Does he say anything *you've* written?

Yes, I said. The picture begins with this young doctor holding up a new-born baby by its legs and slapping life into it. The young doctor says, O.K., baby, this is the world, so inhale and exhale and be with us a while. They're not going to be kind to you out there because nobody was kind to them,

[229]

but don't hate anybody. There's nobody to hate. You're going to be pushed around, and so forth and so on. That's the idea. He tells the baby how it is and what to expect and the story begins.

The director was very kind.

That's very nice, he said.

It's nothing, I said.

It's a nice speech, the director said.

It's like this, I said. The young doctor's been around a little, so he tells the baby it's lousy, but it's the only thing there is, so the baby might as well take it easy and like it. The young doctor says, It's the world. It's not good. It's not bad. But most of us are crazy about it.

That's very good, the director said.

He means it, I said. He knows it's both things at the same time, lousy and good, and he's still young enough and naive enough to wonder what's going to happen to the baby in the world, and of course he can't wait, so he tells the baby what happened to *him* in the world. Your heart is going to break a thousand times before you're twenty, he says, or something like that, but instead of crying about it you're going to learn to laugh, and so on and so forth. It's lousy, I said.

No, the director said, it's very good.

It's not really good, I said. The young doctor is a good guy, an easy-going guy, and he's got to talk when he brings a baby into the world. He feels half-way glad about it and half-way miserable about it. He listens to the baby bawling and it makes him laugh. I don't know who you are, he says to the baby, or who you are going to be, but whoever you are, whatever you do, for Christ's sake don't hurt anybody. But don't let anybody hurt you either.

You see, I said, it doesn't make sense. If you're not going to let anybody hurt you, you're going to have to hurt somebody. There's no two ways about it.

It's a good speech, the director said.

I didn't want to work on this story, I said. They assigned me to it. I need the job badly. I'm paying a lot of old debts. It's a good job. I'm making more money a week than most people in this country make in three or four months. I'm paying a lot of debts.

O.K., baby, this is the world, the director said.

That's right, I said.

It's a swell opening for a picture, he said.

The rebels are near Madrid, I said.

This is the world, the director said. That's fine.

Shall we go? I said.

All right, the director said.

We left the Brown Derby and drove out to the director's home in Beverly Hills, changed our clothes, and went out to the tennis court and played three sets of tennis.

Every once in a while the director would make an excellent drive and say, O.K., baby, this is the world.

As I said before, though, I wouldn't be surprised if they got up and ran to the center of the field and proceeded to kill one another. What the hell, they're alive, and bored, and not overbright; what else is there for them to do, anywhere?

There are too many people, and Fascists are only people, too, so to hell with it. They think they're right and they're willing to die for whatever they believe, so what's the use being amazed about anything?

The Legend-Makers

By WILLIAM SAROYAN

The first thing I heard about when I got down there from San Francisco was that an actress who had been very beautiful and very famous two or three years ago had died of a heart attack. She was twenty-five or so and had been through for a year and a half or so.

The next day I ran into a scenario writer I had gotten drunk with once and he told me that a friend of his, another scenario writer, had died of a heart attack, too. He was older than the actress, forty, and had worked right up to the end. Later, another writer told me this scenario writer's death had grieved him deeply, but it seemed to him that the man had worried too much all the time about the unimportant stuff he was doing, and that the worrying had killed him. The living writer told me the names of some of the pictures the dead writer had been partly responsible for, and they were all pictures I had seen and forgotten. It didn't seem to either of us that he had had any occasion to worry about them. He had, though, and he'd died.

It was quite a sadness in our lives for a while, although he had lived in sunshine for years, had worn the finest clothes, eaten the best of available food, and dwelt in the finest type of modern house. Even with all that, it was sad because there seemed to be something symbolic, or one might say legendary, or even prophetic, about his exit, his wind-up, his life and death, the fulfillment of his destiny. It seemed an awful pointless destiny to fulfill. He had worried himself to death over six B pictures, starring three times that many charming, beautiful, handsome, and perhaps not unduly stupid actresses and actors. In gross figures he had been partly responsible for perhaps seven million different people all over the world finding a

[232]

harmless escape from boredom for from fifty to seventy minutes, during, perhaps, temperate climate, night or day, pleasant weather, unpleasant, rain, snow, or storm. At his best, as a human being, a writer, his functioning had been neither outstanding nor unoutstanding. And when we had had more drinks, toward the end of drinking for the evening, it was felt that he had been a swell guy, a little sad, a little foolish, a little harassed, a little bewildered, with values a little balled up, but always a good guy. Early in the morning we dismissed him with sorrow, regret, and the agreement that women should be brought into the discussion, more or less for the sake of the living. This was done, and the sorrow, the pathos, the regret, was immeasurably increased. As well as the humor.

It was nothing.

The very first day of this visit found the newspapers loaded with fever, hysteria, confusion, bewilderment, energy, accounts of small news on the inside pages, and much copy on the Henry Armstrong-Baby Arizmendi fight, between small men, less light in color than the average of this country, but powerful, clever, and artful in their particular fields. Then Adolf (Hitler) made his reunion in Vienna, marched the men up the field and down again, and Austria, of the Blue Danube, was anschluss, or back in the fold, and a man whose hyphenated name I shall not try to spell roared with love in his voice his welcome to what he called his Führer, one might say his beloved Führer.

We saw the fight between Armstrong and Arizmendi: I mean by we, myself and eleven scenario writers. At the fight it was announced that a ringside patron of the fights for the past forty-two or -three years had finally passed away. A purple wreath or something else sad in image was in his seat, and next to the seat was Al Jolson. The little chubby fight announcer who looks like a real estate salesman asked for silence, during which to count ten for the deceased, which he did. The silence was not exactly whole-hearted or complete: it contained boos, hisses, witty remarks, whistling, and roars of laughter, as well as severe reproofs from anonymous people with a sense of the fitting, or perhaps a classically western regard for the solemnity of death. The deceased was duly counted out and the fighters of the next bout introduced.

The Austrian affair, however, grew in leaps and bounds during the fights, and after the main event, in which the Mexican Arizmendi refused to be annihilated, and in fact fought a handsome fight, the morning papers were full of new developments, so that by the time we got to Musso & Frank's, on Hollywood Boulevard, a writer was found at the bar, drunk, with a paper open in front of him, and tears streaming out of his eyes. There was a map of Spain in the paper which plainly showed how the Rebels were driving the Loyalists to the sea.

It's hopeless, the young writer said, and ordered another scotch and soda.

What is? another writer asked.

Everything, the first writer replied.

In between times, while waiting for new editions of papers, I read a movie story and, finding it lousy, said so. This was an ignorant thing to do, but in a way a pleasing one. As a matter of fact, the story wasn't lousy at all. It was, I believe, a characteristic kind of story. It perhaps only seemed lousy. I probably made a mistake, and if I were to be burned at the stake for my opinion I believe I wouldn't hesitate a moment to recant.

There was a good deal of strange, tense, off-color, and one might say foul-smelling affection between the phonies of Austria and the phonies of Germany over there in Europe, and it all came out in the papers. My Führer, the welcomer said to the invader, and it sounded very much like something slightly opportunistic in some dimension or other.

Then the Polish-Lithuanian border trouble grew in the news, and the scenario writers all worried about that a while, during dinner, and afterwards. They worried also about the executions in Russia. One original scenario writer spent most of his spare worrying-energy worrying about a woman in the newspapers who'd killed her kids and herself because of poverty. For the most part, though, the writers worried about the bigger and more worthwhile subjects for worrying.

I spent only a week in the city where the world's imagination is manufactured, but during the whole week everybody I ran into was worrying, on the whole, about the news. You'd never imagine they were all trying to create a better world, through hook or crook, willy-nilly, or any other way. You got the idea that they were all lost in some grotesque, one might say, desolation in which they were cut off from the world. Nobody worried about having a chance to make a movie that would go out to what is known as the four corners of the world and make the little people realize what monkeys they are being made of, if one may be forgiven a sentence like that.

A fellow passenger on the train back to Frisco was a man named, if memory serves, Louis B. Mayer, a scenario writer, I believe. Less than two hours after getting off the train he spoke to a banquet room full of Lions, or something. I think he told them America is O.K. The people got the lunch out of it, I believe.

I took a cab home and didn't shave because I wasn't invited to dinner.

Irresistible Force

By HERMAN WOUK

Herman Wouk is best known for his best-selling novels *The Caine Mutiny* (1951) and *Marjorie Morningstar* (1955), and has also written for the films. An Easterner by upbringing, he tried briefly to reproduce the Hollywood climate in such stories as "Irresistible Force."

The house was a gigantic stucco imitation of a French château, bright orange and monstrously ugly. It stood on a five-acre grassy knoll off Hollywood Boulevard, fenced around by a low stucco wall, also orange.

A taxi came roaring up the driveway, where ragged brown weeds sprouted abundantly in the gravel. Out of the cab jumped a hatless man in a sleek vicuna topcoat. He thrust a bill at the taxi driver and ran up the steps to the colossal orange portico, his long black hair flying.

"They're not here yet?" he said sharply to a little man with a high starched collar and a furtive face, who stood by the brass-studded oak door holding a bunch of keys.

The little man stared at the newcomer. "Good heavens, Mr. Fauve, you really *came!* I didn't believe—"

"Where are they?"

"They'll be here, sir—but—good heavens—"

"Well, it's a hell of a note. They only have to come from Culver City, and I came three thousand miles from New York, and I'm here first. Well, let's get the story straight, now. He's rich, and retired, you said?"

"Why—why, yes, sir—electrical contractor. Used to be small-time but made a pile on defense orders—very substantial party—how was your plane trip, sir? Dear me, all the way from—"

"Who likes the house—him or his wife or both?"

"Well, mainly Mrs. Erickson, I think—"

"Good, the wife usually makes the decision. What's she like?"

"Why, she seems very nice—"

"Look, Brewsters, I want information! What's her weakness? Why does she want this preposterous barn?"

"Oh—well, sir—" the real-estate broker's face creased in a sly grin—"to be frank, they—I don't think they know what to do with their money. I heard them talk about taking a trip around the world, or even settling in Paris. But I think Mrs. Erickson's decided to go in for a big splash here, to impress her friends, and—"

"What luck! *Nouveau riche* idiots. We're in at last."

"It does look hopeful, sir, that's why I phoned you—"

"The hell with hope." Jeremy Fauve lit a cigarette, looking at the broker with piercing, wild black eyes. "Do you know how long I've been trying to unload this mausoleum? I was drunk when I bought it, and I was rolling in money, and I was generally crazy. Now I've got to sell it, d'you hear, Brewsters? I need money. I will stop at nothing to nail these people down. Any maneuver that occurs to you, I'm for, d'you hear? Maybe we can pick up a silver-mink coat somewhere— tell the wife it goes with the house. A little thing like that can sway a woman, especially such a stupid one—"

"Pardon me, Mr. Fauve. My experience shows it's bad policy to try to influence a buyer. Any kind of pressure usually backfires. We'd better just hope—"

"Who's talking about pressure?" Fauve said irritably. "Just let me handle them, Brewsters, will you? This is the first nibble I've had in two years and I'm going to *land* them. It's a matter of salesmanship, of which you haven't an atom in your make-up. None of you brokers have, you're all sluggish leeches—"

"It's not an easy property to move, sir—"

[237]

"Okay, okay. Is that them?"

A new yellow Cadillac convertible came up the boulevard and turned in under the massive orange gateway.

"Yes, sir—"

"There's three people—" Fauve peered at the car like a hawk.

"The daughter is with them. Only child. That's the catch, Mr. Fauve. She doesn't want to move from Culver City. Says she'll be lonesome without her friends."

Fauve glared at him. "Ye gods, what do you mean, withholding such a piece of crucial information? Do you want to ruin me?"

"Really, sir, you gave me no chance," Brewsters whispered. The Cadillac had stopped and the doors were opening.

"All right. Be quiet now. I'll take over."

Erickson was a stout man with strands of yellow hair over a broad pink scalp, and rimless glasses that shone in the sun. His wife, trotting up the steps behind him, looked as though she had once been very pretty; her features were still doll-like under little puffs of fat, and her figure, lumping and bulging in a tailored beige suit, seemed like the ruin of a good thing. The daughter trailed behind, and Fauve noted unhappily that she was dragging her feet. He came down to greet them, holding out his hand to the wife. "I'm Jeremy Fauve, Mrs. Erickson. Happen to be in Hollywood on a pre-production deal, and so I thought—"

"Why, Mr. *Fauve!* What a surprise! What an honor!" The woman smiled and stared with hungry eagerness. "Dear, this is Mr. Fauve, himself—you know, the famous producer——" She fluttered her small, pretty hands.

"How do? Heard all about you, of course, from Brewsters and Eve here," Erickson said, with a trace of Swedish accent. "Don't get to New York much so I haven't seen your plays but—".

"You've missed nothing. The New York theatre is just a twitching corpse, Mr. Erickson—"

"Oh, don't say that," cried the wife. "I'm a New York girl myself, believe it or not, and the theatre is my first love. I still miss it. I even once had hopes—" she giggled—"before I got kidnaped to California, that is—"

"Of being an actress? My dear, you certainly look the part," Fauve said with a winning warmth which rendered the sudden intimacy quite inoffensive. "And let me congratulate you on escaping such a wretched fate. Mr. Erickson did you an immense favor by kidnaping you." As he talked Fauve sized up the daughter with swift side glances. She stood dejectedly one step lower than her father, her hands in the pockets of a blue cloth jacket.

The wife simpered, and Erickson said with heavy jocularity, "That's telling her, Mr. Fauve. She still throws it up to me that she was the star of her school show."

Fauve laughed merrily. "Well, let's not gossip here on the steps. Come in."

"Mostly I want Ginny here to see it," Erickson said. "Missus and I have been through it twice. This is my daughter Ginny, Mr. Fauve."

"Delighted."

The girl looked dully at him and said, "Hi."

"I just love it," said the wife. "You've furnished it in such exquisite taste, Mr. Fauve."

"I suppose Brewsters told you," Erickson said, "that I have quite a large place in Culver City. I'll have to dispose of that before we talk business on this one—"

"Of course, of course."

Inside, the house was dim, cool, and musty. It had massive dark Spanish furniture and was liberally decorated with tapestries and armor and swords and heavy iron grill work. Fauve lagged behind with the bored daughter as the party

[239]

drifted through the towering rooms on the ground floor. Suddenly, skilfully, he diverted her through a doorway, and they were alone in a pine-paneled study.

"Tell me, Ginny dear," Fauve said, in a good-humored mischievous whisper, "what's he like?"

Her eyes widened. "Who, Mr. Fauve?"

"The boy in Culver City."

Ginny was startled, and for a moment seemed ready to be rude. But Fauve's impish grin infected her; she gave him a low rich laugh. Her face brightened marvelously. She was about seventeen, short and quietly attractive, with brown hair and blue eyes.

"Well, Mr. Fauve! I've heard lots of legends about you. But I didn't know you were clairvoyant—"

"Mighty nice, is he?"

"He's wonderful, since you ask."

"College boy?"

"Oh, no, he's—he wasn't interested in college. He's—he's an actor. But a good one."

"Well! That's in my line. What's his name?"

"Oh, you wouldn't have heard of him. Burt Freeman—he's just nineteen—"

"Ginny dear, it's only half an hour by car to Culver City—"

"He doesn't have a car. He's poor as a rat. Oh, I'm sorry, Mr. Fauve, I know Mama loves your house, but—I hate to be the stumbling block—you see, Burt lives practically next door, and—this would be the end if—"

"My dear, my house is a meaningless trifle compared to young love." He laid his hand lightly on her arm. "The hell with my house. The hell with Mama. You stick to your guns. Queer the deal."

Ginny's eyes shone at him. "Thanks. You're terrific."

"Once, long ago," said Fauve, "I was as terrific as Burt.

[240]

Freeman. Would that I had known you then. Come on, drag
through the formalities. But stand firm, dear."

"He's not a bad actor," Fauve said. He lounged in a
corner of the control booth, out of the line of vision through
the glass wall. It was late afternoon of the same day, and he
needed a shave.

"Adequate juvenile. Dime a dozen," said the fat, pasty-
faced man at the controls, glancing into the studio. Burt
Freeman, a sandy-haired boy in worn tweeds, stood by the
microphone, clutching a script. "All right, thank you, boy.
Sit down for a minute."

The actor's voice boomed in the loud-speaker. "Thank
you very much, Mr. Goldstone." He went scampering across
to Ginny Erickson, who held her hands out to him, smiling,
and her voice came through thin and tinkly. "Oh, Burt, you
were marvelous—"

"No, I was fierce. I only hope he gives me another chance
to—"

Goldstone flipped a switch and cut off the voices. He said
to Fauve, "Want me to send them outside? You look silly
hiding—"

"No, no, don't do that. Damn him for bringing her.
Listen, Herbie, I want you to do exactly as I tell you. First—
can you put him on one of your soap operas, any part, no
matter how small?"

"Well, as a favor to you—though I don't know why you're
so interested in him, he's a small-time nothing, believe me—"

"One thing, Herbie. It's got to be a program that origi-
nates in New York."

"Now, gee whiz, Jerry. What kind of crazy talk is that?
You know the New York office does its own casting. A little
squirt like him—it's preposterous to send him across the
country—"

[241]

"I'll pay his expenses. Do you know someone in the New York office you can count on?"

"Well, Lloyd Fish'll do it for me—Jerry, what the hell kind of maneuver is this now? It's got a rich, ripe Fauve smell."

"Herbie," said Fauve softly, "how would you like to drop this trash and direct a comedy for me?"

Goldstone looked at Fauve with sudden doglike adoration. "*Jerry—really* this time? Are you going into production?"

"I have the new Cowling play."

"*Cowling?*" Goldstone whistled. "Last time I met him he spoke of disembowelling you on sight."

"I know," Fauve said. He drew himself up and his eyes became fanatically proud. "And I loathe him and he knows it. He also knows that I alone can produce that play with the elegance and sensitivity it must have."

"Jerry, any time you say—I'll come running. I'd do anything to work with you again—"

"I will take you into my confidence, Herbie, because you are dear to me. Cowling has given me a sixty-day option on his play. I had to beg him even for that much time—the swine, the boor! He thinks I can't raise the money. I swore I had it already. But he's right. I'm broke, and I have no credit. But if I can get this pipsqueak to New York, I will have seventy thousand in cash within a week. See how important—?"

"Jerry, it's crazy. What has that kid got to do with—"

"Herbie, take my word for it and get him out of town on the morning plane! I'll tell you why in due time. Go on out there and tell him he's sensational. Then tell him he needs grooming. You're going to send him to New York to study with Erwin Piscator while he works in the soap opera. The agency will pay his expenses, you say. I'll give you five hundred dollars to give him. But tell him that unless he can leave tomorrow you're not interested in him. D'you hear?"

"Jerry, I—it's risky, tossing around the agency's name—"

"Am I asking you to put anything on *paper,* you ass? After he's been there a few weeks you can tell him he isn't developing properly, and kick him into the gutter. Go ahead. And phone Lloyd Fish right now, as soon as the squirt says okay. It's got to be absolutely legitimate for a couple of weeks."

The director shrugged and walked to the door.

"And turn out that damned light, will you?" said Fauve. "I want to watch this." Goldstone flipped a switch and the control booth went black. "I needn't tell you that one breath of my name to that boy means sudden death to the whole enterprise."

"Don't worry, Jerry," said Goldstone wearily. "All he knows is he got a call from the casting office. His name was in the file. You're all clear."

Crouched in the gloom, Fauve observed with narrow eyes the pantomime beyond the glass wall. The young actor sprang up respectfully and approached the director as he came through the studio door. Goldstone began to talk. Freeman displayed astonishment, then delight. He asked several questions with wild excitement. He grasped the director's hand and pumped it. Goldstone patted him on the back, grinning tolerantly, and walked out. The boy rushed to Ginny Erickson, hugged her, and gabbled, his eyes glittering, his hands waving. He all but danced. The girl smiled uncertainly for a while, asking questions, then she began to look gloomy.

Fauve leaned forward, turned on the sound switch, and shrank back in his chair.

"—biggest chance of my life, sweetheart, can't you see that?"

"But when will you ever come back, Burt?"

"Well, I don't know. The main thing is, it's an *in.* Once I get set, why—"

"But why must they pick *you* for a radio show in New York? It seems so illogical—"

"Darling," he said in an injured tone, "it's just possible that I happen to suit the part. Actors aren't like cans of soup, you know. One isn't as good as another—"

"Oh, Burt, I know you're a wonderful actor. But there are a million actors in New York."

"You don't seem to grasp what this means. Studying with Piscator! Why, the agency's practically giving me a fellowship!"

"And what about me?"

"I should think you'd be as happy as I am—for me."

"You don't really care at all what happens to us, do you? You're not even thinking about it."

"Be sensible, Ginny. I have to make a living before we can be serious about getting married. Gosh, don't you believe in me at all? As soon as I'm on my feet I'll come back and marry you, or I'll send for you, I swear—"

"You *never* will. You'll meet somebody else. You, all alone in New York . . . you're very good-looking, Burt. This is the end . . ."

"And I suppose it'll be fun for me holed up with Mama and Papa in that horrible orange monstrosity while you're dating a lot of New York debutantes and actesses and what all—"

"Sweetheart, it's not my fault you don't like the house."

"Oh you fool, don't you know why Mama wants that house? For me! So I can meet some rich society boy and— she's got it all figured out—"

"I trust you, Ginny. Can't you trust me?"

"You don't *care*. Not one bit."

"Darling, do you want me to swear on the Bible that I'll be true to you?"

"I don't want you to do anything. I don't care what you do. Go to New York. I'm sure you'll be a great star. Send me an autographed picture sometime."

"Ginny, you just aren't making good sense."

The girl strode rapidly to the door and went out. Burt Freeman took a step or two after her, then stopped and pulled the audition script from his pocket. As he turned the pages a self-satisfied smile spread over his face.

"There it is," Fauve said triumphantly, three days later, showing Herb Goldstone an advertisement in the real-estate section of the Los Angeles *Times*. They were having breakfast in the Wilshire Derby. "Waiter! Phone."

Goldstone peered at the ad. "Culver City . . .you're sure that's the house?"

"My child, I've driven past it ten times. Tudor-style field-stone. That's it." The waiter plugged the telephone into the socket beside the table. Fauve called a number, saying aside, "Herb, you may as well look up reservations on the Chief, and—Hello, Brewsters? Fauve. I just saw the Erickson ad and—yes—yes—"

He nodded and nodded, smiling broadly. Suddenly his expression changed to a horrid glare. "What!" People at other tables turned at the agonized shout. "Say that again!" Then he smashed down the telephone.

"Damn young love!" he choked. "Damn it to the bottom-less fiery pit!"

"Jerry, what—"

"I am ruined, Herb, ruined. Ruined by that girl! The whole bloody Erickson family is moving to New York!"

A Smattering of Bliss

By VIRGINIA FAULKNER

Hal Venner balanced a cigarette carefully on the palm of his hand and attempted to catapult it into his mouth by smacking his wrist forcefully with his other hand.

"Nice try," said his wife, Lorry, retrieving the cigarette from under the piano. "I think you're improving."

"No kidding?" said Hal.

"Absolutely. They stay in the same room now."

"I've never been any good at tricks," said Hal discontentedly.

"Oh, I don't know," said his wife. She turned to their secretary. "Where are we now, Miss B.?"

"George and Louise are in the bathroom," said Miss B. "George has just said: 'Oh-oh! Seven years' bad luck.'"

"Do you know how to pick up broken glass without cutting yourself?" inquired Hal. "You wet a piece of cotton."

"I love cotton," said Lorry. "Listen, Hal, how would this be? Louise takes off her pump and shatters the medicine-cabinet mirror with one good wallop. Then she gives George an arch look and says something like: 'Well, that's seven years for me, too, baby.' Close shot of George's pan as it finally penetrates that she loves him. Then he turns on a big grin and says: 'Maybe we'll get time off for good behavior.' Camera pulls back to a two-shot of the clinch, and fade-out."

"Oh, I like that," said Miss B. enthusiastically. "I think it's sort of nutty and cute."

"Let's not work any more today, darling," said Hal. "Let's just sit."

"Where, for instance?"

"Somewhere indoors, in case of high fog."

"We're indoors now," Lorry reminded him, "and you

need have no qualms about sitting. This is Liberty Hall."

"Sitting here would be too easy. I can't relax unless I've asserted myself."

"You heard him, Miss B.," said Lorry. "When you've typed up those notes, you may scram."

"Ten o'clock tomorrow?" asked Miss B.

"Or so," said Hal. "Better make it at the studio instead of here. It's just as well to give that place a good punch in the time clock now and then. Farewell, Miss B." He slumped down on the sofa, fetching a large sigh. "I wish I were a bricklayer."

"What's stopping you?" asked Lorry. "I bet you'd be a good bricklayer. I hear you were a strong child."

"Half a dozen feet of rusty muscle, that's me," said Hal. "Lorry, let's run away and join a circus. Let's let someone else write movies."

"Oh, goody; let's," said Lorry.

Hal kicked a pillow onto the floor. "Why don't you ever argue with me?" he demanded.

"Listen," said Lorry, "ever since I reached the age of dissent I've argued with people. I've been shrewish and selfish and unpleasant. If I want to be nice to you, I guess I've earned the privilege."

"Would you really walk out on a contract because of a husband's whim?"

"Why not? Your slightest whim is law. Have a slight whim and see."

"I know what you're doing," said Hal. "You're humoring me."

"I can humor a man as well as the next girl," said Lorry complacently. "Matter of fact, if you don't humor a man, the next girl will. The trick is to beat her to the punch. . . . Shall I instruct one of our retinue to call up for plane tickets?"

"Maybe tonight," said Hal, "and maybe tomorrow, and

[247]

maybe not. Come on; let's pack up some dollars and some field glasses and wend our way to Santa Anita."

Loretta Erskine—no one, even after she had been married two years, called her Loretta Venner—had made a success of playwriting since she was twenty-five, but primarily she had established herself in the public eye, ear and hair as a professional wit, a brilliant and merciless commentator on the topics and personalities of the day. Her elopement with Hal had provided columnists with fireworks ample for a month of Roman holidays, since most of the Erskine plays were based on the proposition that all men are created evil, and that marriage, at least among the leisure classes, is an expensive and rather horrid pastime. Moreover, at the time of the elopement, Lorry was thirty-three and Hal only twenty-six.

As her old friend Sim Bailey told her, "It is all right for some women to be inconsistent, but, sweetie, not you. Hordes of people have been hoping and praying for years that you'd slip and break your damned tongue, and this would give 'em just the chance they've been waiting for. They'll rip you to pieces."

"The Grand Old Lady of Gall and Wormwood takes a groom," mused Lorry. "Why, listen to me! I'm my own worst enemy."

"Listen to me," insisted Sim. "If you have to get married —I use the expression in its narrowest sense, of course—why Hal Venner? He's not even a good writer; he's not even as good as I am."

"You're bald."

"I'm taking treatments," said Sim, 'and at least I'm a grown man. If we went to the altar, there would be no unveiled accusations of cradle-snatching. Why don't you take him on a trip and get him out of your system?"

"Because it isn't just a question of that," said Lorry. "Hal and I are what underwear salesmen used to call a good combination. And I want to make it official. I want to step up to home plate and promise to love, honor and cherish Mr. Venner. Because he's the one, see?"

"Oh, dear," said Sim. "My poor friend, you are never going to be the same."

"I guess that will be all right with everyone."

"You wait," warned Sim darkly. "You wait until you're on the receiving end of a few nifties."

"He who lives by the sword must perish by the sword," said Lorry cheerfully.

"You don't know what you're up against, marrying a younger man."

"Maybe you're right about that," said Lorry, "but if ignorance is you-know-what, I'll take a smattering of bliss."

So far, it had been more than a smattering. The first six months they spent on Lorry's farm in Maryland while Hal finished a book. Then they went on a long cruise around South America and, on their return, wrote a play together. The book got good notices; the play ran fourteen months. It looked as if the drinks were on the belittlers in the back room, for it is uphill work to crack wise in the teeth of a hundred and fifty grand, which was the sum Hollywood plunked down for the rights to The Triple Standard. And how the bowl brimmed with sour grape juice when the Venners took off for the Coast to do the picture adaptation, and giving off an unmistakable aura of marital felicity.

"You know what I think we ought to do, since we're in Hollywood?" said Hal as they were driving back from Santa Anita. "I think we ought to have one of those Hollywood parties where everybody comes in slacks and sarongs, or as Franz Josef."

"With real Japanese lanterns," supplemented Lorry, "and platinum hat checks. A white-tie barbecue."

[249]

"That's the idea," said Hal. "Everything very R.S.V.P. and *de rigueur mortis.*"

"Who'll we have?"

"Well, for a starter, how about the cast of the picture? We might say the party was in honor of Desire Hamilton, since she's starring."

"Desire Hamilton? Pardon my rising inflection, but you wouldn't be wanting her autograph, would you?"

"Maybe," said Hal smugly, "she wants mine."

"Look here, my boy. Has she been ogling you?"

"Well, you know Desire," said Hal. "And I'm a healthy male."

"Say no more; I'll put that minx from Minsky's in her place."

"I can defend my honor okay myself," protested Hal. "You're not my ol' shotgun-totin' grandpappy anyway."

Lorry looked at him a moment. "You're the boss," she said at last.

"That's the girl," said Hal, relieved. "Promise, now, no cracks?"

"I won't say a word about you," said Lorry. "I'll just be nasty along general lines."

As the prettiest and most important person at the Venner barbecue, Desire Hamilton could sit in a reclining chair, confident that drinks, cigarettes, matches, compliments and conversation would all be tendered to her without the necessity for any of that ungraceful exertion which lawn furniture seems expressly designed to provoke. To successive suggestions that she join in games of badminton, tennis, ping-pong and bowling, she responded with a shake of her lovely head.

"I'm crazy about sports, though," she said. "Did you know I have an indoor ski slide in my rumpus room? It's the only one in Brentwood."

"It's swell that you ski," said Hal. "We won't have to use a double in the Sun Valley sequence."

"Oh, Sam—Sam Fleishauer, he's my agent—won't let me take a chance with my poor little legs," said Desire, regarding her superb gams with affection. "As he so often says, where would I be without them?"

"Where you are most of the time anyway," said Lorry.

"Oh, I don't go out much," said Desire, after a little thought. "I'm slaving at the studio all day long, and you know when you come home exhausted and dead to the world, all you want is a bed. That's why I.like an ocean voyage. Because of the rest. And on the train. I always just stay in bed from Pasadena to Harmon. That's what I've got against flying. You don't get that three days in bed."

"You might just fly around for three days," said Lorry.

"Oh, but the vibration. These new ships are wonderful, though. I dedicated one, and they made me an honorary stewardess. I want to make a picture about an air stewardess and call it Air Stewardess, but Sam says the flying-picture cycle is over. He wants my next picture to be something where I can be a sort of a female Paul Muni, like Pasteur and Zola. There was one girl scientist, the one that found radium, but M-G-M owns her."

"Madame Bovary?" suggested the hostess.

"That's her. But do you know what I really want to do? I want to play the wife of Genghis Khan!" Desire sat up straight in the long chair. "You know, the Mongolian Hitler. I see myself as a barbarous dancing girl who gains this strange power over Genghis and unwittingly saves civilization." She sank back. "Of course they'd have to be careful not to give Genghis too much to do; he's a strong character."

"It's an inspiration, don't you think, Hal?" said Lorry. "Desire as Puree, the Mongrel Dancing Girl."

"It's a very interesting idea," said Hal reprovingly. "I've

[251]

often wondered why there's never been a play about Genghis Khan."

Desire turned toward him, giving him the full benefit of her enormous blue eyes and enchanting smile. "I have the greatest respect for picture making," she said very earnestly, "but there are times when it just doesn't satisfy me. There is something so quickening about a real live audience. I mean it quickens you; it helps you give. If I could just find a really intelligent play. Something with something to it; not just two hims and a her. And I mean all we people who have come to Hollywood really have a debt we owe to the stage because it is the Mother Art."

"If you're really serious about doing a play," said Hal, "perhaps Lorry and I might whip up something for you."

"There's nothing I'd rather do than a play," said Desire, "but I'm so tied up with contracts and all these silly options and commitments. I mean that's how it's been."

"I know," said Lorry sympathetically. "You couldn't call your soul your own, not even if you had one."

"I think," said Hal, "that those people who just came in are looking for you, Lorry dear."

"What do you want me to do? Leave a paper trail or put up some illuminated arrows?"

"Surely you can work out something simpler than that, pet," said Hal. "A clever girl like you."

"The velvet hand in the iron glove," explained Lorry to the others. "He means he wants me to excuse myself and receive guests."

The party was a great success: three mink coats were stolen, several studio deals were negotiated, and a distinguished character actor was pushed into the swimming pool, so the Venners could consider themselves fairly launched should they care to pursue a social career.

Nevertheless, "I'm glad that's behind us," said Lorry as

they relaxed in the kitchen. "You never really know what's going on when you give a large party. I wish it wasn't conventional to thank the hostess. I'd much rather guests would come clean, because then you could be sure whether or not anyone had fun."

"I had fun," said Hal.

"Pooh, you don't count. You weren't a guest."

"Incidentally," said Hal in a far from incidental tone, "you behaved like a perfect stinker to Desire Hamilton."

"Am I to construe that as a criticism?"

"She was a guest in your house."

"It's a rented house; and anyway, she's so dumb she didn't catch on."

"Then why did you bother to blast her?"

"Oh, force of habit. Or maybe I'm jealous of her legs."

"Your legs are all right."

"What a fellow you are for pretty speeches! Shall we 'whip up' a play around them?"

"Lay off," said Hal. "I had to say something after all those cracks you made."

"I guess I'm a mean lady," said Lorry. "Well, I'm off for my Thropplestance Wonder-Rest Mattress—and that ain't hay. Do you think prexy will be furious if we cut chapel tomorrow? I want to sleep late."

"You do that. I sort of got myself into going over to Desire's to see her new ski slide. Of course I can get myself out of it. If you have anything planned, that is."

"Frankly, I can't think of anything, offhand, but you won't catch me a second time. *Bon soir*, baby. I'll see you in my dreams." *If I can sleep*, she added to herself, for it was a maxim of Lorry's that when you give a man enough rope, it is a 100-to-1 shot he will wind up on the next reservation.

Despite her forebodings, the subject of Desire Hamilton did not recur in the Venner household until several days following,

[253]

and Lorry had relaxed to the extent of keeping her fingers crossed on one hand only. Then, at lunch, apropos of nothing but a dreamy silence, Hal observed that Lorry was not right about Desire.

"In other words, you mean I was wrong."

"Yes, if you must have other words. She's not as dumb as you think."

"Is she dumber?"

"She knew you were making fun of her the other night."

"Oh, Desire never could have worked that out by herself. Somebody's read her the papers." And, as Hal looked baffled, "There was an item in Beau Brash's column saying we girls were feuding."

"Then I definitely think we ought to have her over for dinner. We don't want to be bad friends with our own star," said Hal. "Anyway, these Hollywood feuds are so infantile."

"And what makes you think she'd come to dinner?"

"Well, as a matter of fact, I've asked her, and at first she said no, but I fixed things up. I told her—"

"You told her it was 'just my way.' I say things like that to all the girls."

"Anyhow, I fixed it up. I'm sorry if she bores you, but as you yourself have said, even if all the people bore you some of the time, and some of the people all the time, still a schizophrenic like yourself always has each other."

"Oh, I wouldn't be bored," said Lorry. "I just don't like to look at her, that's all."

"But I've heard you say she was one of the few truly beautiful women in Hollywood!"

"Well, I like the Winged Victory, too, but if I was a sculptor I'd hate to have it around the house."

"I fail to get it."

"Comparisons are odious when you come off second best."

"Are you worrying about your legs again? Because don't.

I like your legs."

"Oh, I'm perfectly satisfied with them; I'm not complaining. They do fine in ordinary competition, but this dame is a pro."

"I see what's in your mind," said Hal cautiously, "and you're all wrong."

"To err is human; that's what makes things so tough," said Lorry.

"Well, what shall I do?" said Hal. I've asked her."

"Take her to Ciro's or some other fleshpot. You're a big boy now. I have to go to New York anyway."

"Now, look here," said Hal.

"It's just a coincidence," said Lorry. "I'm not making anything out of this, honest I'm not. I promised Sim I'd come back for the tryout of his new play, and it opens in New Haven Friday."

"We'll both go."

"No, one of us must stay here on account of the picture. It's in the contract that we hang around until they've finished shooting. Cheer up, I'll bring you a present. A nice scout knife or something."

Sim's play was only a semisuccess, and Lorry stayed with it on the road to help with the doctoring. After two weeks they brought it in, and, if the critics were right, the salvage job had done the trick.

The morning after the New York opening Lorry had late breakfast at Sim's apartment to inspect the notices and to discuss with him the elimination of a scene in the second act, but instead of getting to the business at hand, Sim greeted her with a reproachful air.

"Holding out on me, huh?" he said. "I thought you weren't hanging around New York just on account of my *beaux yeux*." And he extended a paper folded open to a two-column cut of Lorry and Desire at the track. The caption was simple and provocative. RENO-BOUND? was all it said.

"Any comment, Erskine?" inquired Sim.

"There's a question mark," said Lorry serenely.

"I thought it was a typographical error."

"Well, I'll tell you," she said. "Hal has had a little crush on Desire."

"I can see why," said Sim, eyeing the picture.

"I wouldn't have thought too much about it, but he started sticking up for her when I got smart with her at a party. He even hinted we'd write a play built around her legs and Genghis Khan."

"Ouch!"

"But I really got the wind up when he asked her over for a family dinner—the Jolly Threesome gambit, as I call it."

"What's wrong with that? You could keep an eye on them."

"That ain't the pernt. It showed me Hal's state of mind was dangerous. He was trying to convince himself that there was nothing wrong in his seeing Desire. He reasoned that if it was all open and aboveboard, it was harmless. Therefore I checked."

"Gaining what?"

"Plenty. Do you think I'm fatuous enough to try to vamp Hal with that nymph-sized package of dynamite around?"

"So you figured that without you there he'd get bored?"

"Oh, eventually, but it would be quite a while until the first yawn. I thought I'd better nip it in the buderoo."

"You're going great," said Sim, looking at the paper again.

"Oh, I counted on that kind of thing," said Lorry. "You see, the very day I left for New York, Hal took Desire to dinner, and you know how they are out there about putting two people together and getting something barely fit to print. Anyway, after they'd been out together some more—I knew they'd have dates because Hal was smitten, and Desire is sore at me—this was bound to happen." She indicated the picture. "Curtains."

"Yes, but for whom?"

"For them," said Lorry impatiently. "Tantamount has just signed Desire to do a picture with Jack Wiley, and she's supposed to be crazy about him. Besides, she's had two divorces in three years, and the studio doesn't want this kind of publicity."

"Even so—"

"Even so, nothing! Don't kid yourself about Desire; it's career first with that tomato, and Hal isn't a producer. She'll slip him the black spot without a second thought. He'll be furious—the hurt-pride angle—and that's the end of Desire Hamilton as far as the Venner family is concerned."

"It sounds all right," began Sim.

"It works too," said Lorry. She produced a telegram and read dryly:

"FLYING TO NEW YORK TO FLY BACK TO HOLLYWOOD WITH YOU. THAT'S TEN WORDS SO HAVE NO SPACE TO ADD LOVE HAL AND YOU MUST GUESS WHO THIS IS FROM.

"I wish people didn't always feel obliged to be cute in wires."

"Congratulations," said Sim. "In the absence of a hat, I take off my toupee to you."

"Let me see," said Lorry, examining it. "I thought I spied a gray hair." She handed it back to him. "Premature, of course, and so were your congratulations. Desire was only a symptom. You know how guys are. They start looking, and they keep on looking until something happens. My trials have just begun."

"But Hal loves you. Or doesn't he?"

"He certainly does," said Lorry indignantly. "Do you think I'd be taking all this trouble if he didn't? I expect you think I'm a scheming woman fighting a losing battle to keep a

[257]

young husband—not a pretty picture. But, Sim, I'm going to keep right on scheming. I don't want anything to happen to our setup. We've got love and we've got money; we have health and an absorbing interest in common. The fly in the ointment —and every marriage has some handicap—happens to be that I am brighter than Hal. Not that he isn't bright, but I'm just about the brightest woman in the world."

"You been hanging around Bill Saroyan?" asked Sim suspiciously.

"My being brighter wouldn't matter if I was an ordinary woman and Hal was an ordinary man," continued Lorry, after an involuntary *moue*, "because he wouldn't know it. But owing to my reputation, and because Hal is no fool, he does know it. And even though this is 1941 and equality between the sexes is so established it's old hat, that doesn't alter the fact that in happy marriages it is the gentleman who wears the breeks."

"Hooray for men's rights," said Sim. "One day we lads shall get the vote, just wait and see."

"I bet you do too," said Lorry generously. "Didn't you take the place of the horse? Anyway, for my money, the male— as he is called—has to believe that he dominates the female, because if he doesn't, and is a real guy, he'll hunt around until he finds a dame or dames he does dominate. This is technically known as 'being on the make,' which describes Hal's condition at present. The only cure is to convince him that he's the king of the Venner family, and not just a puppet monarch either."

"I never thought to see you honing for a back seat," said Sim.

"One thing on my side is that we work well together. Hal has a lot of warmth and humanity, which I lack, and he's got a sound plot sense; while I have certain perceptions which are missing in his make-up, and can turn a phrase in any direction. Most important of all, we speak the same language. That's a cliché most people don't bother to figure out, but it means an awful lot. It speeds up things when your minds work contrapuntally; it's as exciting a synchronization as, lateral passing in football. You get an idea and you go down the field whipping the ball back and forth until you carry it over. So I don't worry about Hal feeling subordinate in our collaboration, even though the critics and the public persist in handing me top billing. He knows that he's pulling his weight, and that's all that matters to him. As I may have hinted to you, he's a very superior citizen."

"It makes sense," said Sim. "The Triple Standard was a lot more mature and human than the plays you wrote solo."

"And you might add, so am I," said Lorry. "Darn it all, Sim, this marriage is the answer for both Hal and me, and I've got to make it work. It isn't good enough just to go along stuffing up chinks in the armor, pulling fast ones when I see Hal has a yen coming on. The yens don't matter; it's what Hal feels for me that's important. If things are really right between us I can say nuts to all the other women in the world. Every honest-to-God guy has a dash of the chaser; that can be discounted. You just have to make sure that the chase doesn't take him too far away, and that he always wants to come back."

"There's an old saying," observed Sim, "that they never come back."

"Men go where they feel they belong. Of course I don't include congenital so-and-so's, because the main reason they're so-and-so's is that they don't know where they belong. To a man, 'belonging' means someone's belonging to him rather than his belonging to someone else, and he has this feeling of possession only when he is sure that he is absolutely necessary to the other person. So there you have my difficulty. You see, Hal—being the guy he is—is brimming over with chivalry and the protective instinct, but, unfortunately, he

[259]

knows I am quite, quite capable of taking care of myself."

"Hal protecting you," said Sim, "would be like a butterfly escorting a Stuka."

"It isn't funny," said Lorry. "Unless I can find a use for that strong right arm of his—unless I can convince him that I'd be sunk without him—I might as well kiss my boy good-by."

"That oughtn't to stump you; all you have to do is play dumb and helpless."

"Sim, use your head! Supposing for the sake of argument that a leopard can change his spots without causing a commotion, if he blossomed out in green and red stripes even a dope would know something was radically haywire; and my metamorphosis into fluff and nonsense would be just as noticeable.

"I can get away with a lot, but playing dumb isn't on the list."

"Had it occurred to you, dear, that maybe you aren't as smart as you think you are?"

"That's the idea I have to sell Hal," said Lorry. "Because the minute he finds out I'm not as smart as I think I am, then he's smarter than I, and everything will be hunky-dory. If he can't protect me from anything else, he can protect me from myself." She sighed. "The trouble is I am as smart as I think I am."

Sim stared at her.

"Of course I adore you, Erskine," he said thoughtfully, "but it wouldn't hurt you to have your ears knocked down a couple of yards. It wouldn't hurt you at all."

A woman's place—or anyway, one of a woman's places—being the home, Lorry was glad to return with Hal to their complicated nest in Brentwood, a neo-Goldwyn rancho. The light touch was employed by both husband and wife in their comments on the Hamilton episode, Hal stating that Desire's I.Q. could be totted up on the fingers of a single hand, and

Lorry supplementing his observation with the remark that he was too generous; in her opinion, Desire's was the first known case of a negative I.Q. They also agreed that no man was safe with Desire except her own husband, and this disposed of Miss Hamilton as a topic of conversation until, some three weeks later, Lorry announced that they had received a wire bidding them to a revel at Desire's mansion, the occasion being a supper party to commemorate the première of The Triple Standard—retitled for picture purposes, Three's a Crowd.

"We'll regret with pleasure, I presume?"

"I've been meaning to break it to you," said Hal; "we have to go. It's for us."

"What deviltry is this?"

"The studio, probably," said Hal uneasily. "They want us to write her next picture. Seems she's got it in her contract that they let her make that story about Genghis Khan, and she has the idea that I—that we're authorities on the subject."

"I hope you told them to take that bee right out of her bonnet and return it to the hive."

"Oh, sure," said Hal. "I said it was out of the question."

"Good. I suppose we'll have to accept this then," she waved the telegram, "but ask if we can bring Sim Bailey. He's getting here the nineteenth, and I promised to show him Hollywood. If there is a Hollywood, it'll be at Desire's."

Lorry was correct. After the première—which Sim said was a cross between a coronation and a football rally—picture-dom's peerage and four-letter men betook themselves to Sleepy Hollow, the name Desire had selected for her residence from a contest held by her fan clubs. It was, as Lorry did not fail to point out, a name more descriptive of the interior of Desire's head than the scale-model country club which it adorned. The hostess, looking more beautiful than a press agent's dream, received at the foot of her ski slide, informing all comers, as was her wont, that it was the only one in Brentwood. Before she could repeat this fact to the Venners, Lorry observed that they were already in possession of the news. "I half expected to find you in a ski suit," she concluded. "A chinchilla one."

"Did you really?" said Desire. "I suppose you get your information on my wardrobe from Hal."

"We don't talk clothes," said Lorry.

"Oh, darling, you should," said Desire, with a glance that summed up and flicked away Lorry's toilette. "I hope you'll make yourselves at home."

"That will take a bit of doing," said Lorry.

"Hal can show you around," said Desire. "Can't you, pet?"

"Yes," said Hal, without enthusiasm.

"I thought you said she was dumb," remarked Sim as they walked away.

At supper, the Venners found themselves on either side of their hostess, who explained that she had seated them there because they were her guests of honor, and she was sure they wouldn't mind her being between them this once.

"I thought you made a habit of it," said Lorry.

"I haven't any habits," said Desire. "I'm too restless."

"Just call me volatile Sal," murmured Lorry. "What about cohabiting? Or don't you indulge?"

"That's a play upon words, isn't it? said Desire. "It must be wonderful to be a writer. I've often wondered where on earth you get some of your ideas."

"Sometimes from the papers."

"Do you really believe what you read in the papers?"

"Oh, occasionally they get a fact or two straight, the way I look at it. Or don't you believe in the law of averages?"

"I don't think it applies to me," said Desire, with a disarming smile. She turned to Sim, who was sitting on Lorry's right. "I know Miss Erskine finds me awfully dull to talk to.

[262]

I've never bothered to learn repartee. If I have anything to say, I just say it. And it there's something I don't know, I ask. You see, there are so many clever people in the world, it's always easy to find someone to explain."

"It's an angle," admitted the embarrassed Sim.

"What I mean is: why do things the hard way? When I've got a beef, I spill it; I say what's on my mind. For instance, when I think someone's been making passes at my husband—the times I'm married, that is—I just go right to her and tell her to lay off or I'll pull out every hair on her head. You don't need any vocabulary for that, and in the end it's more effective than all this repartee that just makes everybody uncomfortable and louses up a perfectly good party. Maybe I'm dumb—I know Miss Erskine thinks so—but what's the matter with being dumb? The Bible or something says ignorance is bliss, and God knows I'm doing all right."

"I guess you are, at that," said Lorry quietly. "I apologize. For various things. And, if you'll excuse me, I think I'd like to go."

"Sure, if you want to," said Desire. . . . "Nobody feels so hot after they apologize," she explained to Sim. . . . "But you don't have to go!" she exclaimed as Hal pushed back his chair.

"Of course he doesn't," said Lorry.

"Don't be silly," said Hal, starting after her. Then he hesitated and turned. "Uh—good night, Desire," he said politely. "We had a lovely time."

Sim did not see Hal and Lorry again until the day he was leaving for the East. They had gone to Arrowhead, and had just returned that morning. He found Lorry and Miss B. sorting out scripts on the terrace; Hal would be there presently, Lorry explained; he was talking on the phone to the studio.

"How did you like Desire's party?" she asked. "You haven't thanked me for taking you."

[263]

"I thought it might be a delicate subject."

"Well, it is, rather," said Lorry. "By the way, have you noticed anything different about me?"

"Such as what?" hedged Sim.

"Ears are being worn lower this year," said Lorry demurely. "Hal thinks they're awfully becoming."

"Oh, Miss Erskine," said Miss B., "excuse me for interrupting, but shall I send this screen test to the studio?"

"What screen test? We haven't written any screen tests."

"Why, this is the one you worked on by yourself right after your trip to New York, don't you remember? The scene between the two women at the dinner table where they——"

"That's nothing; you can tear that up," said Lorry hastily.

"Just a minute," said Sim, grabbing it from Miss B., and warding Lorry off with one hand. " 'I've never bothered to learn repartee,' " he read aloud. " 'If I have anything to say, I just say it. And if there's something I don't know, I ask. You see, there are so many clever people——' Well, I'll be damned!" He gazed at Lorry with awe and admiration. "You framed yourself," he accused. "Smart. Very smart. But how did you get Desire to do it?"

"Oh, she's a quick study—for a moron."

"You know what I mean. How did you persuade her to cooperate? With a club?"

"We made a deal. And I will say for Desire, she drives a hard bargain."

"But what——"

"Pipe down! Here's Hal."

"Sorry to be so long, darling. . . . Hello, there, Sim. . . . That was B.J., Lorry, and he wants us to have something to show him this afternoon. . . . Now where were we, Miss B.?"

"At the Mongol camp," said Miss B. "Genghis is trying to make Miss Hamilton."

[264]

"Who," said Sim, cocking an eyebrow at Lorry, "drives a hard bargain indeed."

She combined a nod with a warning frown. "So now you know how screen plays are born," she said. "Run along, Sim. Mr. and Mrs. Venner have work to do."

WILLIAM JUSTEMA

Justema, an artist and designer by trade, grew up in the
Los Angeles area, studied both there and around the Bay,
and worked in both California and New York. These
selections are from his *Private Papers* (1944), the record of
his Army service with a camouflage unit stationed at Los
Angeles and the deserts beyond.

How Near

And how far are the scenes of my childhood
in the arms of my family; my soft-spoken family.
Here, open before you, our verbal album.
Listen . . . This is me at three, with teddy-bear
leaving Chicago. This, aged four, under
California sycamores on an Illinois picnic.
Next I am seven, shining among staid
Second-Graders—and—"Oh, Billy,
remember when you played old Scrooge?"
I was eleven then, already a skilled performer
of exacting roles! (Care to hear more?)
I practically dug my way through the first World War—
in backyard trenches. Early film stars visited Glendale,
Fabulous on fake tanks beneath arc lights
selling Liberty Bonds: thrilling sight.
At Community Sings, relatives sang too loud.
My sister—older than I—sent fudge off
and wept a lot. Armistice Night we all went to town
for the excitement . . . I settled down
to an absorbing adolescence.
(Can you bear to hear more?)
Mine was a one-line universe between home
and the local library, veering Eastward.
The exotic, erotic, and the esoteric

were newly mixed by me. (Loti, Havelock Ellis, and the
Bhagavad-Gita—) You should have seen
Agnes and Yours Truly (self-named Indigo and Geranium,
respectively) having tea, framed by peacock feathers.
Living for poetry, we reeked of incense. Once
buried "our friendship"—a leaf-wrapt book—
in the sand of the dry Los Angeles river.
(Which nonsense ended with her getting married.)
Do you dare to hear more?
For this albeit genteel history
has its own pastel pathology: wilful and weak;
trite; tender to a fault; suddenly spiteful
as when surprised.
"My!"—it is mother speaking—"How mad you were
at your birthday party. You locked yourself
in the bathroom: we couldn't get you out.
And where did you say you spent the one last year?"
—referring to my natal December seventh
which was drear in gray New England,
in gay Honolulu drear.
"Of what, Dear, are you thinking?
Your little family's here!"

No Place for a Puritan

is the desert. No place to draw curtains.
And what is a hymn in the open
but a pity, or a sin . . .
Where God does not exist—invent Him.
Regard then the Great American Desert God
morbid and elegant, His kingdom almost emptied.
The sea was here and left its shapes
to wither. Only my "aigrette" (or Smoke) tree;
my rare "flute bush" (?) show vividly

[267]

the rush of water. Filigree weeds
reach for they know not what—
finally breaking in the hush-hush wind,
their odd jewelry strewn on the ancient beach.
We have forgotten the islands;
see the mountains (my "Potpourris") each
evening—as an iris, a violet, and a rose
gathering when the sun drops out of reach
and the moon takes over: a lunar
landscape too barren and too bold
for homely virtues . . .
Our God is a sensuous God—Who
would not be, from a couch of sand?
The soldier on the desert
rears the most worldy altar that he can
and serves in serpent skin, with curses.
It is the right degree of the wrong ecstasy:
do you blame the man? He never sees
the fountains he continually hears,
nor finds the bare feet dancing his mosaic floors.
While far above him clouds are whirled
carnation colored and carnation curled—
hardly Christian.

The Whore at Easter

ordered another drink, so deeply was she offended.
The torn mouth, the ragged eyes
were typical, and that the despised did despise.
"I think," she said, "you soldiers stink,"
and we were both offended
however blurred our reasons why.
I should have persuaded her she was deprived
of nothing she had had

[268]

though she might be more reminded.
That for me the War was the same
dire opportunity: an education
at the brink of savagery.
Her "home and a family"; my precious "gifts"
were in their usual jeopardy, especially
from ourselves . . . Yet we remained
offended, she and I.
The fool of desire and the tool of words!
How should we be defended
save by ourselves?
The language of her horrid room
is heard around the earth; and womankind
in bearing man gives birth
to marching blasphemies
. . . so they crucified Him.
From my tower I saw them.
And who am I? And who is she—to be offended?
rising from our drinks.

That Hill

that barrier which tempted you, tempts you still.
Yesterday you were a child, and the upper way
from school was best. "There's my house,
down there"—much the prettiest,
mother in the kitchen getting supper.
And it was from heights, too, that you dreamt
of flying above your schoolfellows' heads
simply by keeping your arms rigid,
your breathing steady. "Look at Billy Justema!"
—landing after you were out of sight.
And it was a sort of hill, called Bee Rock,
you and your dad climbed Sunday afternoons

into the highest crannies of delight
so different seemed the'air at the top.
All of your triumphs had to do with hills.
They still do.
Show me a soldier who, racked on his cot,
has not said: "I am going over, I have got
to go over—" knowing full well beyond each
is another. They reach to eternity—
till he fall back exhausted,
crying to his pillow:
"Excelsior! We have made it!
We have stayed in the valley."

Los Angeles at War

By JAMES LEIGH

James Leigh has published several short stories. He
teaches at San Francisco State College. As indicated in
"Los Angeles at War," he was raised chiefly in the Los
Angeles area, mostly in Santa Monica.

Here in hygiene-conscious America we have succeeded
splendidly in deodorizing and sanitizing not only our bodies
and homes but also the modern history we have helped make.
Even as recent and enormous a phenomenon as the World War
of 1939-45 is already stashed neatly away in history books,
with all its huge stink and horror reduced to production
graphs and rigorously dispassionate accounts of major cam-
paigns. It may be said that we have enough raw material for
nightmares in the present, without dredging the past for more.
But blank spots are weak spots, and when I hear four-starred
Chiefs of Staff publicly urging the national adoption of "war
psychology," I wonder what that phrase can possibly mean to
full-grown young Americans born, say, in 1941.

I was born in 1930, and am thus a member of that undis-
tinguished demi-generation which was too young to fight in
Normandy and New Guinea but exactly the right age to get
its feet frozen off in Korea. By pure good luck, I missed taking
part in that strange episode of 1950-1, that peculiarly un-
official war which was real only to those who fought it and
their close relations—and perhaps to those who made money
out of it. World War II was different: it was real not only to
those who fought it but to those too young or old or female
to fight. It was spectacularly real in thronged and booming
Southern California. The war and its "psychology" changed
our lives—the way we thought and felt about things, the way

we acted. Even I, going most unheroically through junior high and high school on the western ocean fringe of immense Los Angeles, even I knew that. And the war hit some people my age much harder than it hit me.

Of course the war proper touched California only once, and Los Angeles not at all. That once—the token lobbing of a few small shells into the Goleta oil fields by a lone Japanese submarine—though it seems only laughable at a remove of fifteen-odd years, did create then a sizable ripple of anxiety in L. A. and the rest of the state. And many of those tireless old ladies, who during the war seemed to pause in their knitting of socks and mittens only long enough to write letters to newspapers, did bombard the press with demands that the 800 miles of California coastline be patrolled closely enough to prevent a recurrence of the disaster at Goleta. But the shelling functioned most effectively as a painlessly thrilling reminder that a real shooting war was going on: doubtless many Angelenos leaned harder on their rivet guns for at least a few days afterward (and perhaps swallowed a little more of the virulent wartime alcohol which spurted nonstop behind the thousand jammed bars of the city).

There had been, of course, the great phoney Los Angeles air raid of 1943, during which for several early morning hours the sky over the city was crosshatched with searchlights and festooned with the small white flowers of anti-aircraft shells, whether aimed at something or nothing the city never knew. I bought a paper on the way to school the next morning: under the 72-point headline the lead story began, "A fleet of enemy bombers roared off into a purple dawn. . . ." (An interesting study might be made of the slantings and misrepresentations perpetrated during the war years by the Los Angeles press. But, then, I expect the same would hold true in any other American city.)

For several days after the "raid," we talked of nothing

else. The vastly uninformed consensus, abetted by the shotgun conjectures of the press, held that *something* had been up there. There were rumors of wreckage falling in certain vacant lots in East Los Angeles (a stray P-38 with radio trouble? An unauthorized light-plane?) Clearly, the city did not wish to admit that the target of so much gorgeously objectified hostility could have been only a mote in the eye of a nervous watcher; it surely would have felt better if only there could have been, say, a single lost Japanese plane up there to drop a single small but bona fide bomb on one of those vacant lots in East L. A. before being blown to satisfyingly-recognizable bits by our flak.

What I remember most clearly about the "raid" is the esthetes' detachment with which we watched the pattern of lights and shell-bursts over central Los Angeles ten miles away. Standing in pajamas on our front porch, we were "afraid," I suppose, and I'm sure we felt the raid was a real one; but, in a way, even experiencing the sight and sound of it did not convince us of it. I cannot, of course, say what my mother, father and sister thought or felt, but we behaved more like people watching a Fourth of July display than people transfixed by a sense of their own powerlessness, and I was certain that wherever bombs might fall they would not fall on me. I recall that the neighborhood Air Raid Warden, always so annoyingly present during blackouts with his white helmet and red-muted flashlight, was nowhere to be seen during the commotion. Probably home on his front porch watching with his family, my father said.

Things proceeded afterward very much as before. At school we had resigned ourselves to being non-combatants, all Japanese, the only people upon whom we could have (and doubtless would have) wreaked our patriotism, having been snatched up en masse and interned a few weeks after Pearl Harbor. We heard and repeated with variations the story of

[273]

the Little Old Lady who had been done in (raped, shot, stabbed, poisoned, strangled or asphyxiated) by her treacherous Japanese gardener before the bombs had stopped falling on Pearl Harbor. And I remember clearly my pang of joy on realizing that the seventh grade would now be deprived of its hero and scourge, a tall, handsome, sharp-eyed, straight-toothed fellow named Roy, who dominated all athletic competition and who happened to be Japanese. Being patriotic at his expense would have been no cinch.

However, we did our part as best we could. There were the War Stamps and War Bonds in which we were interminably urged to invest every spare dime or dollar (and these were increasingly plentiful throughout the war). There were endless drives in which different home-rooms, grades and entire schools competed to collect old newspapers, old tires, old toothpaste tubes. There was, too, the war itself, which we followed like some colossal World Series, marking advances and retreats on maps with tiny flagged pins, memorizing the silhouettes of ME-109's and Zeroes just in case, arguing tirelessly about the relative merits of different pistols, machine-guns, tanks, planes, ships, divisions, generals, branches of the service, whole armies and nations.

And there were the movies. Indeed, the false-alarm air raid, carried off with an apparently spontaneous flair for spectacle worthy of Cecil B. De Mille, was for us like nothing so much as an exceptionally realistic passage in one of the countless war movies we consumed. For the older people there was other fare: Lou Costello being funny in various misfitting uniforms, or jolly wartime musicals in which platoons of starlets frolicked in form-fitting khaki or Navy blue. The war movies seemed truly ours, though most of us soon ceased to be moved by them. It was hard to feel any visceral reaction to the celluloid barbarism of those Chinese character actors who had been hurriedly resurrected before Christmas 1941, thrust into

[274]

what looked like old Salvation Army uniforms, and equipped with wooden samurai swords or placed behind cardboard periscopes to hiss, "Die, foorish American," through false buckteeth. And we had gotten used to Nazi villains even before Pearl Harbor. So we readily became cynical critics, who knew to the instant when the mortally-wounded fighter pilot would release from the corner of his mouth the neat trickle of chocolate syrup, who knew infallibly (and were never disappointed) that it would be the less handsome of the two leading men who would be killed in the climactic battle; we became bored connoisseurs of "realism," snickering at plywood tanks and bath-tub model warships, impressed only by a greater admixture of real-looking blood and dirt than most films contained. Under it all, we were afraid to take it seriously, I suspect. At least we were always silent during the newsreels.

Yet even if the movies and scrap drives weren't real to me; even if rationing was no worse than an itch, since we'd never had a lot of money and I had no car for which to swindle A-ration stamps: still the war was real to Los Angeles, which became perhaps the biggest perpetual-motion boom town in American history. It was real enough to the hundreds of thousands of war workers and servicemen who poured into and through it. And though, as you can see, I had it easy enough, the war was real to people my age, too. I know this now in the way people usually know these things: by remembering what I saw the war do to individual people. I think of two of them, a girl I knew slightly and a boy I didn't know at all.

The girl's name was Louise. She lived in a trailer camp a couple of blocks from my house, and in our last year at junior high school I had conceived a wholly futile but perfectly valid 14-year-old passion for her. She was very pretty, tall and sweet-faced but much too thin, with what seemed to me then an excitingly electric quality, but which I suppose was just nervous anxiety. Maybe it was both. She chewed her fingernails and ate all the candy she could get her hands on, although her skin stayed clear. Both her parents (they were from Oklahoma or West Texas, I think), worked long day shifts in a war plant. Her brother, a sailor, had been killed in the Pacific the first year of the war. There was a framed photograph of him on the wall of the trailer's long, low-ceilinged, living-dining-bedroom, and scattered about were various cheap oddments of souvenirs he had sent home, paper leis and a big pink sateen pillow with "Honolulu" printed on it above a picture of a hula dancer.

We started high school about a year before the war ended. I noticed that Louise was absent a lot, sometimes for whole weeks, and I began to hear things about her at school. Telling myself, with that willful dishonesty practiced by even the least sophisticated lovers, that she might be ill, I detoured past the trailer camp after school one day in the middle of one of those weeks. A blond, pink-faced sailor, very young-looking, passed me in a hurry at the entrance to the camp, and I felt almost sick with the certainty that he had been with Louise.

I could hear radio music from inside the trailer but it seemed several long minutes before Louise opened the door. The way she looked made me feel hopelessly young and useless: her curly bobbed hair was only a little less tidy than usual, but her eyes were oddly moist, not as if from crying, and her lipstick-smeared mouth looked red and mushy like a piece of stepped-on fruit. Nor could I feel reassured to see her in school clothes, for her thin tight red sweater was only half tucked inside her short skirt, and she wore nothing beneath it, so that her trivial little adolescent breasts were hardly more prominent than her collarbones.

She was alone, and asked me inside, although she seemed neither pleased nor displeased to see me, and not even much surprised. I hesitated, stammering I don't remember what about having thought she might have been sick, but I finally came in, sitting on the edge of the open sofa-bed so that I wouldn't have to look at it. The room was not much disordered, really, except for the bed and an empty jelly glass on the floor by my feet. On the sink in the kitchenette I saw a half-pint whiskey bottle and a Pepsi-Cola bottle, neither quite empty. Louise sat opposite me on a folding chair, legs crossed, smoking a cigaret. I think she asked me how school was, but I don't remember what I said, or how long I sat there. Probably no more than ten minutes. There was a knock on the door. another sailor, this one dark-haired, saying, "Louise? I'm a buddy of Chick's." Of course I left then.

All this was soon common knowledge at school. There was some sort of scuffle at Louise's, I heard, involving a sailor and a couple of eager high-school boys. Louise dropped out of school altogether. A few months later I saw her talking to two sailors in a parked car outside the trailer camp. Still later, I gathered, she had gotten pregnant. (Her baby, if she had it, would now be a little older than she was then.) The last time I saw her was in West Los Angeles several years after the war, behind the counter of a hot dog stand patronized by the motorcycle crowd. Her hair was dyed an unearthly pink.

The other person I remember, the boy I didn't know at all, was a Mexican whom I saw only once, at a distance of about a hundred yards, from the rail of Santa Monica Pier. But his story needs a preface.

The way the Los Angeles press covered the phoney air raid seemed funny; its treatment of what it called the "Zoot Suit Wars" was not. The Mexicans of California, then as now, were second-class citizens in many respects. (Perhaps the easiest of countless ways to illustrate this is to compare the number of elected or appointed public officials in California who are Mexicans with the number of Mexicans, period.) This inferior status did not, of course, keep Mexicans from volun-

[277]

teering or being drafted, from fighting and dying at least in proportion with non-Mexicans. But it doubtless helped produce among young Los Angeles Mexicans the familiar pattern of gang membership and "delinquent behavior" which such discrimination always produces. Given the existence of these gangs, the huge and constant population of servicemen (great numbers of them restlessly fresh from boot camp or basic training, anxious to exercise their new skill in violence), and the prickly heat of the wartime weather in Los Angeles—how could there not have been clashes? Yet it now seems incredible that the Los Angeles papers could have treated the situation as they did, implying a great conspiracy on the part of the gangs to "prey on servicemen". With the local Japanese population long since put away in camps, and the war itself well on its way to being won, there seems to have been a fresh need for "bad guys": new targets had to be found for the mass-produced aggressions of the city, lest it erupt (as it did anyway) in civil disturbance and interservice brawling. The press found—indeed, seemed almost to create—these targets, in the image of the "zoot suit gangs". Hardly anyone questioned the essentially ludicrous conception of a relative handful of Mexican youths in broad-brimmed hats, draped jackets and pegged pants (almost all of them too young for the service), declaring war on thousands of soldiers, sailors and Marines. And for many weeks this was exactly the song which the Los Angeles papers sang, and which, by and large, L. A. believed.

The revenges exacted by bands of servicemen for a few isolated but hugely-ballyhooed affronts by zoot-suiters were limited only by the availability of fall guys wearing the officially stigmatized cheap finery. With the convulsive regularity of hysteria came reports, in the papers or by word of mouth, of imminent pitched battles between these forces of Good and Evil. The only one I saw, however, was no contest.

A friend came by my house about noon one Saturday:

there was talk of a "go" that afternoon somewhere near the pier at Santa Monica, and he proposed that we should go and watch. When we got off the bus, a big convertible full of whooping Marines brandishing cans of beer slammed to a stop in the bus zone behind us; the civilian driver, a red-faced man wearing dark glasses, yelled "Kill the bastards" as they piled out and started toward the beach. My friend and I walked out on the pier, expecting to see fighting break out at any moment.

But except for half a dozen sailors on a prowling reconnaissance of the half-empty parking lot next to the dance pavilion, the pier looked quiet and ordinary. Further out I could see the still, angled rods of the old men fishing for perch. We paused near the first fried shrimp stand: the man there seemed to know what we were looking for. "No fight today, boys," he said. "*Pachucos* didn't show up." Three Marines passed us, coming from the end of the pier. They glanced sharply at us, as if the shrimp stand were a bunker full of storm troopers, but they didn't stop. We bought cokes from the shrimp man, and were drinking them when we heard yelling which seemed to come from under the pier. We crossed to the rail and looked down on the beach.

Out from between the piles ran a boy certainly no older than we. He looked even younger, perhaps because his long dark hair was a wild mop which made his face seem baby-small. He wore a white T-shirt and a pair of dark slacks which ballooned as he ran, a few yards ahead of a phalanx of seven or eight Marines. He stumbled and half-fell to the sand for a moment, long enough for his pursuers to reach him. The foremost Marine half ran into him, half pushed him down and the rest of them closed around him in a circle perhaps six feet wide. Two of the Marines, leaders or delegates, began cursing him, apparently daring him to fight. He stood up slowly and tossed the hair out of his eyes. One of the Marines slapped him hard across the face and stood back. Rather deliberately he

[279]

reached into his pocket and took out what must have been not a switchblade but, from the motion I glimpsed, a small penknife at which he dug desperately with his thumbnail for just an instant before the Marine who had slapped him knocked him down. The other one had his belt off then, and I saw the buckle flash down where the boy was lying.

The beating took only about a minute, I suppose. Four of them picked him up and carried him down to the edge of the beach where, with a one-two-three, they heaved him a surprising distance into the water. The rest of them, including the one rethreading his belt, followed and cheered. Only then I noticed a middle-aged man a few yards to our left at the rail watching through binoculars. One of the Marines who had not taken part hung behind the rest as they returned, glancing back over his shoulder until the boy had dragged himself on all fours out of the water.

Clear-eyed liberals who look at human history with the social scientist's detachment may point out that girls "get into trouble" in peacetime as well as wartime, and that scapegoating of ethnic minorities continues, alas, to this day. But when I think of Louise, lying beneath one sailor after another through those long trailer afternoons, and when I remember that Mexican boy run down and beaten while we looked on, with or without binoculars, I know that they were victims of the war. And so, though perhaps less obviously and less immediately, were Louise's sailors and even that little lynch party of Marines.

I was too young, lucky, or afraid to be one of those first- or second-degree victims, but I felt then and realized later that "war psychology" had made all who shared it for a time less than fully human, in the name of a single massive "superhuman" effort. As military discipline necessarily demands that a man become a sort of robot for the sake of efficiency, so does the psychology of war demand that people become things to be used. People use one another like things in peacetime, too, and thus become things themselves. The difference is that war psychology not only condones, but encourages and even glorifies this dehumanization. (Girls like Louise were called "Victory Girls".) Debauchery and lynching may be a very real part of human potential, but at the same time they are profoundly anti-human. Only in the poisonous chemistry of war psychology do they become inseparably compounded with gallantry and the selfless, purposeful focusing of energy.

A few years after the war ended I saw another Marine on trial for his life in a Los Angeles court-room. The papers were calling him a "mad dog killer". Caught without fare after taking a taxi to El Toro Marine Base, he had shot the driver in the back of the head with a .45. He broke loose for a few moments in the court-room and hurled himself at the photographers as if he meant to kill them and everyone else. He really was like a mad dog at that instant, and I doubt if anyone present will have forgotten the look in his eyes. On the other hand, I doubt if many reflected that, in a way, he was not the shameful exception which officially he had to be called, but rather the extreme logical end product of a war psychology perhaps familiar to many times and places, but certainly familiar to our own.

Poems from The New Colony

By MADELINE GLEASON

Madeline Gleason was born in North Dakota. She has
lived in San Francisco since 1932. The author of two
volumes of poetry, *Poems,* 1945, and *Metaphysical
Needle,* 1950, she has in addition contributed to various
publications, among them *Botteghe Oscure* and *Evergreen Review.*

I

GULLS soar in the sky
Then glide down to the water
Where refuse attracts,
They inherit the air
And the sea's scum.
We rise, but sometimes falter
And fall again, and we inherit
That sea's flood
To which men and gulls come,
We inherit our own praise or blame
And bear it.

Each moves out on the dangerous sea,
Fearing rip-tide and under-tow
And the blasts that blow
We pray through bitter tears
That we will not drown
In the terrifying flood
Of waters;
That high waves be leveled
And run calm on the sea,
That a quiet sea
Come to our assistance

And make safer the distance
Between us and the shore;
That we will not crash on the rocks,
That battering waves
Rip no oar from the oar-locks.

We pray through bitter tears
That we live to reach the shore,
And explore beyond the shore;
That we be saved and given strength
For the other journey:
The journey through a wood,
Where with every shaking gust,
Our trust will not be turned into distrust.

We would do many times
What is but once required of us.
But each is restless, restless and afraid,
Doubting the virtue of the life he's made,
Crowned with the vanity of flowers.
There is no relief from sorrow or necessity,
And in our anxiety we show but little charity
Each is kindled and put out
Like a light in the night time.

Each moves through a dangerous wood
Where sharp branches threaten
Like shapes that frighten children
In unlighted rooms;
We move from light into the tombs
Of our imaginations, and fall among shadows;
Each prays that no branch will ensnare
And lift him up, like Absalom, by the hair.

Each hopes to come safely through
Into an open place,

Into the light again;
And stand with those
Made patient in extremity,
Reborn in heart and mind,
Who have the courage to find
Among old ruins the new colony.

II

O THAT fine morning on the slope
Of Tamalpais, when our hope
Was fresh as the cold mountain side,
And strong as the sea's incoming tide,

With such light hearts, alert and well,
It was our time then to excel
In climbing mountains without a fall,
In loving none, desiring all.

We lived from minute to minute, and
Youthful, vigorous, could withstand
Setbacks to hope, attacks of pain,
Knowing we should be whole again.

O that fine morning, when for us,
Still foolish and still credulous,
The morning and the mountain shone
On us, and all we looked upon.

Among the faces and the voices,
How difficult to make our choices!
But at the last there is only one
We would have close as flesh to bone.

And when the final choice is made,
Lord, with what care our plans are laid!
And with what caution, for none can tell
Which morning dream night may dispel!

III

THE air of heaven fills with stars that rise
Above the Gate; Orion's sword is bright,
And Sirius, his dog, runs through the night
Among constellations in the ancient skies.

Now Russian Hill is dark, a cold wind blows;
Cassiopeia and Aldebaran
Still rise immortal; only mortal man
Is uncertain of the place to which he goes.

Walk down the hill and hurry homeward now;
Always the thought of war is uppermost;
Violence, and the suffering homeless host
For whom the falling flare obscures the Plough.

IV

WHILE we escape, night after night,
The scattered rocks are struck waves
Swelling the coves, far out of sight,
Far from the coast the petrel cries.

Like lifting wave on lifting wave,
Hope leaps and overpowers thought,
All that we feared to lose, we save;
All that eluded us is caught.

The heart is restless and must bear
As the cut-rock the sea-ferment
And sharpness of the salt-sea air,
All cold, change and astonishment.

Nothing is won, nothing is lost,
Shapes shift, yet all remains the same;
Evening by evening towards the coast
New birds come as the old ones came.

[285]

Somebody Has To Be Nobody

By BUDD SCHULBERG

Schulberg (born 1914) established his place among the California novelists with *What Makes Sammy Run* (1941) and *The Disenchanted* (1950), the latter a fictionized account of the terrible last days of F. Scott Fitzgerald. He has lived mostly in the East, but springs from a movie family—his father was head of a studio—and his successfully combined work in the two arts—e.g. by basing the film *On the Waterfront* upon his original novel *Waterfront*.

At half past five, Ciro's looks like a woman sitting before her dressing table just beginning to make up for the evening. The waiters are setting up the tables for the dinner trade, the cigarette and hat-check girls are changing from slacks to the abbreviated cancan costumes which are their work clothes, and an undiscovered Alice Faye who is making her debut tonight is rehearsing, *Oh, daddy, I wanna bran'-new cah, champagne, caviah, oh, daddy. . . .*

A telephone rings and the operator who is suffering from delusions of looking like Bette Davis answers, "Ci-ro's. . . . A table for Mr. Nathan? . . . For six. . . . His usual table?" This was not what she had come to Hollywood for—to take reservations over the telephone—but even the small part she played in A. D. Nathan's plans for the evening brought her a little closer to the Hollywood that was like a mirage, always in sight but never within reach. For, like everyone else in Hollywood, the telephone operator at Ciro's had a dream. Once upon a time, ran this one, there was A Famous Movie Producer—called Goldwyn, Zanuck or A. D. Nathan—and one evening this F.M.P. was in Ciro's placing a million-dollar telephone call when he happened to catch sight of her behind the switchboard. "Young lady," he said, "you are wasting your time at that switchboard. You may not realize it, but you are Naomi in my forthcoming farm epic, Sow the Wild Oat."

Reluctantly the operator plugged out her dream and sent word of Nathan's reservation to André. André belonged to that great international race, headwaiters, whose flag is an unreadable menu and whose language is French with an accent. Headwaiters are diplomats who happened to be born with silver spoons in their hands instead of their mouths. André would have been a typical headwaiter. But he had been in Hollywood too long. Which meant that no matter how good a headwaiter he was, he no longer wished to be one. André wanted to be a screen writer. In fact, after working only three years, André had managed to finish a screen play entitled, surprisingly enough, Confessions of a Hollywood Waiter, which he had written all by himself, in English.

With casual deliberateness—hadn't Jimmy Starr called him the Poor Man's Adolphe Menjou?—André picked out a table one row removed from the dance floor for Mr. Nathan. The waiter whose ringside table was A. D. Nathan's "Usual" raised a protest not entirely motivated by sentiment. In Waiters' Local 17, A. D. Nathan's fame was based not so much on his pictures as on his tips.

"Mr. Nathan will have to be satisfied with this table," André explained. "All the ringside tables are already reserved."

André had to smile at his own cleverness. A. D. Nathan did not know it yet, but André had had him in mind from the beginning as the producer of his scenario. A. D. seemed the logical contact because he remembered André as an ordinary waiter in Henry's, back in the days before pictures could talk. But André knew he needed something stronger than nostalgia to bring himself to A. D.'s attention. Every Saturday night Nathan presided at the same table overlooking the floor. Tonight André would make him take a back seat. Nathan would threaten and grumble, and André would flash his suave headwaiter smile and be "so sorry, Monsieur Nathan. If there were only something I could do." Then, at the opportune moment, just as the floor show was about to begin, André would discover that something could be done. And when Nathan would try to thank André with a crisp green bill for giving him the table André had been saving for him all evening, André's voice would take on an injured tone: "*Merci beaucoup*, Mr. Nathan. Thank you just the same, but André is glad to do a favor for an old friend."

André thought of the scene in terms of a scenario. That was the dialogue, just roughed in, of course. Then the business of Nathan insisting on rewarding André for his efforts. And a close-up of André, shyly dropping his eyes as he tells M'sieu Nathan that if he really wants to reward André, he could read Confessions of a Hollywood Waiter, by André de Selco.

So that was André's dream, and he dreamed it all the while he was fussing over last-minute details, like a nervous hostess getting ready for a big party.

By the time Nathan's party arrived, the big room with the cyclamen drapes and pale green walls of tufted satin was full of laughter, music, shop talk and an inner-circle intimacy that hung over the place like the smoke that rose from lipsticked cigarettes and expensive cigars. Everyone turned to stare at the newcomers, for Hollywood celebrities have a way of gaping at one another with the same wide-eyed curiosity as their supposedly less sophisticated brothers waiting for autographs outside.

Nathan entered with assurance, conscious of the way "There's A. D." was breathed through the room. His figure was slight but imposing, for he carried himself with the air of a man who was used to commanding authority. There was something ghostly about him, with his white hair and pale skin, but his eyes were intensely alive, dark eyes that never softened, even when he smiled. As he followed André toward the dance floor, actors, agents, directors and fellow producers were anxious to catch his eye. It was "Hello, A. D. . . . How are you tonight, A. D.?" and he would acknowledge them with a word or a nod, knowing how to strike just the right balance between dignity and cordiality.

At his side was his wife, a tall brunette with sculpture-perfect features, hardened by a willful disposition. Some still remembered her as Lita Lawlor, who seemed on the verge of stardom not so many years ago. But she had sacrificed her screen career for love, or so the fan magazines had put it, though gossipers would have you believe that Lita was just swapping one career for another that promised somewhat more permanent security.

Accompanying the Nathans were a plain middle-aged couple whom no one in Ciro's could identify, a girl of seventeen who managed to be astonishingly pretty without the aid of the Westmore Brothers, and Bruce Spencer, a young man whom Nathan was grooming as the next Robert Taylor. And grooming was just the word, for this male ingénue pranced and tossed his curly black mane like a horse on exhibition.

André led the party to the inferior table he had picked out for them.

"Wait a minute. André, this isn't my table," Nathan protested.

He frowned at André's silky explanations. He was in no mood to be crossed this evening. It seemed as if everything was out of focus today. First his three-thousand-dollar-a-week writer had turned in a script with holes big enough to drive a tank through. Then he had decided that what he needed was a date with a cute little thing like this Jenny McBride, and instead here he was with his wife, that young ham of hers and those Carters he'd been ducking for months. And to top everything, there was that business in New York.

[289]

Impatiently, Nathan beckoned the waiter. "I want a magnum of Cordon Rouge, 1929."

1929, Nathan thought. That was the year he almost lost his job. It was a funny thing. All these people hoping to be tossed a bone never thought of A. D. Nathan as a man with a job to hold. But that year, when the panic came and the banks moved in, he had had to think fast to hold on to that big office and that long title.

He wondered what would have become of him if he had lost out. He thought of some of the magic names of the past, like Major Adams and Eddie Selbert, who could walk into Ciro's now without causing a head to turn. And he thought how impossible it would be to enter Ciro's without the salaaming reception he always complained about, but could not have given up.

But that was nothing to worry about now, as he looked across at Jenny, with that incredibly young face, so pretty and soft, like a marmalade kitten, he thought. He lifted his glass in a toast to her.

"Happy birthday," he said. "May you always be seventeen."

"Seventeen!" Mrs. Carter exclaimed. "I'd forgotten there were any seventeen-year-olds left in the world!"

They all laughed and Nathan looked at Mimi Carter, suddenly shocked to see how old she and Harry had become. He could remember when they were the stand-bys at the Embassy Club and the Cocoanut Grove. Now their eyes were shining like tourists', because they had never been to Ciro's before.

"Is the wine all right, Harry?" Nathan asked.

Harry looked up, his face flushed with pleasure. "All right? I haven't had wine like this——" He paused to think. "In a long time," he said.

There was a silence, and Nathan felt embarrassed for him.

He was glad when Mimi broke in with the anecdote about the time they were leaving for Europe with their Western star, Tex Bradely, and Tex insisted on bringing his own Scotch along because he was afraid to trust those foreign bootleggers.

Nathan was only half listening, though he joined in the laughter, for he found himself wondering, *When is Carter going to put the bite on me for that job he wants? And how am I going to con this McBride kid?* And though he could not divine André's plans or guess how he figured in the dreams of the telephone operator who looked like Bette Davis, he could not help feeling that Ciro's was a solar system in which he was the sun and around which all these satellites revolved.

"André," he beckoned, "will you please tell the operator I'm expecting a very important long-distance call?" An empty feeling of excitement rose inside him, but he fought it down. The dancers were swaying to a tango. Nathan saw Spencer and Lita, whirling like professionals, conscious of how well they looked together. He looked at Jenny, and he thought, with a twinge of weariness, of all the Jennies he had looked at this way. "Would you like to dance, my dear?"

He was an old man to Jenny, an old man she hardly knew, and it seemed to her that everybody in the room must be saying, "There goes A. D. with another one. Kids like that will do anything to get ahead." But she tried to smile, tried to be having a terribly good time, thinking, *If I want to be an actress, this is part of the job. And if I can't look as if I'm getting the thrill of my life out of dancing with this old fossil, what kind of an actress am I, anyway?*

Nathan could have told her what kind of an actress she was. He had expressed himself rather vividly on that subject after seeing her test that afternoon.

"McBride stinks," he had told his assistants as the lights came on in the projection room that afternoon. "She'll never be an actress and she photographs even younger than she is."

[291]

That's what he wanted to tell her. But he was reaching that age when it is reassuring to be surrounded with Jenny McBrides. That meant feeding her the old come-on, tossing her just enough crumbs of encouragement to keep her hopes alive. "I'd like to talk to you about that test sometime soon," was all he had said.

"Enjoying your birthday party, Jenny?" he said as he led her back to the table.

"Oh, I'm having an elegant time, Mr. Nathan," she said. She tried to say it with personality, her eyes bright and her smile fixed. But only her ambition was in it, not her heart.

Her heart was not in Ciro's. Her heart was on Orange Grove Avenue. That's where Bill Mason lived. Bill worked as a grip on Nathan's lot. The grip is the guy who does the dirty work on a movie set. Or, as Bill liked to explain it, "I'm the guy who carries the set around on his back. I may not be the power behind the throne, but I'm sure the power under it."

Jenny thought of the way she and Bill had planned to celebrate her birthday, down at the amusement pier. They always had fun down there together.

"Oh, I'm so sorry, Mr. Nathan," Jenny had told the producer when he phoned, "but this—this happens to be my birthday, and I——"

"I know it's your birthday, my dear," he had lied wearily. "Why do you think I called? I thought we might have a birthday party—just the two of us."

She hesitated, not knowing what to do. Bill would never forgive her. But this was A. D. Nathan calling her in person.

"Thanks, very much; I'd love to. But I do have an appointment——"

"Well, bring your appointment along," Nathan had conceded; "we'll make a real party of it. How would you like to go to Ciro's?"

She had never been to Ciro's. "Next to heaven," she said,

[292]

"I can't think of a nicer place."

Bill had looked in on his way home as usual, an energetic kid with laughter in his eyes and unruly brown hair that Jenny was forever scolding him for forgetting to comb.

"Sorry to keep you waiting, Mac," he called from the door. "But that old bag"—he was referring to one of the screen's most glamorous personalities—"blew her lines in the big love scene fifteen straight times. I thought one of the juicers was going to drop a lamp on her!"

He lifted Jenny off her feet the way he always did and kissed the tip of her nose. "That schnoz is too little to work," he grinned. "Too bad you haven't got a nice big practical one like me."

She took a kitten bite out of his cheek. "Aren't you going to say anything?" she pouted.

"That's my cue," he said. "Happy birthday, child. How old are you this year, twelve?"

She shut her eyes childishly and lapsed into baby talk, "I want my serpwise."

She was surprised. Bill was holding up a diamond engagement ring.

"Like it?"

"Oh, it's beautiful. But, Bill——"

Bill grimaced with boyish embarrassment. "Try it on. What's a little thing like a diamond to us Masons? Know what Leon Shamroy told me today? Said he'd put me on the camera crew, starting the next picture.

He kissed her again, this time for keeps. "I'll run home and slip into something more comfortable, as they say in the movies," he laughed, indicating his blue jeans and work shirt.

Jenny advanced cautiously, fearing the storm ahead. "Bill—Bill darling, do you have any evening clothes?"

Bill stopped at the door. "Evening clothes? We'd look like a couple of jerks, riding the roller coaster in evening clothes."

[293]

"But, Bill, we aren't going to the pier. We're going to Ciro's."

"Ciro's!" Honey, are you crazy? It costs you five clams just to get a glass of water in that joint!"

"I guess A. D. Nathan can afford it," she said, watching his expression change and hurrying to explain. "Darling, I'd of given anything to get out of it. But you know how important he is. I don't want to sound dramatic, but—well, my whole career may depend on this."

"You don't sound dramatic," he said; "you sound touched." The playfulness was gone from his eyes now, the gaiety between them snapped like a violin string. "Listen, Mac, you may be kidding yourself, but you can't kid me. I was on the set when you made that test. I love you enough to tell you what a lousy actress you are."

Jenny tightened with indignation. "I suppose you know more about acting than Mr. Nathan? He says he wants to keep the test to look at again."

"Are you sure he meant the test, and not you?"

Here at this table in Ciro's the waiter was filling her glass again, and she was laughing at something funny and off-color that Bruce Spencer had just said. But she couldn't forget what she had done to Bill, how she had slapped him, melodramatically handed back the ring, and how, according to the few choked words exchanged at the door, they had parted forever.

Jenny had cried, because she loved Bill. And then she had stopped crying and called A. D. Nathan, because she had read too many movie magazines. *This is what makes a great actress of you—sorrow and sacrifice of your personal happiness*, she thought, and she saw herself years later as a great star, running into Bill in Ciro's after he had become a famous cameraman. *"Bill,"* she would say, *"perhaps it is not too late. Each of us had to follow his own path until they crossed again."*

By the time Jenny phoned Nathan to say she would come

alone, he had already asked his wife. "Now we have to find an escort," he grumbled. "Fine chance of finding an extra man at this hour."

"We might be able to get hold of Bruce Spencer," said Lita. "He said something about being free when we left the club this afternoon."

Nathan knew they could get hold of Bruce Spencer. Lita and Bruce were giving the Hollywood wives something to talk about over their bridge tables of an afternoon. Sometimes he dreamed of putting an end to it. But that meant killing two birds with bad publicity. And they were both his birds, his wife and his leading man.

"All right," he said, "I'll give Spence a ring. Might not be bad publicity for the McBride girl if we decide to use her."

Lita pecked him on the cheek with preoccupation. Bruce was dying to get that star-making part in Suicide Squad. This might be the ideal evening to talk A. D. into it.

And then, since the four of them might look too obvious, Nathan had wanted an extra couple. He tried several, but it was too late to get anybody in demand. That's how he had happened to think of the Carters.

When you talked about old-time directors, you had to mention Harry Carter in the same breath with D. W. Griffith and Mickey Neilan. Carter and Nathan had been a famous combination until sound pictures and TB knocked Carter out of the running. The last job he had had was a quickie Western over a year ago. And a year in Hollywood is like an era anywhere else. A. D. had forgotten all about Carter until he received a letter from him a few months ago, just a friendly letter, suggesting dinner some evening to cut up touches about old times. But A. D. knew those friendly dinners, knew he owed Carter a debt he was reluctant to repay, and so, somehow, the letter had gone unanswered. But, in spite of himself, his conscience had filed it away for further reference.

[295]

"I know who we'll get. The Harry Carters. Been meaning to take them to dinner for months."

"Do we have to fall back on the Old Ladies' Home?" Lita said, drawing on a pair of long white gloves that set off her firm tan arms.

"It might not be so bad," Nathan said, giving way to the sentimentalism that thrives in his profession. "Mimi Carter always used to be a lot of fun."

"I can just imagine," said Lita. "I'll bet she does a mean turkey trot."

So that's how it happened chance plucked the Carters out of the obscurity of a bungalow court and dropped them down in the middle of a world they had never expected to see again.

"Harry, I just know this means A. D.'s going to give you a chance again," Mimi Carter whispered as they walked off the dance floor with their arms around each other, and she saw how his eyes were shining and hastened to warn, "Not too much wine, Harry. Be careful. You aren't used to it, and you've got to impress A. D. tonight."

"Don't worry, sweetheart," he answered. "I'm watching. I'm waiting for the right moment to talk to him."

Lita and Bruce were dancing again, and Jenny was alone with A. D. at the table when the Carters returned. It was the moment Jenny had been fishing for. She could hardly wait to know what he thought of the test.

"I don't think it does you justice," Nathan was saying. "The cameraman didn't know how to light you at all. I think you have great possibilities."

Jenny grinned trumphantly, the wine and encouragement going to her head, and Nathan reached over and patted her hand in what was meant to seem a fatherly gesture, though he lingered a moment too long. But Jenny saw nothing but "A. D. Nathan Presents Jenny McBride——" For this was Jenny's dream, a dream that seemed to be coming true as

André presented her with an ornate birthday cake, the orchestra played a special swing arrangement of Happy Birthday and everyone in Ciro's applauded, applauded her, even famous people like George Raft and Betty Grable and Marlene Dietrich. Jenny blew out the candles, candles that seemed to spell "A. D. Nathan Presents Jenny McBride," and she laughed with embarrassment and delight and the thought that *You're on your way, Jenny McBride. If Bill could only see you now.*

Then she looked up and a forkful of birthday cake stopped in mid-air. Bill Mason was seeing her now. He was sitting at the bar with a highball in his hand, staring down at her. As she stared back, he drained his glass, his face terribly red and terribly serious. She had never seen him drunk before. Horrified, she saw him rise slowly and start toward her table, with a desperate effort to preserve his dignity.

He stopped at their table, weaving slightly, bowed low like a foreign director and kissed Jenny's hand.

"Allow me to eentroduce myself," he said to Nathan with mock seriousness. "I am ze great foreign director, Vilhelm von Mason. I yust vant to tell you vat a vunderful actress you haf here. Ven she plays drama, you bust out crying, you are laughing so hard."

"Bill!" she cried. "Bill, what are you doing here?"

"I am getting drunk here," Bill answered. "Drunk enough to get up courage to come over and take you home."

People were beginning to stare, and Nathan hated scenes. "Who is this man?" he demanded. "What is he doing here?"

"I'm nobody you ever heard of," said Bill. "Just a lousy grip who works on your lot. Just the dope this great tragedienne of yours is going to marry."

Everyone looked at Jenny, and she felt her dream smashing up, and she fought to hold the pieces together. She used the old words, but she poured them out as if no one had ever spoken them before, "Get out of here! I hate you! I never want

[297]

to see you again!"

Bill smiled, sadly and drunkenly. "Don't believe her, A. D. We're a natural, Mac and me. And if you'd just get your mind off that casting couch for a minute, you'd tell her to go home and forget this stuff."

"If you work on my lot, you're fired," Nathan said, and he called to André, "Have this man thrown out of here."

A couple of bouncers closed in on Bill. He waited for them calmly. He was sober now. "Might as well save yourself the trouble, boys. You couldn't keep me here if you gave me the joint. I'm going to a place with real class, Barney's Beanery."

Then he bowed to Jenny and kissed her hand again. "Good-by, Miss Garbo. It's been thrilling to meet you. Don't forget to send me that autographed picture."

The birthday cake was eaten and the champagne was drunk, but it was no longer the same. A. D. continued to stare at Jenny, but the expression in his eyes had changed to thoughtful inspection.

Harry Carter looked at his watch nervously. It was almost time for the floor show. And after that, the party would be over, before he had a chance to talk about that comeback. He looked at Mimi, trying to find the courage to put it up to A. D. But A. D. seemed in no mood to listen. Lita and Bruce were watching, too, wondering how to bring the subject around to Suicide Squad. And André, behind that headwaiter's mask, was thinking, *Only twenty more minutes and I will be speaking to A. D. about my scenario.*

"André," Nathan called, and the headwaiter snapped to attention. "Are you sure there hasn't been a call for me?"

"No, monsieur. I would call you right away, monsieur."

Nathan frowned. "Well, make sure. It should have been here by now." He felt angry with himself for losing his patience. There was no reason to be so upset. This was just another long-distance call. He had talked to New York a thousand times before, about matters just as serious.

But when André came running with the message that New York was on the wire, he could not keep the old fear from knotting his stomach, and he jostled the table in his anxiety to rise.

"You may take it in the second booth on the left, Mr. Nathan," said "Bette Davis" as she looked up from her switchboard with a prefabricated smile. But he merely brushed by her and slammed the door of the booth behind him.

The telephone girl looked after him with the dream in her eyes. *When he comes out I'll hafta think of something arresting ta say ta him,* she decided. *Wouldn't it be funny if he did notice me?*

Five minutes later she heard the door of the booth sliding open and she looked up and smiled.

"Was the connection clear, Mr. Nathan?"

That might do for a starter, she thought. But he didn't even look up as he murmured, "Yes. I heard very well. Thank you," and he put half a dollar down and walked on. He felt heavy, heavy all over, his body too heavy for his legs to support and his eyes too heavy for the sockets to hold. He walked back to the table no longer seeing the people who tried to catch his glance, erect through force of habit.

"Everything all right?" said his wife.

"Yes. Yes," he said. "Everything."

Was that my voice? It didn't sound like my voice. It sounded more like Harry Carter's voice. Poor old Harry. Never forget the days we ran the World-Wide lot together. Or that time I lost my shirt in the market and Harry loaned me fifty G's. Wonder what ever happened to Harry.

Then he realized it was Harry Carter talking, "A. D., this has sure been a tonic for Mimi and me. And I know we didn't come here to talk shop. But you always used to have faith in me and—well——"

All heads were turning toward the entrance again and

[299]

Nathan saw Joe Morris, a rival producer, coming in. "Excuse me. I'll be right back," he said, and he rose to his feet in slow motion.

With that same somnambulistic rhythm he walked toward Morris.

"Well, Joe, guess I put one over on you this time. Guess who's going to do my next picture? Harry Carter."

"Harry Carter!" Morris unclenched his cigar. "Why, he's dead, isn't he?"

"You should be so dead. I've got him over at my table now, talking a deal. I just saw a swell little picture he did for Tec-Art. Looks like the old master is better than ever, and we're crying about the dearth of directors."

Joe Morris chewed his cigar irritably. If there was anything he couldn't stand, it was letting A.D. Nathan outsmart him. Then a shrewd gleam came into his eyes.

"Harry and I used to be great pals," he said. "Think I'll walk back to your table and say hello to him."

Carter looked up in amazement as Morris came toward him, with his friendly face on. "Well, Harry, old kid," he greeted him. "Where you been keeping yourself lately? How about dropping in at the beach tomorrow for a drink?"

"You see!" Harry told his wife proudly as they did an especially fancy turn around the floor. "Is Hollywood a crazy place! One minute you're a bum who can't get by the gate, the next minute they're fighting over you."

Jenny and Nathan were sitting at the table alone again. *This will be quick*, he thought—*this will be quick and sharp, like a scalpel cut.*

"Miss McBride," his voice began in a monotone, "what would you say if I were to tell you that your screen test was so bad it even made the projectionist laugh?"

Jenny flushed with the pain of it, and she looked at the emptied magnum of champagne.

"Why, Mr. Nathan, you must be—you must be——"

"No, I am not drunk," he said, with terrible finality. "You're the one who's drunk. I've filled you full of false hopes that have made you drunk. You see, I have a very bad habit of lying to pretty girls who can't act. So, if you have any brains at all in that very pretty head of yours, you'll run home and marry that grip of yours before it's too late."

He didn't move his head, and his face seemed to show no emotion at all when she gritted her teeth to fight back the tears. But there was a faint, tired smile around his mouth as he watched her jump up from the table and run toward the door.

At the entrance, the autograph crowd pushed forward to see who it was, and when they found it was no one they recognized, they relaxed in disappointment.

"Don't get her! She's nobody!" someone called out, and suddenly Jenny thought, *Well, I guess somebody has to be nobody,* and she felt better when she gave the cab driver Bill's address on Orange Grove Avenue.

"What did you do to that kid?" Lita asked when the music stopped and she returned to the table arm in arm with Bruce.

"I told her that as an actress she'll make a good wife for a grip," Nathan said.

"I didn't think she had much on the ball," Bruce said, lighting a cigarette, and proud of the smooth way he shifted into, "By the way, A.D., Lita let me read the script on Suicide Squad. That's a terrific part, that aviator who goes blind, but doesn't let anybody know it. Who's going to play it?"

"Any leading man in Hollywood except you," Nathan said.

Bruce looked undressed without his assurance. The silence was awkward, and then Lita said, "But, A.D., that part was written for Bruce."

All the rest of his face seemed to be sagging, but Nathan's

hard black eyes watched them with bitter amusement. "There isn't a part in the studio that's written for Bruce. The only thing that kept Bruce from being fired months ago was me. And now there's no longer me."

Lita looked up at him, really frightened now.

·"A.D., what do you mean?"

His face was white, white as a ghost, the ghost he was about to become. "I mean I'm out," he said. "Finished. Washed up. Through. Hudson called to say the board voted to ask for my resignation."

"What are you going to do now?" she said.

He thought of the thing he had promised himself to do when his time came—drop out of sight, break it off clean. Hollywood had no use for anticlimaxes on or off the screen. But as he sat there, he knew what would really happen.

Move over, Major Adams and Eddie Selbert, he thought. *Make room for another ghost.*

The floor show was just starting. The undiscovered Alice Faye was putting everything she had into *"Oh, daddy, I wanna bran'-new cah, champagne, caviah."*

And as she sang, André smiled in anticipation. So far everything had gone just as he had planned. And now the time had come to move A.D. up to that ringside table.

The World in the Evening

By CHRISTOPHER ISHERWOOD

The following selection is the first chapter of Isherwood's novel *The World in the Evening* (1954). Born in England in 1904, Isherwood has been an American citizen since 1946 and has commonly lived in and around Los Angeles. Among his film-world books are *Prater Violet* (1945) and *Goodbye to Berlin* (1954), from which came the great film *I Am a Camera*.

The party, that evening, was at the Novotnys'. They lived high up on the slopes of the Hollywood hills, in a ranch-style home complete with Early American maple, nautical brasswork and muslin curtains; just too cute for words. It looked as if it had been delivered, already equipped, from a store; and you could imagine how, if the payments weren't kept up, some men might arrive one day and take the whole place back there on a truck, along with Mrs. Novotny, the three children, the two cars and the cocker spaniel. Most of the houses Jane and I visited were like that.

It was quite late already and several people were drunk; not acting badly, just boastful and loud and thick-voiced. I was about halfway; which was the best way for me to be. As long as I was sober, I sulked. If I went on drinking, I was apt to turn nasty and say something embarrassing, or else fall asleep and snore. Jane was always worried about that, and yet she never could tear herself away until the end. "Why in hell don't you go on back home, if you're so bored," she sometimes whispered to me furiously, "instead of drooping around like a Goddam martyr? What's the matter? Afraid I might do something *you* wouldn't do?" I used to grin at her without answering. That was exactly how I wanted her to feel: unsure of me and uneasy and guiltily aggressive. It was the only way I knew of hitting back at her.

[303]

I was alone, now, at the uncrowded end of the living room. A mirror on the opposite wall showed me how I appeared to the outside world: a tall, blond, youngish-oldish man with a weakly good-looking, anxious face and dark over-expressive eyes, standing in a corner between a cobbler's table and a fake spinning wheel, holding a highball glass in my hand. A miniature brass ship with a fern growing out of it was fastened to the wall beside my cheek. I looked as if I were trying to melt into the scenery and become invisible, like a giraffe standing motionless among sunlit leaves.

I was wearing my usual crazy costume, the symbol of my protest against this life I was leading: a white tuxedo jacket, with a crimson bow tie and carnation to match my moiré cummerbund. Elizabeth, if she could have seen me, would have said, "Darling, what on *earth* are you supposed to be? No—don't tell me. Let me guess...." In a way, I think I did dress like this just because it would have amused Elizabeth. Certainly, no one here saw the joke, not even Jane; my masquerade as a musical-comedy Hollywood character passed entirely unnoticed. And why, after all, should any of these people notice it? This was the only way they knew me—as I appeared, night after night, at Jane's side, in the doorways of their homes. (We never stayed home alone together in the evenings, any more; it would have been unthinkable.)

If you had asked who I was, almost every one of them would have answered "Jane Monk's husband," and let it go at that. It had been the same right from the start, when we'd first arrived in California, the previous year. Even the society columnists decided I was no fun and had better be ignored. They never mentioned me directly if they could avoid it, though they bubbled with items like "Saw Jane (Mrs. Stephen) Monk looking gorgeous (as usual) in white satin with some stunning antique Brussels lace. They're here from New York, via Nassau. Plan to settle for a while. Jane tells me..." etc.,

etc. Jane loved it. She never seemed to get tired of being talked about, no matter how bitchily. She even told me once—taking it as a huge joke—how a man at Chasen's had been overheard saying "Well, he may be a Monk—but, brother, she's no nun." That was one of the things about her I still found charmingly innocent and touching.

"Out here on the Coast," someone declared, in the group nearest to me, "you just don't know what the score is. Why, back East, we're practically in the war already." Someone else agreed that F.D.R. would get us in as soon as he could find an excuse. There was talk about the London blitz, and Rommel and the fighting in Africa (this was April, 1941) but you could tell that none of them cared very much. Their fears and their interests were elsewhere. Sid Novotny was a screen writer, and this party was just in case the studio might be hesitating to take up his option. Alice Faye, who was to have been the guest of honor, hadn't shown up. However, several of the front-office executives were present, a couple of second-magnitude stars, and a lot of young actresses and actors. Such as Roy Griffin, for instance.

A man disengaged himself from the conversation and came over to me. I'd been watching him preparing to do this for several minutes. We'd been introduced to each other earlier in the evening; I knew he was a producer, though I'd forgotten his name. He had a crew cut, clean hairy hands, inquisitive eyes and a very sincere manner.

"Say, Mr. Monk, you know I've been wanting to get together with you ever since I heard you were out here? It was quite a thrill, meeting you tonight. It really was. Believe it or not, I'm one of the old original Rydal fans. Yes, I'll bet I was one of the very first in this country."

I made a suitable noise.

"*The World in the Evening:* Jesus—that's a great book! One of the truly great books written in our time." The producer lowered his voice, as though we were just entering a church. "You know something?" He glanced quickly at the group he had left, afraid, apparently, that they might be listening. "Somewhere in that book, there's a great movie. *One hell of a movie.* Most people wouldn't be able to see that. But I can. I can give you my word that it's there. Did anyone ever buy the rights?"

"I don't think so." I was looking over the crowd at the other end of the room. I had just noticed that Jane wasn't there. "I could find out, if you're interested." Roy Griffin wasn't there, either.

"I'm definitely interested. Definitely. Say, supposing we manage to work something out, would you possibly consider helping us on the screen play?"

"I'm not a writer, you know." Jane might be in the bar, of course. Or with Mrs Novotny, admiring some new clothes. Maybe she wasn't with Roy at all.

"Not a writer, Mr. Monk? Come now—let's not be so darned modest! What about that introduction you did to the *Collected Stories?* I read that over and over. You did a beautiful job. Fine. Sensitive. No one but yourself could have written that way. No one else was in a position to know her as you did."

"Well—I'm glad you liked it, but . . ."

"And it's not a question of movie experience. Let me put it this way—we'd need you as a sort of a, well, an artistic conscience. Someone to tell us when we're getting off the beam. You're the only man who could tell us that. And we've got to watch every darned little nuance, or we're sunk. Every word Elizabeth Rydal wrote is sacred to me. Sacred. I'm not kidding. I'd want to make this picture just as she'd have wished it— catch that wonderful delicate style and preserve it in celluloid, if you get what I mean. . . ."

I've got to find them, I said to myself. Now, at once. I

can't stand any more of this. This time, I've got to absolutely sure.

The producer's voice faded in again: "Say, how about lunch, some time? Say, why don't I call you around the first of the week?"

"All right." I tore a leaf from my notebook and scribbled the telephone number, substituting one wrong digit; a favorite trick of mine. If they finally track you down you can always pretend it was a slip.

"And Mrs. Monk too, of course. If she'd care to join us."

"I'll ask her." I thrust the paper into his hand and walked away before he could say another word.

At the entrance to the bar I ran into Mrs. Novotny, dainty and haggardly bright, in a dirndl costume with slave bangles.

"Getting yourself a drink? Good!" She smiled brilliantly, squeezing the crow's-feet around her eyes. "I like a man who knows how to look out for himself."

I grinned at her numbly. ("Your dying-god grin," Jane called it, when she was mad at me.)

"Sid and I were both so glad you could come, this evening. Jane's such a lot of fun. She enjoys herself so. She always gets a party going. She's such a *happy* person. . . ."

"Yes," I said.

"Excuse me. . . ." She gave me another smile, touched my arm lightly and headed eagerly back into the crowd. I'd been getting ready to ask her if she knew where Jane was. It was so hard to hit on exactly the right tone of voice; casual, but not too casual. Now I felt glad that I hadn't tried.

The bar was three steps down from the living room. Here, the dueling pistols and the ships' compasses, the Toby jugs, the clay pipes and the Currier and Ives prints clustered around a gay altar of colored bottles, and the air was thick with smoke and chatter. I stood on the top step, looking down. A couple of men recognized me and nodded, and I nodded back; but I

[307]

knew very well that none of them really wanted me to join them. A cold, bored, boring highbrow: that was how I seemed to them, no doubt. Or else a snooty, half-Europeanized play-boy with a limey accent and a Riviera background, who knew Italian princesses and French counts. An alien, in any case, who didn't belong to their worried movie world, where you lived six months ahead of your salary and had to keep right on spending lest anyone should suspect that your credit wasn't good. I had no part in their ulcers and anxieties, their mort-gages and their options. I had never sweated it out at a sneak preview or a projection-room post-mortem. And so, when these people thought of me, they certainly envied me my unearned money but probably also despised me for my irresponsible freedom.

I came near to startling them all, at that moment, with a great bellow of despair, like an animal trapped in a swamp. Somehow or other, I'd wandered into this gibbering jungle of phonies and now here I was, floundering stupidly in the mud of my jealous misery and sinking deeper with every movement. I hadn't even the consolation of being able to feel sorry for my-self. I wasn't in the least tragic or pitiable; no, merely squalid and ridiculous. I knew that, and yet I couldn't help myself. I couldn't get out of the swamp. I tried to think of Elizabeth and what she would have said, but it was no good. Elizabeth wasn't here. I was all alone. I should go on struggling and sinking. I had no control, any more, over what was going to happen.

Jane wasn't in the bar. Neither was Roy Griffin.

Turning from the steps, I walked quickly along a short passage, opened a glass door and stepped out into the garden. It was cut from the steep hillside in two terraces; a dichondra lawn above, and, below, a small kidney-shaped swimming pool. The water of the pool must have been heated for it steamed gently in the beams of submerged lamps, its green-lit fumes rising theatrically against the enormous cheap-gaudy night-scape of Los Angeles which sparkled away out to the horizon like a million cut-rate engagement rings.

There was nobody in the garden.

I came to a halt at the edge of the pool. It was brilliantly clean; not one leaf floating on its surface, not one speck of dirt on its tiled floor. God curse this antiseptic, heartless, hateful neon mirage of a city! May its swimming pools be dried up. May all its lights go out for ever. I drew a deep dizzying breath in which the perfume of star jasmine was mixed with chlorine.

So this time was going to be like all the other times. I wasn't going to find her. I wasn't going to know for certain. Later, she'd walk into the living room quite casually, smiling as she said, "We took a ride. I felt like I needed some fresh air." Or else simply smiling and not bothering to explain at all. And Roy would either be casual too, as some of the others had been, or else embarrassed and in need of a stiff drink, avoiding my eyes. And I'd look at Jane and she'd look right back at me; and there would be nothing to say about it because I could prove nothing.

She and Roy had probably driven off into the hills to-gether, the way the high-school kids did. The other day, at another party, a man had told us how he'd had a flat tire on Mulholland Drive, and how he'd gone over to car parked near by, after suitable warning coughs, to borrow a jack, and sur-prised a couple of them—the boy around sixteen, the girl maybe less—stark naked. "Holy smoke," the boy had said, "for a minute I thought you were a cop!" They hadn't seemed the least ashamed of themselves. Jane's comment on this story had been, "Well, good for *them!*"

I became suddenly aware of my hand, and the glass in it flashing green with the magic light of the water. The glass was empty, asking to be filled. I would have to go back into the house to fill it. I'd fix myself a huge drink and then sit down somewhere and figure out a very clever way to trap her once and for all, and be sure.

Wait, though. What was that?

Not the distant noises from the house. Not the crickets, which were chirping all over the hillside. Not the beating of my own heart.

There it was again. Quite close.

But—of course! I had entirely forgotten about the doll's house.

It was a playhouse, actually; fixed up to look like the witch's candy cottage in *Hansel and Gretel*, with curly pillars that were supposed to be sugar sticks and shingles painted the color of toffee. The three Novotny children were still just small enough to squeeze into it together; Mrs. Novotny thought it was cute to make them demonstrate this to her guests, on Sunday afternoons. All you could see of it now was a black outline, standing back among the shadows of the oleanders around the pool.

I set my glass down very gently on the paving and tiptoed across to it, holding my breath.

Small but unmistakable sounds. Out of the darkness, right at my feet.

And then Jane's voice in a faint gasping whisper: "Roy . . . !"

I stood there, death-still, clenching my fists. But I was grinning.

For now, suddenly—now that there was never again to be any more doubting, dreading, suspecting—here, right in the brute presence of the simple unbelievable fact—I felt what I had never guessed I would feel; a great, almost agonizing upsurge of glee, of gleeful relief.

Caught. Caught her at last.

At my first boarding school in England, on winter evenings, we had played hide-and-seek sometimes, turning out the lights and hiding all over the big house. When you were It, you tip-toed around holding your breath and listening, until your ears grew so keen it seemed you could hear every sound within miles. I had always hated being It, but it was worth bearing the tense, spooky loneliness just for the sake of that one intoxi-cating, gleeful instant when you knew you'd caught them, those whispers lurking and mocking you in the darkness.

A funny thought flashed through my head: I've been It for nearly four years. What a long game . . .

Right at my feet, Jane giggled. "Roy—you sonofabitch..."

And, as if this were the signal they had been waiting for, my clenched fists jumped from my sides and pounded thunder-ing on the doll's house roof.

Then, light and quick as a murderer, I turned and ran laughing up the steps from the pool, jumped a flower bed, burst through a line of bushes and was out on the driveway. Luckily, my car was parked some distance from the front door of the house. I fumbled frantically for the key, started the engine, backed out like a rocket, smashed into another car—crumpling the fenders, probably—bounced off it, whirled the steering wheel around, and was away.

After that, everything came unstuck. The car bolted head-long with me down the road, squealing and skidding around the curves. My left hand wanted to swing it over the edge and plunge it to a blazing wreck in a gully; but my right hand re-fused, and was stronger. My voice was yelling dirty insane words about the things it would do to Jane. My mind sat away off somewhere, calm and strangely detached, disclaiming all responsibility for this noisy madman, just watching, listening and waiting for what would happen next.

And then I was up in the bedroom of our house. I had found one of her lipsticks and scribbled the mirror and the walls with the words I had been shouting, in big scarlet letters. Now I was throwing stuff into a suitcase as if the place were on

[311]

fire. Reaching into the closet for clothes, my hands touched an evening gown, gripped and crumpled it and dragged it out, and it was Jane I was going to kill. "Rip her up. Rip her wide open," I muttered, hunting for a razor blade in my shaving kit. The blade was double-edged, awkward to hold. I cut my thumb deeply as I slashed with obstinate rage at the dress; the silk was amazingly tough. But it was done at last. Sobbing, I flung the poor, beautiful, harmless thing into a corner, all gashed and bloodied and spoiled. How horrible! I was going to vomit. I stumbled into the bathroom with my bleeding thumb in my mouth and reached the toilet bowl just in time.

When I had washed myself, I came back into the bedroom for my suitcase, feeling weak and shaken and nearly sober. It was then I remembered Elizabeth's letters. They were in a file, standing on the desk in the room I called my study but never used; I hadn't looked at them in months. I couldn't leave them alone with Jane. She might burn them. She might even read them. I should have to take them along with me—wherever it was that I was going.

At the front door I paused and turned for a last look at our little hate-nest. Perhaps I had never seen it properly until this moment; my feelings about Jane had reduced it to a sort of flat, colorless backdrop. Actually, it had considerable comic possibilities. The hall was Hollywood-Spanish, with decorated beams and a staircase of curlicue ironwork and tiled steps gaily painted with birds and flowers. High up the wall, which had a surface like very expensive cream note paper, there was a balcony draped with an Indian blanket. "Romeo and Juliet," I said aloud. Then I noticed a bottle of whisky standing unopened in a paper bag on the carved Italian dower-chest. I picked it up and ran down the crazy pavement to the car, leaving the door ajar and all the lights burning.

In the darkened hotel lobby, only the reception desk was

illuminated. It was quiet here and calm like a chapel, with the desk clerk keeping his vigil amidst the shadows of big, sleepy, indoor leaves. I signed the guest card, saying to myself as I often did: After all, I suppose I do actually exist. Anyhow, I seem to have a name, just like anybody else.

"Stopping with us long, Mr. Monk?" the desk clerk asked, with an instant's glance at my signature. His manner was perfect; correct, yet discreetly understanding. It was as if he knew what I was thinking. You can trust us, his reassuring smile seemed to say. We shall accept you for what you tell us you are. We shall assume that you are a real person. All our guests, by definition, are real people.

"I'm not sure about my plans, yet." (But, even as I said this, I knew suddenly what I was going to do.)

The clerk nodded pleasantly and wrote something in a book. He was dressed for this death-watch job as if for a lively party; his suit, shirt, tie and teeth were immaculate, and his handsome, sunburned young face showed not the least sign of fatigue. How is it, I wanted to ask him, that you can sit there, hour after hour, so calm and alone? What's your secret? How did you learn to inhabit the Night? I would have liked to stay and talk to the young man, telling him everything exactly as it had happened, without shame or excuse, as you might tell a doctor or a priest. But already the porter stood behind me with my suitcase; and the clerk was saying: "Four sixty-two, sir. I hope you'll be comfortable."

"Will you put a call through for me, please?" I said. "Long distance to Dolgelly, Pennsylvania. You'll have to get the number from Information. It'll be listed under Pennington, Miss Sarah Pennington. The house is called Tawelfan. T-a-w-e-l-f-a-n. It's on Boundary Lane."

"Surely." The clerk was scribbling this down. "Good night, Mr. Monk."

The call came through very quickly; only a few minutes

after the porter had left me alone in my room.

"Go ahead, Los Angeles. Your party's on the line."

"Hello . . ."

"Yes . . .?" Sarah's voice sounded faint and anxious and old. I could picture her—with her hair in pigtails, probably—startled from sleep in the gray of dawn and fearing news of some disaster.

"Aunt Sarah, it's me, Stephen. I woke you, didn't I? I'm so sorry, but I had to tell you this at once. I . . ."

"*Stephen!* It's you! Where are you?"

"Still here. In California. But listen . . ."

"I'm sorry, Stephen dear. I can't hear you. . . ."

"What I want to know is—could you possibly have me at Tawelfan? I mean, right away?"

"*Stephen!* You mean, to *stay?* To *live* here?"

"Well—it might be only for a day or two. Or maybe longer. I'm not sure, yet. But are you quite certain it won't be inconvenient?"

"Inconvenient! Listen to the man! He expects *me* to tell *him* that it's inconvenient to have him *here.* Oh, Stephen dear, I'm so excited I can hardly believe it! When do you suppose you'll be coming?"

"I ought to be with you tomorrow. That is, if I can get on a plane sometime later today. I'll send you a telegram when I know for sure."

"Oh, how wonderful . . . Stephen, I'm not dreaming, am I? You really *are* coming?"

"Of course I'm coming, Aunt Sarah. Now you go right back to bed and finish your sleep."

"Oh, I shan't sleep another wink. Besides, it's getting light already. I must be up and doing. Good night, Stephen, my dearest. I suppose it *is* still night with you? How odd that seems! God bless you."

"Good night, Aunt Sarah."

I hung up with a sigh of pain and relief. Her joy made me feel sad and guilty, as though I had somehow cheated her. But what a relief to know that it was done, now; I had taken the single, necessary, irrevocable step. And now I knew what I hadn't realized or admitted to myself until this moment—that I'd taken it only just in time. The least delay in getting that phone call through, and perhaps—no, it was certain; I'd have gone back to the house. Back to Jane, on her own terms, any terms. That was the simple, miserable truth.

"But it's done now," I repeated aloud. I opened my suitcase and took out the whisky bottle. First I would get into bed, then drink until I slept. Very soon it would be morning. Things would start to happen of themselves, and Life would begin to carry me slowly, slowly away from the wreck.

But the whisky nauseated me. I couldn't touch it. Instead, I lay there staring at the ceiling and was shaken by another trembling fit of hate. Grinning savagely, I thought of Roy Griffin, that film-fairy, that pansy male-impersonator who fooled nobody but himself, stuck with a very expensive nymphomaniac. Stuck with her, and not knowing how to wriggle out of it, and scared silly because of his career. Maybe he'd even have to marry her. Ha ha, what a laugh! The poor, miserable little pansy bastard, married to a bitch who's been accustomed to spend more on herself in one week that he earns in six months. Or did he think he was going to live on alimony! Well, if he did, he certainly had another guess coming. Not one cent would that whore get. Not one single cent. Not even if she took the case to the Supreme Court. I'd go to jail, first.

But I got hot, then, thinking of them together; two mating giants filling the dwarf world of the doll's house, and nearly bursting it apart with their heavings and writhings. I played the scene over and over to myself, elaborating every detail, until if left me sick with disgust and exhaustion. And so, toward dawn, I fell asleep.

Big Sur and the Good Life

By HENRY MILLER

Unlike most writers in this anthology, Henry Miller has used California chiefly as a place of retirement. Born in 1891, Miller spent his youth in New York and published his famous *Tropic of Cancer* (1931) and *Tropic of Capricorn* (1939), as well as many of his short stories, during a long residence in France. As a sage and philosopher he has attracted thousands of pilgrims to Big Sur.

It was twelve years ago on a day in February that I arrived in Big Sur—in the midst of a violent downpour. Toward dusk that same day, after a rejuvenating bath outdoors at the hot sulphur springs (Slade's Springs), I had dinner with the Rosses in the quaint old cottage they then occupied at Livermore Edge. It was the beginning of something more than a friendship. It would be more just, perhaps, to call it an initiation into a new way of life. . . .

Years ago our great American poet Robinson Jeffers began singing of this region in his narrative poems. Jack London and his friend George Sterling made frequent visits to Big Sur in the old days; they came on horseback, all the way from the Valley of the Moon. The general public, however, knew almost nothing of this region until 1937 when the Carmel-San Simeon highway, which skirts the Pacific for a distance of sixty miles or more, was opened up. In fact, until then it was probably one of the least known regions in all America.

The first settlers, mountain men mostly, of hardy pioneer stock, came around 1870. They were, as Lillian Ross puts it, men who had followed the buffalo trails and knew how to live on meat without salt. They came afoot and on horseback; they touched ground which no white men had ever set foot on before, not even the intrepid Spaniards.

So far as is known, the only human beings who had been here before were the Esselen Indians, a tribe of low culture which had subsisted in nomadic fasion. They spoke a language having no connection with that of other tribes in California or elsewhere in America. When the padres came to Monterey, around 1770, these Indians spoke of an ancient city called Excelen of which no vestiges have ever been found.

But perhaps I should first explain where the Big Sur region is located. It begins not far north of the Little Sur River (Malpaso Creek) and extends southward as far as Lucia, which, like Big Sur, is just a pin point on the map. Eastward from the coast it stretches to the Salinas Valley. Roughly, the Big Sur country comprises an area two or three times the size of Andorra.

Big Sur has a climate of its own and a character all its own. It is a region where extremes meet, a region where one is always conscious of weather, of space, of grandeur, and of eloquent silence. Among other things, it is the meeting place of migratory birds coming from north and south. It is said, in fact, that there is a greater variety of birds to be found in this region than in any other part of the United States. It is also the home of the redwoods; one encounters them on entering from the north and one leaves them on passing southward. At night one can still hear the coyote howling, and if one ventures beyond the first ridge of mountains one can meet up with mountain lions and other beasts of the wild. The grizzly bear is no longer to be found here, but the rattlesnake is still to be reckoned with. On a clear, bright day, when the blue of the sea rivals the blue of the sky, one sees the hawk, the eagle, the buzzard soaring above the still, hushed canyons. In summer, when the fogs roll in, one can look down upon a sea of clouds floating listlessly above the ocean; they have the appearance, at times, of huge iridescent soap bubbles, over which, now and then, may be seen a double rainbow. In January and February the hills are greenest, almost as green as the Emerald Isle. From November to February are the best months, the air fresh and invigorating, the skies clear, the sun still warm enough to take a sun bath.

From our perch, which is about a thousand feet above the sea, one can look up and down the coast a distance of twenty miles in either direction. The highway zigzags like the Grande Corniche. . . . It now forms part of the great international highway which will one day extend from the northern part of Alaska to Tierra del Fuego. By the time it is finished the automobile, like the mastodon, may be extinct. But the Big Sur will be here forever, and perhaps in the year A.D. 2,000 the population may still number only a few hundred souls. Perhaps, like Andorra and Monaco, it will become a Republic all its own. Perhaps the dread invaders will not come from other parts of this continent but from across the ocean, as the American aborigines are said to have come. And if they do, it will not be in boats or in airplanes.

And who can say when this region will once again be covered by the waters of the deep? Geologically speaking, it is not so long ago that it rose from the sea. Its mountain slopes are almost as treacherous as the icy sea in which, by the way, one scarcely ever sees a sail boat or a hardy swimmer, though one does occasionally spot a seal, an otter or a sperm whale. The sea, which looks so near and so tempting, is often difficult to reach. We know that the Conquistadores were unable to make their way along the coast, neither could they cut through the brush which covers the mountain slopes. An inviting land, but hard to conquer. It seeks to remain unspoiled, uninhabited by man.

Often, when following the trail which meanders over the hills, I pull myself up in an effort to encompass the glory and the grandeur which envelops the whole horizon. Often, when the clouds pile up in the north and the sea is churned with white caps, I say to myself: "This is the California that men dreamed of years ago, this is the Pacific that Balboa looked out on from the Peak of Darien, this is the face of the earth as the Creator intended it to look."

This little community of one, begun by the fabulous "outlander," Jaime de Angulo, has multiplied into a dozen families. The hill (Partington Ridge) is now nearing the saturation point, as things go in this part of the world. The one big difference between the Big Sur I encountered eleven years ago and that of today is the advent of so many new children. The mothers here seem to be as fecund as the soil. The little country school, situated not far from the State Park, has almost reached its capacity. It is the sort of school which, most unfortunately for our children, is rapidly disappearing from the American scene.

In another ten years we know not what may happen. If uranium or some other metal vital to the warmongers is discovered in these parts, Big Sur will be nothing but a legend.

Today Big Sur is no longer an outpost. The number of sightseers and visitors increases yearly. Emil White's "Big Sur Guide" alone brings swarms of tourists to our front door. What was inaugurated with virginal modesty threatens to end as a bonanza. The early settlers are dying off. Should their huge tracts of land be broken up into small holdings, Big Sur may rapidly develop into a suburb (of Monterey), with bus service, barbecue stands, gas stations, chain stores and all the odious claptrap that makes Suburbia horrendous.

This is a bleak view. It may be that we will be spared the usual horrors which accompany the tides of progress. Perhaps the millennium will be ushered in before we are taken over!

I like to think back to my early days on Partington Ridge,

[319]

when there was no electricity, no butane tanks, no refrigera-
tion—and the mail came only three times a week. In those
days, and even later when I returned to the Ridge, I managed
to get along without a car. To be sure, I did have a little cart
(such as children play with), which Emil White had knocked
together for me. Hitching myself to it, like an old billy goat,
I would patiently haul the mail and groceries up the hill, a
fairly steep climb of about a mile and a half. On reaching the
turn near the Roosevelts' driveway, I would divest myself of
everything but a jock-strap. What was to hinder?

The callers in those days were mostly youngsters just entering or just leaving the service. (They're doing the same
today, though the war ended '45.) The majority of these lads
were artists or would-be artists. Some stayed on, eking out
the weirdest sort of existence; some came back later to have a
serious go at it. They were all filled with a desire to escape the
horrors of the present and willing to live like rats if only they
might be left alone and in peace. What a strange lot they were,
when I think on it! Judson Crews of Waco, Texas, one of the
first to muscle in, reminded one—because of his shaggy beard
and manner of speech—of a latter-day prophet. He lived almost exclusively on peanut butter and wild mustard greens,
and neither smoked nor drank. Norman Mini, who had already had an unusual career, starting as in Poe's case with his
dismissal from West Point, stayed on (with wife and child)
long enough to finish a first novel—the best first novel I have
ever read and, as yet, unpublished. Norman was "different"
in that, though poor as a church mouse, he clung to his
cellar, which contained some of the finest wines (native and
foreign) anyone could wish for. And then there was Walker
Winslow, who was then writing *If a Man Be Mad*, which
turned out to be a best seller. Walker wrote at top speed, and
seemingly without interruption, in a tiny shack by the roadside
which Emil White had built to house the steady stream of

[320]

stragglers who were forever busting in on him for a day, a week, a month or a year.

In all, almost a hundred painters, writers, dancers, sculptors and musicians have come and gone since I first arrived. At least a dozen possessed genuine talent and may leave their mark on the world. . . .

Almost every art colony owes its inception to the longing of a mature artist who felt the need to break with the clique surrounding him. The location chosen was usually an ideal one, particularly to the discoverer who had spent the better years of his life in dingy holes and garrets. The would-be artists, for whom place and atmosphere are all important, always contrive to convert these havens of retreat into boisterous, merry-making colonies. Whether this will happen to Big Sur remains to be seen. Fortunately there are certain deterrents.

It is my belief that the immature artist seldom thrives in idyllic surroundings. What he seems to need, though I am the last to advocate it, is more first-hand experience of life—more bitter experience, in other words. In short, more struggle, more privation, more anguish, more disillusionment. These goads or stimulants he may not always hope to find here in Big Sur. Here, unless he is on his guard, unless he is ready to wrestle with phantoms as well as bitter realities, he is apt to go to sleep mentally and spiritually. If an art colony is established here it will go the way of all the others. Artists never thrive in colonies. Ants do. What the budding artist needs is the privilege of wrestling with his problems in solitude—and now and then a piece of red meat. . . .

In addition to all the other problems he has to cope with, the artist has to wage a perpetual struggle to fight free. I mean, find a way out of the senseless grind which daily threatens to annihilate all incentive. Even more than other mortals, he has need of harmonious surroundings. As writer or painter, he can

[321]

do his work most anywhere. The rub is that wherever living is cheap, wherever nature is inviting, it is almost impossible to find the means of acquiring that bare modicum which is needed to keep body and soul together. A man with talent has to make his living on the side or do his creative work on the side. A difficult choice!

If he has the luck to find an ideal spot, or an ideal community, it does not follow that his work will there receive the encouragement he so desperately needs. On the contrary he will probably find that no one is interested in what he is doing. He will generally be looked upon as strange or different. And he *will* be, of course, since what makes him tick is that mysterious element "X" which his fellow-man seems so well able to do without. He is almost certain to eat, talk, dress in a fashion eccentric to his neighbors. Which is quite enough to mark him out for ridicule, contempt and isolation. If, by taking a humble job, he demonstrates that he is as good as the next man, the situation may be somewhat ameliorated. But not for long. To prove that he is "as good as the next man" means little or nothing to one who is an artist. It was his "otherness" which made him an artist and, given the chance, he will make his fellow-man other too. Sooner or later, in one way or another, he is bound to rub his neighbors the wrong way. Unlike the ordinary fellow, he will throw everything to the winds when the urge seizes him. Moreover, if he *is* an artist, he will be compelled to make sacrifices which worldly people find absurd and unnecessary. In following the inner light he will inevitably choose for his boon companion poverty. And, if he has in him the makings of a great artist, he may renounce everything, even his art. This, to the average citizen, particularly the good citizen, is preposterous and unthinkable. Thus it happens now and then that, failing to recognize the genius in a man, a most worthy, a most respected, member of society may be heard to say: "Beware of that chap, he's up to no good!"

The world being what it is, I give it as my candid opinion that anyone who knows how to work with his two hands, anyone who is willing to give a fair day's work for a fair day's pay, would be better off to abandon his art and settle down to a humdrum life in an out of the way place like this. It may indeed be the highest wisdom to elect to be a nobody in a relative paradise such as this rather than a celebrity in a world which has lost all sense of values. But this is a problem which is rarely settled in advance.

There is one young man in this community who seems to have espoused the kind of wisdom I refer to. He is a man with an independent income, a man of keen intelligence, well educated, sensitive, of excellent character, and capable not only with his hands but with brain and heart. In making a life for himself he has apparently chosen to do nothing more than raise a family, provide its members with what he can, and enjoy the life of day to day. He does everything single-handed, from erecting buildings to raising crops, making wine, and so on. At intervals he hunts or fishes, or just takes off into the wilderness to commune with nature. To the average man he would appear to be just another good citizen, except that he is of better physique than most, enjoys better health, has no vices and no trace of the usual neuroses. His library is an excellent one, and he is at home in it; he enjoys good music and listens to it frequently. He can hold his own at any sport or game, can vie with the toughest when it comes to hard work, and in general is what might be called "a good fellow," that is, a man who knows how to mix with others, how to get along with the world. But what he also knows and does, and what the average citizen cannot or will not do, is to enjoy solitude, to live simply, to crave nothing, and to share what he has when called upon. I refrain from mentioning his name for fear of doing him a disservice. Let us leave him where he is, Mr. X, a master of the anonymous life and a wonderful example to his fellow-man....

[323]

Voyage en Icarie (By Fernand Rude, *sous-préfet* of Vienne.) is the account of two workers from Vienne (France) who came to America just a hundred years ago to join Étienne Cabet's experimental colony at Nauvoo, Illinois. The description given of American life, not only at Nauvoo but in the cities they passed through—they arrived at New Orleans and left by way of New York—is worth reading today, if only to observe how essentially unchanged is our American way of life. To be sure, Whitman was giving us about this same time (in his prose works) a similar picture of vulgarity, violence and corruption, in high and low places. One fact stands out, however, and that is the inborn urge of the American to experiment, to try out the most crack-brained schemes having to do with social, economic, religious and even sex relations. Where sex and religion were dominant, the most amazing results were achieved. The Oneida Community (New York), for example, is destined to remain as memorable an experiment as Robert Owen's in New Harmony (Indiana). As for the Mormons, nothing comparable to their efforts has ever been undertaken on this continent, and probably never will again.

In all these idealistic ventures, particularly those initiated by religious communities, the participants seemed to possess a keen sense of reality, a practical wisdom, which in no way conflicted (as it does in the case of ordinary Christians) with their religious views. They were honest, law-abiding, industrious, self-sustaining, self-sufficient citizens with character, individuality and integrity, somewhat corroded (to· our present way of thinking) by a Puritan sobriety and austerity, but never lacking in faith, courage and independence. Their influence on American thought, American behavior, has been most powerful.

Since living here in Big Sur I have become more and more aware of this tendency in my fellow-American to experi-

[324]

ment. Today it is not communities or groups who seek to lead "the good life" but isolated individuals. The majority of these, at least from my observation, are young men who have already had a taste of professional life, who have already been married and divorced, who have already served in the armed forces and seen a bit of the world, as we say. Utterly disillusioned, this new breed of experimenter is resolutely turning his back on all that he once held true and viable and is making a valiant effort to start anew. Starting anew, for this type, means leading a vagrant's life, tackling anything, clinging to nothing, reducing one's needs and one's desires, and eventually—out of a wisdom born of desperation—leading the life of an artist. Not, however, the type of artist we are familiar with. An artist, rather, whose sole interest is in creating, an artist who is indifferent to reward, fame, success. One, in short, who is reconciled from the outset to the fact that the better he is the less chance he has of being accepted at face value. These young men, usually in their late twenties or early thirties, are now roaming about in our midst like anonymous messengers from another planet. By force of example, by reason of their thoroughgoing nonconformity and, shall I say, "nonresistance," they are proving themselves a more potent, stimulating force than the most eloquent and vociferous of recognized artists.

The point to note is that these individuals are not concerned with undermining a vicious system but with leading their own lives—on the fringe of society. It is only natural to find them gravitating toward places like Big Sur, of which there are many replicas in this vast country. We are in the habit of speaking of the "last frontier," but wherever there are "individuals" there will always be new frontiers. For the man who wants to lead the good life, which is a way of saying *his own life*, there is always a spot where he can dig in and take root.

[325]

But what is it that these young men have discovered, and which, curiously enough, links them with their forebears who deserted Europe for America? That the American way of life is an illusory kind of existence, that the price demanded for the security and abundance it pretends to offer is too great. The presence of these "renegades," small in number though they be, is but another indication that the machine is breaking down. When the smashup comes, as now seems inevitable, they are more likely to survive the catastrophe than the rest of us. At least, they will know how to get along without cars, without refrigerators, without vacuum cleaners, electric razors and all the other "indispensables" . . . probably even without money. If ever we are to witness a new heaven and a new earth, it must surely be one in which money is absent, forgotten, wholly useless.

Ozymandias, The Utopia That Failed

By ALDOUS HUXLEY

Born in England in 1894, Huxley has resided principally in Southern California since the late 1930's. His many important novels include *Point Counter Point* (1928), *Brave New World* (1932), and the Los Angeles novel *After Many a Summer Dies the Swan* (1940). It has been suggested by David Daiches that Huxley's "real genius is as an essayist"; and he is represented here by one of his many California essays.

In this part of the desert Ozymandias consists of an abandoned silo and the ruins of a cow byre. "The hands that mocked"—mocked themselves in the very act of so laboriously creating these poor things—were the hands of a thousand idealists; "the heart that fed" belonged to a Marxist lawyer, with a Gladstone collar and the face of a revivalist or a Shakespearean actor. Job Harriman was his name; and if the McNamara brothers had not unexpectedly confessed to the dynamiting of the *Times* building, he would in all probability have become the first Socialist mayor of Los Angeles. But with that confession, his passionately defended clients ceased to be proletarian martyrs and became the avowed killers of twenty-six unfortunate printers and newspapermen. Job Harriman's chance of winning the election abruptly declined to zero. Another man would have admitted defeat. Not Harriman. If Los Angeles would not have him as its mayor, he would go out into the wilderness and there create a new, better city of his own. On May Day, 1914, the Llano del Rio Co-operative Colony (incorporated first in California and later under the more easy-going laws of Nevada) received its first contingent of settlers.

Three years later, in the *Llano View Book*, an anonymous

enthusiast wrote of the event with a mixture of biblical and patriotic solemnity. "May first, 1914, a hardy little band of pioneers, likened unto those who courageously founded the Plymouth Colony in Massachusetts so many years ago, went forth into the Antelope Valley to found another Colony, destined through the years to be quite as historical and quite as significant of the founding of a New Civilization." And this May Day promise had already been fulfilled. "The success of complete cooperation has now been demonstrated convincingly. The demonstration is the most thorough that can be asked for." The colony is now "too firmly established to be affected by anything except a concerted and organized effort backed by Capital. Its future is clear." These words were penned and printed, at the Llano publishing house, in the summer of 1917. Before the year was out, that clear future was a thing of the past. The company was bankrupt, the colonists had dispersed. Within twenty-four hours of their departure playful iconoclasts had smashed five hundred dollars' worth of windows; within a week, a large frame hotel and several scores of houses and workshops had been demolished and carried off piecemeal by the homesteaders who precariously represented capitalism in the wilderness. Only the silo and the foundations of the cow byre remained; they were made of concrete and could not be hauled away.

> Round the decay
> Of that collossal wreck, boundless and bare,
> The lone and level sands stretch far away.

A more squeamish artist than Shelley would have avoided the reduplication of those alliterative epithets. "Boundless and bare," "lone and level"—one is reminded of a passage in Lewis Carroll's versified essay on poetic diction: "The wild man went his weary way to a strange and lonely pump." But the general effect, albeit a little cheap, is dramatically good and even sufficiently true, despite the fact that the sands hereabouts are neither bare nor indefinitely level. A few miles south of Ozymandias the desert tilts upwards to a range of wooded and, in winter, snow-covered mountains. To the north stretches a plain; but its levels are dotted with isolated buttes and rimmed, in the far distance, by other ranges of mountains. And over all the ground spreads the thin carpet of those astonishingly numerous plants and bushes which have learned to adapt themselves to a land where it rains eight or nine inches during the winter and not at all from May to November.

To the brute facts of meteorology in arid country Job Harriman was resolutely indifferent. When he thought of human affairs, he thought of them only as a Socialist, never as a naturalist. Thus, with a population of only three hundred thousand, Los Angeles was already becoming uncomfortably dry. But because its water would enrich the real-estate operators, Job Harriman opposed the construction of the Owens Valley Aqueduct. Worse, he rationalized his opposition by the obviously absurd statement that the city could grow indefinitely on its local resources. The same ill-informed optimism made nonsense of his plan for Llano. In a good year (and every other year is bad) water from the Big Rock Creek makes possible the raising, at Llano, of crops and cattle worth perhaps a hundred thousand dollars. The Colony owned rights to part of this water. On its irrigated acres fifty or, at the most, a hundred persons might have eked out a precarious living. But by the beginning of 1917 Harriman had accepted the applications of almost a thousand eager co-operators. Every applicant had to buy two thousand shares of the company's stock, for which he was to pay five hundred, or preferably a thousand, dollars in cash, and the balance in labor. In a year or two, it was assumed, the Colony would be self-sufficient; until then, it would have to live on the cash invested by its members.

[329]

For as long as the cash lasted, times were good, enthusiasm high and achievement correspondingly great. A wagon road was driven through the foothills, up into the timberland of the San Gabriel Mountains. Trees were felled and laboriously brought down to the sawmill in the plain, below. A quarry was opened, a lime kiln constructed. The tents of the first colonists gave place to shacks, the shacks to houses. Next a hotel was built, to accommodate the interested visitors from the infernal regions of capitalism. Schools and workshops appeared as though by magic. Irrigation ditches were dug and lined. Eighty horses and a steam tractor cleared, leveled, plowed and harvested. Fruit trees were planted, pears canned, alfalfa cut and stored, cows milked and "the West's most modern rabbitry" established. Nor were the spiritual needs of the colonists neglected. From the print shop issued two weekly newspapers and a stream of pamphlets. Among the amenities were a woman's exchange, a Socialist local, several quartets, two orchestras, a brass band and a mandolin club.

One of the old-timers has often talked to me nostalgically of that brass band, those mandolins and barber-shop ensembles. What pleasure, on a mild night in May or June, to sit out of doors under one's privately owned cottonwood tree and listen, across a mile of intervening sagebrush, to the music of Socialists! The moon is full, the last snow still glitters on the summit of Mount Baden Powell and, to the accompaniment of the steady croaking of frogs along the irrigation ditch and the occasional frantic shrieks of the coyotes, the strains of Sousa and "Sweet Adeline" and the Unfinished Symphony transcribed for mandolins and saxophone, come stealing with extraordinary distinctness upon the ear. Only Edward Lear can do full justice to such an occasion. It must have been, in the very highest degree, "meloobious and genteel." But, alas, every magical night is succeeded by yet another busy morning. The *al fresco* concert was delightful; but that did not make it any easier to collect, next day, from the communal treasury. As well as the mandolins, my old-timer friend recalls his efforts to get paid for services rendered. After long haggling he would think himself lucky if he came away with two dollars in silver and the rest in hay or pumpkins.

For most of the co-operators, the morning after a concert was less disillusioning. I have met three or four ex-colonists—older, sadder, possibly wiser—and all of them bore witness to the happiness of those first months at Llano. Housing, to be sure, was inadequate; food monotonous, and work extremely hard. But there was a sense of shared high purpose, a sustaining conviction that one had broken out of an age-old prison and was marching, shoulder to shoulder with loyal comrades, towards a promised land. "Bliss was it in that dawn to be alive." And this applies to all dawns without distinction—the dawn of a war and the dawn of a peace, the dawn of revolution and the dawn of reaction, the dawn of passion and in due course the blessed coolness of the dawn of indifference, the dawn of marriage and then, at Reno, the long awaited dawn of divorce. In cooperative communities dawns are peculiarly rosy. For this very reason, midday is apt to seem peculiarly stifling, and the afternoons intolerable and interminable. To the ordinary hazards of community life Llano added the insurmountable obstacles of too many people, too little water and, after three years, no money.

As the situation grew worse, the propagandists became more lyrical. "Llano offers hope and inspiration for the masses. . . .Its purpose is to solve unemployment, to assure safety and comfort for the future and old age." And the words were accompanied by a detailed plan of the city which was just about to be built. "It will be different in design from any other in the world. Its houses will be comfortable, sanitary, handsome, home-like, modern and harmonious with their surroundings, and will insure greater privacy than any other houses

[331]

ever constructed. They are unique and designed especially for Llano." The publicity worked. Applications and, more important, checks kept steadily coming in. With each arrival of an idealist's life savings, there was a respite. But a respite at a price. For with those life-savings came another member and his family. The Colony had acquired three days' supply of food, but it had also acquired five extra mouths. Each successive windfall went a little less far. And meanwhile our old friend, Human Nature, was busily at work.

In his office and in court Harriman was a successful attorney. Outside he was an idealist and theorizer, whose knowledge was not of men and women but of sociological abstractions and the more or less useful fictions of economics.

In a preface which he contributed in 1924 to Ernest Wooster's *Communities Past and Present* Harriman writes, (how touchingly!) about his self-imposed ignorance and subsequent enlightenment. "Believing that life arose out of chemical action and that form was determined by the impinging environment. I naturally believed that all would react more or less alike to the same environment." But in fact they didn't. Against all the rules, "we found more well-to-do-men among the unselfish than there were among the selfish." Worse still, "we found to our surprise that there were more selfish men among the poor in proportion to their number, than there were among the well-to-do. . . ." Worst and most unexpected was the fact that the selfish "persisted in their course with a persistence that was amazing." From amazement the poor man passed to downright "confusion" at the discovery that there are "those who are extremely active (in the work of the Colony) and yet who are also extremely selfish. If their behavior is closely observed, they will invariably be found to be working for self-glory or for power." These discoveries of the immemorially obvious led him to two conclusions, whose extremely unoriginal character is the guarantee of their soundness. First, "theories and intellectual concepts play a very small part in our reactions." And, second, "economic determination seems to play no part in separating the sheep from the goats." In the process of reaching these conclusions, Job Harriman had to pass through ten years of an excruciatingly educative purgatory.

No effort had been made to exclude from Llano the sort of people whose presence is fatal to any close-knit community, and there was no system of rules by which, having been admitted, such persons might be controlled. From the first Harriman found himself confronted by a cantankerous minority of troublemakers. There were the idealistic purists, who complained that he was making too many compromises with the devils of capitalism; there were the malingerers, who criticized but refused to work; there were the greedy, with their clamor for special privileges; there were the power lovers who envied him and were ambitious to take his place. Meeting secretly in the desert, the "brush gang," as these malcontents were called, plotted his overthrow. It came at last at the hands of a trusted lieutenant who, in Harriman's absence, disposed of the Llano property to private owners—including, in a big way, himself. But, long before this final catastrophe, there had been nothing to eat, and the majority of the colonists had returned, without their savings, to the world of free competition. A few, under Harriman's leadership, migrated in a special train to Louisiana, where they had collectively bought an abandoned lumber camp and several thousand denuded acres. There was another blissful dawn, followed by a prolonged struggle with a hundred ferocious Texans, who had been invited to join the community, but had not, apparently, been told that it was a co-operative. When these extremely rugged individualists had gone, taking with them most of the Colony's livestock and machinery, the survivors settled down to the dismal realities of life on an inadequate economic foundation. Work was hard, and for diversion there were only the weekly dances, the intrigues of several

[333]

rival brush gangs and the spectacle of the struggle for power between the ailing Harriman and an ex-insurance salesman of boundless energy, called George T. Pickett. By 1924, Harriman was out—for good.

The new manager was one of those "born leaders," who have no patience with democratic methods and are seriously convinced that they always know best. "I'd rather work with a bunch of morons than with a lot of over-educated kickers." But the colonists—or at least some of them—refused to accept his benevolent dictatorship. Brush gangs bored from within; heretics and seceders campaigned from without. From the neighboring town of Leesville two dissident and mutually hostile groups bombarded the loyalists with anonymous letters and denounced the management and, of course, one another in any left-wing paper that would print their articles.

And all the time New Llano was as far as ever from self-sufficiency. The Colony could boast of no less than thirty-eight industrial and agricultural departments. But all of them, unfortunately, were running at a loss. The only solid asset was Pickett's incomparable salesmanship; the only steady source of income, his far-ranging drives for funds. Through the years a trickle of money flowed in—never quite enough to buy the colonists new shoes, but sufficient at least to prevent actual starvation. In the thirties wildcatters persuaded the management that there was oil on the colony's property. A number of idealists were talked into a speculative investment, and three wells were drilled. Needless to say, all of them were dry.

Then came the Revolution. While Pickett was away, soliciting Federal funds at Washington, his enemies called a meeting of the entire membership. By a majority vote of the minority who attended, Pickett was deposed. For the dominant brush gang and its supporters, what a blissful dawn! For the rest, it looked like the midnight of all hope. The author of a rare little book, *The Crisis in Llano Colony, An Epic Story*, belonged to the second group. To express his feelings about Pickett, mere prose seemed inadequate. The history of the conspiracy culminates in a lyric.

> He came from out the Land of Graft
>   To lend a hand to Llano,
> Its industry and handicraft,
>   And added to its cargo.
>
> He quit the struggle in the bog,
>   Where devil take the hindmost,
> He left the realm where dog eat dog,
>   With Equity his guide-post.
>
> A better life the world to show,
>   A work he tires of never,
> While men may come and men may go,
>   Will he go on forever.

"Forever" was perhaps a little too optimistic. But the fact remains that, in due course, George T. Pickett did come back to Llano. In his *Can We Co-operate?* Bob Brown prints a letter from one of the surviving colonists, dated November, 1937. "Things in hell of a shape here. No food for the past week but sweet potatoes, and darn small ones at that. . . . No electricity for two months, and I buy plenty kerosene. . . . Very little money coming in, and what little there is Pickett takes it for his own use. Seems to think everything belongs to him. . . . Lots of people pretty mad here since Pickett took over again. . . . I expect few people on the outside would believe the truth about this place. Just try and tell some of those old friends, who sent money in through *The Colonist*, that one works 365 days a year in this Socialist paradise, then supplies one's own clothes, most of one's own food, light, etc., and they might say one was a liar."

Two years later it was finished. All the Colony property

had been sold up, and the colonists (most of them old people who had invested their savings and their work in Llano for the sake of security in their declining years) were on relief. All that remained, after twenty-five years of idealistic struggle, was a small brick hotel and a recreation hall.

> And on the pedestal these words appear:
> "My name is Ozymandias, king of kings:
> Look on my work, ye Mighty, and despair!"

But *despair* is only the penultimate word, never the last. The last word is *realism*—the acceptance of facts as they present themselves, the facts of nature and of human nature, and the primordial fact of that spirit which transcends them both and yet is in all things. The original Ozymandias was no realist; nor was poor Mr. Harriman. In the conditions prevailing at Llano and, later, at New Llano, integral co-operation was as fatally condemned to self-destruction as are, in any circumstances, the ambitions of a king of kings. Fortunately, unrealistic co-operation does no harm except to the co-operators. Unrealistic imperialism, on the other hand, cannot commit suicide without inflicting misery and death upon innumerable victims.

The economic problems of community living can be solved by any group possessed of common sense and capital. The psychological problems are much more difficult and demand, for their solution, something rarer than either cash or shrewdness.

Life in a community is life in a crowd—the same old crowd, day in, day out. At Llano the colonists divided mankind into two groups—themselves and people "on the outside." The same distinction, in the same words, is made by convicts. "On the inside" are we; "on the outside" lies the whole wide world. Of those nineteenth-century American communities which survived long enough to rear a second generation of co-operators, few were able to resist the impact of the bicycle.

[336]

Mounted on a pair of wheels, the young people were able to explore that unredeemed but fascinating world "on the outside." After each expedition, it was with mounting reluctance that they returned to the all too familiar crowd. In the end reluctance hardened into refusal. They went out one day and never came back.

The attraction of life "on the outside" can be counteracted in several ways. Shared religious faith is helpful, but not, of itself, enough. One can believe as the others believe, and yet detest the sight of them. "*Ave Virgo!*—Gr-rr—you swine!" Browning's fictional soliloquist is echoed, more decorously, by such real and historical figures as the saintly Dame Gertrude More. "Living in religion (as I can speak by experience), if one is not in a right course of prayer and other exercises between God and our soul, one's nature groweth much worse than it would have been if one had lived in the world." It grows worse because there is no escape from the objects of one's unreasoned abhorrence. "On the outside," we are constantly imitating the conduct of the Old Man in the limerick, "who purchased a steed, which he rode at full speed, to escape from the people of Basing." "On the inside," be it of Alcatraz, of Llano, of a cloister, there are no steeds; and unless they can learn the difficult art of being charitable, the inmates of such penal, socialistic or religious colonies will find themselves condemned to a life sentence of boredom, distaste and loathing. Vows, rules and a hierarchy can forcibly constrain a man to remain in his community. Only "a course of prayer, by which the soul turneth towards God and learneth from Him the lesson of truly humbling itself," can soften his heart to the point where it becomes susceptible of loving even his exasperating brothers.

At Llano shared religious faith was replaced, less effectively, by a vague Pickwickian belief that, thanks to Socialism, everything would be much better in the twenty-second century. "You've got to get up on some private hill to view the future.

I've been on this job ten years, and there has been some real progress. But when I'm overwhelmed by the ugliness, the seemingly useless struggle of it all, I just climb up my hill and see the whole place as it should be."

More effective, as a binding force, than religious or Utopian belief, is the presence among the faithful of some dominant and fascinating personality. These are the human magnets, in relation to whom ordinary men and women behave like iron filings. Their attractive power is hard to analyze and explain. Impressiveness of appearance and high intelligence are sometimes present, but not invariably. A glittering eye, a mysterious manner, a disconcerting fluctuation between remoteness and concern—these are never amiss. A gift of the gab is useful, and becomes quite invaluable when combined with the right kind of voice—the kind of voice which seems to act directly on the autonomic nervous system and the subconscious mind. Finally, indispensably, there is the will of iron, there is the unswerving tenacity of purpose, the boundless self-confidence—all the qualities which are so conspicuously absent in the common run of anxious, bewildered and vacillating humanity. A community having capital, sound management and a leader possessed of magnetic qualities can hardly fail to survive.

Unfortunately (or rather, thank God!) the magnetic leader is not immortal. When his current is turned off, the iron filings fly apart, and yet another experiment in integral co-operation is at an end.

Is there any reason, someone may ask, why it should ever have been begun? For the Marxist, a religious community is anathema and a secular co-operative colony represents no more than"a working-class form of escape, corresponding to the white-collar boy's flight to Montparnasse." For the capitalist, any kind of integral co-operation is a gratuitous absurdity which might, if it worked too well, become dangerously subversive. But for anyone who is interested in human beings and their so largely unrealized potentialities, even the silliest experiment has value, if only as demonstrating what ought not to be done. And many of the recorded experiments were far from silly. Well planned and carried out with skill and intelligence, some of them have contributed significantly to our knowledge of that most difficult and most important of all the arts—the art of living together in harmony and with benefit for all concerned. Thus, the Shakers cultivated the sense of togetherness by means of the sacramental dance, through collective "speaking with tongues" and in spiritualistic séances, at which mediumship was free to all. The Perfectionists practiced mutual criticism—a drastic form of group therapy which often worked wonders, not only for neurotics, but even for the physically sick. Sex is "the lion of the tribe of human passions"; to tame the lion, John Humphrey Noyes devised, and for thirty years his community at Oneida put into effect, a system of "Complex Marriage," based upon "Male Continence." Separated, by means of a carefully inculcated technique, from propagation, the "amative function" was refined, taught good manners, reconciled with Protestant Christianity and made to serve the purpose of religious self-transcendence. "Amativeness," Noyes could truthfully write, "is conquered and civilized among us." A similar conquest had been achieved, in India, by those Tantrik prophets, in whom the world-affirming spirit of the Vedas had come to terms, through sacramentalism, with the world-denying spirit of Jainism, Yoga and early Buddhism. In the West, however, Noyes's experiment stands alone—not indeed in its intention (for many before him had tried to do the same thing), but in the realistic and therefore successful way it was carried out. The members of the Oneida Community seem to have been happier, healthier, better behaved and more genuinely religious than most of their contemporaries "on the outside." That they should have been forced, under the threat of ecclesiastical persecution, to abandon their experiment is a real misfortune. The course of Freudian and post-Freudian psychology would have run a good deal more smoothly, if there had been a place, like Oneida, where theorists might have tested their frequently preposterous notions against the realities of a co-operating group, in which the lion no longer raged and a reconciliation between sex, religion and society was an accomplished fact.

Except in a purely negative way, the history of Llano is sadly uninstructive. All that it teaches is a series of don'ts. Don't pin your faith on a water supply which, for half the time, isn't there. Don't settle a thousand people on territory which cannot possibly support more than a hundred. Don't admit to your fellowship every Tom, Dick and Harry who may present himself. Don't imagine that a miscellaneous group can live together, in closest physical proximity, without rules, without shared beliefs, without private and public "spiritual exercises" and, without a magnetic leader. At Llano everything that ought not to have been done was systematically done. A pathetic little Ozymandias is all that remains to tell the tale.

From where I used to live, on the fringes of what had been the colony's land, this Ozymandias was the only visible trace of human handiwork. Gleaming in the morning light or against the enormous desert sunsets, that silo was like a Norman keep rising, against all the probabilities, from the sagebrush. *The splendour falls on castle walls. Childe Roland to the dark tower came*—came, and looking through the opening in the dark tower's wall, saw within a heap of tin cans, some waste paper and half a dozen empty bottles of Pepsi-Cola. The ruin stands very close to the highway and there are still a few motorists prepared, at a pinch, to walk a quarter of a mile.

But Ozymandias is not the only relic of the co-operative

past. Two or three miles to the southeast, on the almost ob-
literated wagon road over which the colonists once hauled
their timber from the mountains, is the Socialist cemetery.

It lies astride of the four-thousand-foot contour line, that
ecological frontier where the creosote bushes abruptly give
place to junipers, the Joshua trees to common yuccas. One
ancient and gigantic Joshua—the last outpost of the great
army of Joshuas encamped on the wide plains below the
foothills—stands like a sentinel on guard over the dead. In a
little tumbledown enclosure of wooden palings and chicken
wire three or four anonymous mounds have returned completely to the desert.

On what was once bare and weeded ground, the sage and
the buckwheat have taken root again and are flourishing as
though they had never been disturbed. Nearby a concrete
headstone commemorates someone who, to judge by his name,
must have been of Scandinavian origin. His epitaph is purely
quantitative, and all the inscription tells us is that he lived
sixty-eight years, seven months, four days and eleven hours.
The most pretentious of the tombs is a mausoleum in the form
of a hollow cube of cement. Entering through the broken door
one finds a slab, headstone and an incredible quantity of the
desiccated droppings of small rodents. The dance goes on. A
human pattern, made up of the patterns of patterns, is resolved into the simpler forms that are its elements. Another
vortex catches and draws them into itself. Patterns are built up
into patterns of a higher order, and for a few months a little
pattern of these patterns of patterns hurries, squeaking along
the rat roads.

Outside, the Joshua tree stands guard in the empty sunlight, in the almost supernatural silence. A monstrous yucca
at the limit of its natural habitat? A symbol within the cosmic
symbol? The eye travels out across the plain. The buttes are
like kneeling elephants and beyond them, far away, are the

blue ghosts of mountains. There is a coolness against the cheek, and from overhead comes the scaly rattling of the wind in the dead dry leaves of the Joshua tree. And suddenly the symbol is essentially the same as what it symbolizes; the monstrous yucca in the desert is at once a botanical specimen and the essential Suchness. What we shall all know, according to the *Barbo Thodol,* at the moment of Death may also be known by casual flashes, transfiguringly, while we inhabit this particular pattern of patterns. There is a consciousness of the Pure Truth, like a light "moving across the landscape in springtime in one continuous stream of vibration." Be not afraid. For this "is the radiance of your own true nature. Recognize it." And from out of this light comes "the natural sound of Reality reverberating like a thousand thunders." But, again, be not afraid. For this is the natural sound of your own real self—a thousand thunders which have their source in silence and in some inexpressible way are identical with silence.

Hook

By WALTER VAN TILBURG CLARK

Although born in Maine (1909), Clark has spent most of
his life in Nevada and California. His novels include
The City of Trembling Leaves (1945), *The Ox-Bow Incident* (1940), and *The Track of the Cat* (1949). He has
written poetry, worked as a teacher and editor, and produced a number of convincing short stories, some of
which were collected in a volume entitled *The Watchful Gods* (1950).

Hook, the hawk's child, was hatched in a dry spring
among the oaks beside the seasonal river, and was struck from
the nest early. In the drouth his single-willed parents had to
extend their hunting ground by more than twice, for the
ground creatures upon which they fed died and dried by the
hundreds. The range became too great for them to wish to return and feed Hook, and when they had lost interest in each
other they drove Hook down into the sand and brush and went
back to solitary courses over the bleaching hills.

Unable to fly yet, Hook crept over the ground, challenging all large movements with recoiled head, erected, rudi-
mentary wings, and the small rasp of his clattering beak. It
was during this time of abysmal ignorance and continual fear
that his eyes took on the first quality of a hawk, that of being
wide, alert and challenging. He dwelt, because of his helplessness, among the rattling brush which grew between the oaks
and the river. Even in his thickets and near the water, the
white sun was the dominant presence. Except in the dawn,
when the land wind stirred, or in the late afternoon, when
the sea wind became strong enough to penetrate the half-mile
inland to this turn in the river, the sun was the major force,
and everything was dry and motionless under it. The brush,

[343]

small plants and trees alike husbanded the little moisture at their hearts; the moving creatures waited for dark, when sometimes the sea fog came over and made a fine, soundless rain which relieved them.

The two spacious sounds of his life environed Hook at this time. One was the great rustle of the slopes of yellowed wild wheat, with over it the chattering rustle of the leaves of the California oaks, already as harsh and individually tremulous as in autumn. The other was the distant whisper of the foaming edge of the Pacific, punctuated by the hollow snoring of the waves. But these Hook did not yet hear, for he was attuned by fear and hunger to the small, spasmodic rustlings of live things. Dry, shrunken, and nearly starved, and with his plumage delayed, he snatched at beetles, dragging in the sand to catch them. When swifter and stronger birds and animals did not reach them first, which was seldom, he ate the small, silver fish left in the mud by the failing river. He watched, with nearly chattering beak, the quick, thin lizards pause, very alert, and raise and lower themselves, but could not catch them because he had to raise his wings to move rapidly, which startled them.

Only one sight and sound not of his world of microscopic necessity was forced upon Hook. That was the flight of the big gulls from the beaches, which sometimes, in squealing play, came spinning back over the foothills and the river bed. For some inherited reason, the big, ship-bodied birds did not frighten Hook, but angered him. Small and chewed-looking, with his wide, already yellowing eyes glaring up at them, he would stand in an open place on the sand in the sun and spread his shaping wings and clatter his bill like shaken dice. Hook was furious about the swift, easy passage of gulls.

His first opportunity to leave off living like a ground owl came accidentally. He was standing in the late afternoon in the red light under the thicket, his eyes half-filmed with drowse

[344]

and the stupefaction of starvation, when suddenly something beside him moved, and he struck, and killed a field mouse driven out of the wheat by thirst. It was a poor mouse, shriveled and lice ridden, but in striking, Hook had tasted blood, which raised nest memories and restored his nature. With started neck plumage and shining eyes, he tore and fed. When the mouse was devoured, Hook had entered hoarse adolescence. He began to seek with a conscious appetite, and to move more readily out of shelter. Impelled by the blood appetite, so glorious after his long preservation upon the flaky and bitter stuff of bugs, he ventured even into the wheat in the open sun beyond the oaks, and discovered the small trails and holes among the roots. With his belly often partially filled with flesh, he grew rapidly in strength and will. His eyes were taking on their final change, their yellow growing deeper and more opaque, their stare more constant, their challenge less desperate. Once during this transformation, he surprised a ground squirrel, and although he was ripped and wing-bitten and could not hold his prey, he was not dismayed by the conflict, but exalted. Even while the wing was still drooping and the pinions not grown back, he was excited by other ground squirrels and pursued them futilely, and was angered by their dusty escapes. He realized that his world was a great arena for killing, and felt the magnificence of it.

The two major events of Hook's young life occurred in the same day. A little after dawn he made the customary essay and succeeded in flight. A little before sunset, he made his first sustained flight of over two hundred yards, and at its termination struck and slew a great buck squirrel whose thrashing and terrified gnawing and squealing gave him a wild delight. When he had gorged on the strong meat, Hook stood upright, and in his eyes was the stare of the hawk, never flagging in intensity but never swelling beyond containment. After that the stare had only to grow more deeply challenging and

[345]

more sternly controlled as his range and deadliness increased. There was no change in kind. Hook had mastered the first of the three hungers which are fused into the single, flaming will of a hawk, and he had experienced the second.

The third and consummating hunger did not awaken in Hook until the following spring, when the exultation of space had grown slow and steady in him, so that he swept freely with the wind over the miles of coastal foothills, circling, and ever in sight of the sea, and used without struggle the warm currents lifting from the slopes, and no longer desired to scream at the range of his vision, but intently sailed above his shadow swiftly climbing to meet him on the hillsides, sinking away and rippling across the brush-grown canyons.

That spring the rains were long, and Hook sat for hours, hunched and angry under their pelting, glaring into the fogs of the river valley, and killed only small, drenched things flooded up from their tunnels. But when the rains had dissipated, and there were sun and sea wind again, the game ran plentiful, the hills were thick and shining green, and the new river flooded about the boulders where battered turtles climbed up to shrink and sleep. Hook then was scorched by the third hunger. Ranging farther, often forgetting to kill and eat, he sailed for days with growing rage, and woke at night clattering on his dead tree limb, and struck and struck and struck at the porous wood of the trunk, tearing it away. After days, in the draft of a coastal canyon miles below his own hills, he came upon the acrid taint he did not know but had expected, and sailing down it, felt his neck plumes rise and his wings quiver so that he swerved unsteadily. He saw the unmated female perched upon the tall and jagged stump of a tree that had been shorn by storm, and he stooped, as if upon game. But she was older than he, and wary of the gripe of his importunity, and banked off screaming, and he screamed also at the intolerable delay.

[346]

At the head of the canyon, the screaming pursuit was crossed by another male with a great wing-spread, and the light golden in the fringe of his plumage. But his more skillful opening played him false against the ferocity of the twice-balked Hook. His rising maneuver for position was cut short by Hook's wild, upward swoop, and at the blow he raked desperately and tumbled off to the side. Dropping, Hook struck him again, struggled to clutch, but only raked and could not hold, and, diving, struck once more in passage, and then beat up, yelling triumph, and saw the crippled antagonist side-slip away, half-tumble once, as the ripped wing failed to balance, then steady and glide obliquely into the cover of brush on the canyon side. Beating hard and stationary in the wind above the bush that covered his competitor, Hook waited an instant, but when the bush was still, screamed again, and let himself go off with the current, reseeking, infuriated by the burn of his own wounds, the thin choke-thread of the acrid taint.

On a hilltop projection of stone two miles inland, he struck her down, gripping her rustling body with his talons, beating her wings down with his wings, belting her head when she whimpered or thrashed, and at last clutching her neck with his hook and, when her coy struggles had given way to stillness, succeeded.

In the early summer, Hook drove the three young ones from their nest, and went back to lone circling above his own range. He was complete.

2

Throughout that summer and the cool, growthless weather of the winter, when the gales blew in the river canyon and the ocean piled upon the shore, Hook was master of the sky and the hills of his range. His flight became a lovely and certain thing, so that he played with the treacherous currents of the air with a delicate ease surpassing that of the gulls. He could sail for hours, searching the blanched grasses below him with telescopic eyes, gaining height against the wind, descending in mile-long, gently declining swoops when he curved and rode back, and never beating either wing. At the swift passage of his shadow within their vision, gophers, ground squirrels and rabbits froze, or plunged gibbering into their tunnels beneath matted turf. Now, when he struck, he killed easily in one hard-knuckled blow. Occasionally, in sport, he soared up over the river and drove the heavy and weaponless gulls downstream again, until they would no longer venture inland.

There was nothing which Hook feared now, and his spirit was wholly belligerent, swift and sharp, like his gaze. Only the mixed smells and incomprehensible activities of the people at the Japanese farmer's home, inland of the coastwise highway and south of the bridge across Hook's river, troubled him. The smells were strong, unsatisfactory and never clear, and the people, though they behaved foolishly, constantly running in and out of their built-up holes, were large, and appeared capable, with fearless eyes looking up at him, so that he instinctively swerved aside from them. He cruised over their yard, their gardens, and their bean fields, but he would not alight close to their buildings.

But this one area of doubt did not interfere with his life. He ignored it, save to look upon it curiously as he crossed, his afternoon shadow sliding in an instant over the chicken-and-crate-cluttered yard, up the side of the unpainted barn, and then out again smoothly, just faintly, liquidly rippling over the furrows and then over the stubble of the grazing slopes. When the season was dry, and the dead earth blew on the fields, he extended his range to satisfy his great hunger, and again narrowed it when the fields were once more alive with the minute movements he could not only see but anticipate.

Four times that year he was challenged by other hawks blowing up from behind the coastal hills to scud down his slopes, but two of these he slew in midair, and saw hurtle down to thump on the ground and lie still while he circled, and a third, whose wing he tore, he followed closely to earth and beat to death in the grass, making the crimson jet out from its breast and neck into the pale wheat. The fourth was a strong flier and experienced fighter, and theirs was a long, running battle, with brief, rising flurries of striking and screaming, from which down and plumage soared off.

Here, for the first time, Hook felt doubts, and at moments wanted to drop away from the scoring, burning talons and the twisted hammer strokes of the strong beak, drop away shrieking, and take cover and be still. In the end, when Hook, having outmaneuvered his enemy and come above him, wholly in control, and going with the wind, tilted and plunged for the death rap, the other, in desperation, threw over on his back and struck up. Talons locked, beaks raking, they dived earthward. The earth grew and spread under them amazingly, and they were not fifty feet above it when Hook, feeling himself turning toward the underside, tore free and beat up again on heavy, wrenched wings. The other, stroking swiftly, and so close to down that he lost wing plumes to a bush, righted himself and planed up, but flew on lumberingly between the hills and did not return. Hook screamed the triumph, and made a brief pretense of pursuit, but was glad to return, slow and victorious, to his dead tree.

In all these encounters Hook was injured, but experienced only the fighter's pride and exultation from the sting of wounds received in successful combat. And in each of them he learned new skill. Each time the wounds healed quickly, and left him a more dangerous bird.

In the next spring, when the rains and the night chants of the little frogs were past, the third hunger returned upon Hook with a new violence. In this quest, he came into the taint of a young hen. Others too were drawn by the unnerving perfume, but only one of them, the same with which Hook had fought his great battle, was a worthy competitor. This hunter drove off two, while two others, game but neophytes, were glad enough that Hook's impatience would not permit him to follow and kill. Then the battle between the two champions fled inland, and was a tactical marvel, but Hook lodged the neck-breaking blow, and struck again as they dropped past the tree-tops. The blood had already begun to pool on the gray, fallen foliage as Hook flapped up between branches, too spent to cry his victory. Yet his hunger would not let him rest until, late in the second day, he drove the female to ground among the laurels of a strange river canyon.

When the two fledglings of this second brood had been driven from the nest, and Hook had returned to his own range, he was not only complete, but supreme. He slept without concealment on his bare limb, and did not open his eyes when, in the night, the heavy-billed cranes coughed in the shallows below him.

3

The turning point of Hook's career came that autumn, when the brush in the canyons rustled dryly and the hills, mowed close by the cattle, smoked under the wind as if burning. One midafternoon, when the black clouds were torn on the rim of the sea and the surf flowered white and high on the rocks, raining in over the low cliffs, Hook rode the wind diagonally across the river mouth. His great eyes, focused for small things stirring in the dust and leaves, overlooked so large and slow a movement as that of the Japanese farmer rising from the brush and lifting the two black eyes of his shotgun. Too late Hook saw and, startled, swerved, but wrongly. The surf muffled the reports, and nearly without sound, Hook felt the minute whips of the first shot, and the astounding, breath-breaking blow of the second.

Beating his good wing, tasting the blood that quickly swelled into his beak, he tumbled off with the wind and struck into the thickets on the far side of the river mouth. The branches tore him. Wild with rage, he thrust up and clattered his beak, challenging, but when he had fallen over twice, he knew that the trailing wing would not carry, and then heard the boots of the hunter among the stones in the river bed and, seeing him loom at the edge of the bushes, crept back among the thickest brush and was still. When he saw the boots stand before him, he reared back, lifting his good wing and cocking his head for the serpent-like blow, his beak open but soundless, his great eyes hard and very shining. The boots passed on. The Japanese farmer, who believed that he had lost chickens, and who had cunningly observed Hook's flight for many afternoons, until he could plot it, did not greatly want a dead hawk.

When Hook could hear nothing but the surf and the wind in the thicket, he let the sickness and shock overcome him. The fine film of the inner lid dropped over his big eyes. His heart beat frantically, so that it made the plumage of his shot-aching breast throb. His own blood throttled his breathing. But these things were nothing compared to the lightning of pain in his left shoulder, where the shot had bunched, shattering the airy bones so the pinions trailed on the ground and could not be lifted. Yet, when a sparrow lit in the bush over him, Hook's eyes flew open again, hard and challenging, his good wing was lifted and his beak strained open. The startled sparrow darted piping out over the river.

Throughout that night, while the long clouds blew across the stars and the wind shook the bushes about him, and throughout the next day, while the clouds still blew and massed until there was no gleam of sunlight on the sand bar, Hook remained stationary, enduring his sickness. In the second evening, the rains began. First there was a long, running patter of drops upon the beach and over the dry trees and bushes. At dusk there came a heavier squall, which did not die entirely, but slacked off to a continual, spaced splashing of big drops, and then returned with the front of the storm. In long, misty curtains, gust by gust, the rain swept over the sea, beating down its heaving, and coursed up the beach. The little jets of dust ceased to rise about the drops in the fields, and the mud began to gleam. Among the boulders of the river bed, darkling pools grew slowly.

Still Hook stood behind his tree from the wind, only gentle drops reaching him, falling from the upper branches and then again from the brush. His eyes remained closed, and he could still taste his own blood in his mouth, though it had ceased to come up freshly. Out beyond him, he heard the storm changing. As rain conquered the sea, the heave of the surf became a hushed sound, often lost in the crying of the wind. Then gradually, as the night turned toward morning, the wind also was broken by the rain. The crying became fainter, the rain settled toward steadiness, and the creep of the waves could be heard again, quiet and regular upon the beach.

At dawn there was no wind and no sun, but everywhere the roaring of the vertical, relentless rain. Hook then crept among the rapid drippings of the bushes, dragging his torn sail, seeking better shelter. He stopped often and stood with the shutters of film drawn over his eyes. At midmorning he found a little cave under a ledge at the base of the sea cliff. Here, lost without branches and leaves about him, he settled to await improvement.

When, at midday of the third day, the rain stopped altogether, and the sky opened before a small, fresh wind, letting light through to glitter upon a tremulous sea, Hook was so weak that his good wing trailed also to prop him upright, and his open eyes were lusterless. But his wounds were hardened, and he felt the return of hunger. Beyond his shelter, he heard the gulls flying in great numbers and crying their joy at the cleared air. He could even hear, from the fringe of the river, the ecstatic and unstinted bubblings and chirpings of the small birds. The grassland, he felt, would be full of the stirring anew of the close-bound life, the undrowned insects clicking as they dried out, the snakes slithering down, heads half erect, into the grasses where the mice, gophers and ground squirrels ran and stopped and chewed and licked themselves smoother and drier.

With the aid of this hunger, and on the crutches of his wings, Hook came down to stand in the sun beside his cave, whence he could watch the beach. Before him, in ellipses on tilting planes, the gulls flew. The surf was rearing again, and beginning to shelve and hiss on the sand. Through the white foam-writing it left, the long-billed pipers twinkled in bevies, escaping each wave, then racing down after it to plunge their fine drills into the minute double holes where the sand crabs bubbled. In the third row of breakers two seals lifted sleek, streaming heads and barked, and over them, trailing his spider legs, a great crane flew south. Among the stones at the foot of the cliff, small red and green crabs made a little, continuous rattling and knocking. The cliff swallows glittered and twanged on aerial forays.

The afternoon began auspiciously for Hook also. One of the two gulls which came squabbling above him dropped a freshly caught fish to the sand. Quickly Hook was upon it. Gripping it, he raised his good wing and cocked his head with open beak at the many gulls which had circled and come down at once toward the fall of the fish. The gulls sheered off, cursing raucously. Left alone on the sand, Hook devoured the fish and, after resting in the sun, withdrew again to his shelter.

4

In the succeeding days, between rains, he foraged on the beach. He learned to kill and crack the small green crabs.

Along the edge of the river mouth, he found the drowned bodies of mice and squirrels and even sparrows. Twice he managed to drive feeding gulls from their catch, charging upon them with buffeting wing and clattering beak. He grew stronger slowly, but the shot sail continued to drag. Often, at the choking thought of soaring and striking and the good, hot-blood kill, he strove to take off, but only the one wing came up, winnowing with a hiss, and drove him over onto his side in the sand. After these futile trials, he would rage and clatter. But gradually he learned to believe that he could not fly, that his life must now be that of the discharged nestling again. Denied the joy of space, without which the joy of loneliness was lost, the joy of battle and killing, the blood lust, became his whole concentration. It was his hope, as he charged feeding gulls, that they would turn and offer battle, but they never did. The sandpipers, at his approach, fled peeping, or, like a quiver of arrows shot together, streamed out over the surf in a long curve. Once, pent beyond bearing, he disgraced himself by shrieking challenge at the businesslike heron which flew south every evening at the same time. The heron did not even turn his head, but flapped and glided on.

Hook's shame and anger became such that he stood awake at night. Hunger kept him awake also, for these little leavings of the gulls could not sustain his great body in its renewed violence. He became aware that the gulls slept at night in flocks on the sand, each with one leg tucked under him. He discovered also that the curlews and the pipers, often mingling, likewise slept, on the higher remnant of the bar. A sensation of evil delight filled him in the consideration of protracted striking among them.

There was only half of a sick moon in a sky of running but far-separated clouds on the night when he managed to stalk into the center of the sleeping gulls. This was light enough, but so great was his vengeful pleasure that there broke from him a shrill scream of challenge as he first struck. Without the power of flight behind it, the blow was not murderous, and this newly discovered impotence made Hook crazy, so that he screamed again and again as he struck and tore at the felled gull. He slew the one, but was twice knocked over by its heavy flounderings, and all the others rose above him, weaving and screaming, protesting in the thin moonlight. Wakened by their clamor, the wading birds also took wing, startled and plaintive. When the beach was quiet again, the flocks had settled elsewhere, beyond his pitiful range, and he was left alone beside the single kill. It was a disappointing victory. He fed with lowering spirit.

Thereafter, he stalked silently. At sunset he would watch where the gulls settled along the miles of beach, and after dark he would come like a sharp shadow among them, and drive with his hook on all sides of him, till the beatings of a poorly struck victim sent the flock up. Then he would turn vindictively upon the fallen and finish them. In his best night, he killed five from one flock. But he ate only a little from one, for the vigor resulting from occasional repletion strengthened only his ire, which became so great at such a time that food revolted him. It was not the joyous, swift, controlled hunting anger of a sane hawk, but something quite different, which made him dizzy if it continued too long, and left him unsatisfied with any kill.

Then one day, when he had very nearly struck a gull while driving it from a gasping yellowfin, the gull's wing rapped against him as it broke for its running start, and, the trailing wing failing to support him, he was knocked over. He flurried awkwardly in the sand to regain his feet, but his mastery of the beach was ended. Seeing him, in clear sunlight, struggling after the chance blow, the gulls returned about him in a flashing cloud, circling and pecking on the wing. Hook's plumage showed quick little jets of irregularity here and there.

[355]

He reared back, clattering and erecting the good wing, spreading the great, rusty tail for balance. His eyes shone with a little of the old pleasure. But it died, for he could reach none of them. He was forced to turn and dance awkwardly on the sand, trying to clash bills with each tormentor. They banked up squealing and returned, weaving about him in concentric and overlapping circles. His scream was lost in their clamor, and he appeared merely to be hopping clumsily with his mouth open. Again he fell sideways. Before he could right himself, he was bowled over, and a second time, and lay on his side, twisting his neck to reach them and clappering in blind fury, and was struck three times by three successive gulls, shrieking their flock triumph.

Finally he managed to roll to his breast, and to crouch with his good wing spread wide and the other stretched nearly as far, so that he extended like a gigantic moth, only his snake head, with its now silent scimitar, erect. One great eye blazed under its level brow, but where the other had been was a shallow hole from which thin blood trickled to his russet gap.

In this crouch, by short stages, stopping repeatedly to turn and drive the gulls up, Hook dragged into the river canyon and under the stiff cover of the bitter-leafed laurel. There the gulls left him, soaring up with great clatter of their valor. Till nearly sunset Hook, broken spirited and enduring his hardening eye socket, heard them celebrating over the waves.

When his will was somewhat replenished, and his empty eye socket had stopped the twitching and vague aching which had forced him often to roll ignominiously to rub it in the dust, Hook ventured from the protective lacings of his thicket. He knew fear again, and the challenge of his remaining eye was once more strident, as in adolescence. He dared not return to the beaches, and with a new, weak hunger, the home hunger, enticing him, made his way by short hunting journeys

[356]

back to the wild wheat slopes and the crisp oaks. There was in Hook an unwonted sensation now, that of the ever-neighboring possibility of death. This sensation was beginning, after his period as a mad bird on the beach, to solidify him into his last stage of life. When, during his slow homeward passage, the gulls wafted inland over him, watching the earth with curious, miserish eyes, he did not cower, but neither did he challenge, either by opened beak or by raised shoulder. He merely watched carefully, learning his first lessons in observing the world with one eye.

At first the familiar surroundings of the bend in the river and the tree with the dead limb to which he could not ascend, aggravated his humiliation, but in time, forced to live cunningly and half-starved, he lost much of his savage pride. At the first flight of a strange hawk over his realm, he was wild at his helplessness, and kept twisting his head like an owl, or spinning in the grass like a small and feathered dervish, to keep the hateful beauty of the wind-rider in sight. But in the succeeding weeks, as one after another coasted his beat, his resentment declined, and when one of the raiders, a haughty yearling, sighted his up-staring eye, and plunged and struck him dreadfully, and failed to kill him only because he dragged under a thicket in time, the second of his great hungers was gone. He had no longer the true lust to kill, no joy of battle, but only the poor desire to fill his belly.

Then truly he lived in the wheat and the brush like a ground owl, ridden with ground lice, dusty or muddy, ever half-starved, forced to sit for hours by small holes for petty and unsatisfying kills. Only once during the final months before his end did he make a kill where the breath of danger recalled his valor, and then the danger was such as a hawk with wings and eyes would scorn. Waiting beside a gopher hole, surrounded by the high, yellow grass, he saw the head emerge, and struck, and was amazed that there writhed in his

[357]

clutch the neck and dusty coffin-skull of a rattlesnake. Holding his grip, Hook saw the great, thick body slither up after, the tip an erect, strident blur, and writhe on the dirt of the gopher's mound. The weight of the snake pushed Hook about, and once threw him down, and the rising and falling whine of the rattles made the moment terrible, but the vaulted mouth, gaping from the closeness of Hook's gripe, so that the pale, envenomed sabers stood out free, could not reach him. When Hook replaced the grip of his beak with the grip of his talons, and was free to strike again and again at the base of the head, the struggle was over. Hook tore and fed on the fine, watery flesh, and left the tattered armor and the long, jointed bone for the marching ants.

When the heavy rains returned, he ate well during the period of the first escapes from flooded burrows, and then well enough, in a vulture's way, on the drowned creatures. But as the rains lingered, and the burrows hung full of water, and there were no insects in the grass and no small birds sleeping in the thickets, he was constantly hungry, and finally unbearably hungry. His sodden and ground-broken plumage stood out raggedly about him, so that he looked fat, even bloated, but underneath it his skin clung to his bones. Save for his great talons and clappers, and the rain in his down, he would have been like a handful of air. He often stood for a long time under some bush or ledge, heedless of the drip, his one eye filmed over, his mind neither asleep or awake, but between. The gurgle and swirl of the brimming river, and the sound of chunks of the bank cut away to splash and dissolve in the already muddy flood, became familiar to him, and yet a torment, as if that great, ceaselessly working power of water ridiculed his frailty, within which only the faintest spark of valor still glimmered. The last two nights before the rain ended, he huddled under the floor of the bridge on the coastal highway, and heard the palpitant thunder of motors swell and roar over him. The trucks shook the bridge so that Hook, even in his famished lassitude, would sometimes open his one great eye wide and startled.

5

After the rains, when things became full again, bursting with growth and sound, the trees swelling, the thickets full of song and chatter, the fields, turning green in the sun, alive with rustling passages, and the moonlit nights strained with the song of the peepers all up and down the river and in the pools in the fields, Hook had to bear the return of the one hunger left him. At times this made him so wild that he forgot himself and screamed challenge from the open ground. The fretfulness of it spoiled his hunting, which was now entirely a matter of patience. Once he was in despair, and lashed himself through the grass and thickets, trying to rise when that virgin scent drifted for a few moments above the current of his own river. Then, breathless, his beak agape, he saw the strong suitor ride swiftly down on the wind over him, and heard afar the screaming fuss of the harsh wooing in the alders. For that moment even the battle heart beat in him again. The rim of his good eye was scarlet, and a little bead of new blood stood in the socket of the other. With beak and talon, he ripped at a fallen log, and made loam and leaves fly from about it.

But the season of love passed over to the nesting season, and Hook's love hunger, unused, shriveled in him with the others, and there remained in him only one stern quality befitting a hawk, and that the negative one, the remnant, the will to endure. He resumed his patient, plotted hunting, now along a field of the Japanese farmer, but ever within reach of the river thickets.

Growing tough and dry again as the summer advanced, inured to the family of the farmer, whom he saw daily, stoop-

[359]

ing and scraping with sticks in the ugly, open rows of their fields, where no lovely grass rustled and no life stirred save the shameless gulls, which walked at the heels of the workers, gobbling the worms and grubs they turned up, Hook became nearly content with his share of life. The only longing or resentment to pierce him was that which he suffered occasionally when forced to hide at the edge of the mile-long bean field from the wafted cruising and the restive, down-bent gaze of one of his own kind. For the rest, he was without flame, a snappish, dust-colored creature, fading into the grasses he trailed through, and suited to his petty ways.

At the end of that summer, for the second time in his four years, Hook underwent a drouth. The equinoctial period passed without a rain. The laurel and the rabbit-brush dropped dry leaves. The foliage of the oaks shriveled and curled. Even the night fogs in the river canyon failed. The farmer's red cattle on the hillside lowed constantly, and could not feed on the dusty stubble. Grass fires broke out along the highway, and ate fast in the wind, filling the hollows with the smell of smoke, and died in the dirt of the shorn hills. The river made no sound. Scum grew on its vestigial pools, and turtles died and stank among the rocks. The dust rode before the wind, and ascended and flowered to nothing between the hills, and every sunset was red with the dust in the air. The people in the farmer's house quarreled, and even struck one another. Birds were silent, and only the hawks flew much. The animals lay breathing hard for very long spells, and ran and crept jerkily. Their flanks were fallen in, and their eyes were red.

At first Hook gorged at the fringe of the grass fires on the multitudes of tiny things that came running and squeaking. But thereafter there were the blackened strips on the hills, and little more in the thin, crackling grass. He found mice and rats, gophers and ground-squirrels, and even rabbits, dead in the stubble and under the thickets, but so dry and fleshless that only a faint smell rose from them, even on the sunny days. He starved on them. By early December he had wearily stalked the length of the eastern foothills, hunting at night to escape the voracity of his own kind, resting often upon his wings. The queer trail of his short steps and great horned toes zigzagged in the dust and was erased by the wind at dawn. He was nearly dead, and could make no sound through the horn funnels of his clappers.

Then one night the dry wind brought him, with the familiar, lifeless dust, another familiar scent, troublesome, mingled and unclear. In his vision-dominated brain he remembered the swift circle of his flight a year past, crossing in one segment, his shadow beneath him, a yard cluttered with crates and chickens, a gray barn and then again the plowed land and the stubble. Traveling faster than he had for days, impatient of his shrunken sweep, Hook came down to the farm. In the dark wisps of cloud blown among the stars over him, but no moon, he stood outside the wire of the chicken run. The scent of fat and blooded birds reached him from the shelter, and also within the enclosure was water. At the breath of the water, Hook's gorge contracted, and his tongue quivered and clove in its groove of horn. But there was the wire. He stalked its perimeter and found no opening. He beat it with his good wing, and felt it cut but not give. He wrenched at it with his beak in many places, but could not tear it. Finally, in a fury which drove the thin blood through him, he leaped repeatedly against it, beating and clawing. He was thrown back from the last leap as from the first, but in it he had risen so high as to clutch with his beak at the top wire. While he lay on his breast on the ground, the significance of this came upon him.

Again he leapt, clawed up the wire, and, as he would have fallen, made even the dead wing bear a little. He grasped the top and tumbled within. There again he rested flat, searching the dark with quick-turning head. There was no sound or motion but the throb of his own body. First he drank at the chill metal trough hung for the chickens. The water was cold, and loosened his tongue and his tight throat, but it also made him drunk and dizzy, so that he had to rest again, his claws spread wide to brace him. Then he walked stiffly, to stalk down the scent. He trailed it up the runway. Then there was the stuffy, body-warm air, acrid with droppings, full of soft rustlings as his talons clicked on the board floor. The thick, white shapes showed faintly in the darkness. Hook struck quickly, driving a hen to the floor with one blow, its neck broken and stretched out stringily. He leaped the still pulsing body and tore it. The rich, streaming blood was overpowering to his dried senses, his starved, leathery body. After a few swallows, the flesh choked him. In his rage, he struck down another hen. The urge to kill took him again, as in those nights on the beach. He could let nothing go. Balked of feeding, he was compelled to slaughter. Clattering, he struck again and again. The henhouse was suddenly filled with the squawking and helpless rushing and buffeting of the terrified, brainless fowls.

Hook reveled in mastery. Here was game big enough to offer weight against a strike, and yet unable to soar away from his blows. Turning in the midst of the turmoil, cannily, his fury caught at the perfect pitch, he struck unceasingly. When the hens finally discovered the outlet, and streamed into the yard, to run around the fence, beating and squawking, Hook followed them, scraping down the incline, clumsy and joyous. In the yard, the cock, a bird as large as he, and much heavier, found him out and gave valiant battle. In the dark, and both earthbound, there was little skill, but blow upon blow, and only chance parry. The still squawking hens pressed into one corner of the yard. While the duel went on, a dog, excited by the sustained scuffling, began to bark. He continued to bark, running back and forth along the fence on one side. A light flashed on in an uncurtained window of the farmhouse, and streamed whitely over the crates littering the ground.

Enthralled by his old battle joy, Hook knew only the burly cock before him. Now, in the farthest reach of the window light, they could see each other dimly. The Japanese farmer, with his gun and lantern, was already at the gate when the finish came. The great cock leapt to jab with his spurs and, toppling forward with extended neck as he fell, was struck and extinguished. Blood had loosened Hook's throat. Shrilly he cried his triumph. It was a thin and exhausted cry, but within him as good as when he shrilled in mid-air over the plummeting descent of a fine foe in his best spring.

The light from the lantern partially blinded Hook. He first turned and ran directly from it, into the corner where the hens were huddled. They fled apart before his charge. He essayed the fence, and on the second try, in his desperation, was out. But in the open dust, the dog was on him, circling, dashing in, snapping. The farmer, who at first had not fired because of the chickens, now did not fire because of the dog, and, when he saw that the hawk was unable to fly, relinquished the sport to the dog, holding the lantern up in order to see better. The light showed his own flat, broad, dark face as sunken also, the cheekbones very prominent, and showed the torn-off sleeves of his shirt and the holes in the knees of his overalls. His wife, in a stained wrapper, and barefooted, heavy black hair hanging around a young, passionless face, joined him hesitantly, but watched, fascinated and a little horrified. His son joined them too, encouraging the dog, but quickly grew silent. Courageous and cruel death, however it may afterward sicken the one who has watched it, is impossible to look away from.

In the circle of the light, Hook turned to keep the dog in

front of him. His one eye gleamed with malevolence. The dog was an Airedale, and large. Each time he pounced, Hook stood ground, raising his good wing, the pinions newly torn by the fence, opening his beak soundlessly, and, at the closest approach, hissed furiously, and at once struck. Hit and ripped twice by the whetted horn, the dog recoiled more quickly from several subsequent jumps and, infuriated by his own cowardice, began to bark wildly. Hook maneuvered to watch him, keeping his head turned to avoid losing the foe on the blind side. When the dog paused, safely away, Hook watched him quietly, wing partially lowered, beak closed, but at the first move again lifted the wing and gaped. The dog whined, and the man spoke to him encouragingly. The awful sound of his voice made Hook for an instant twist his head to stare up at the immense figures behind the light. The dog again sallied, barking, and Hook's head spun back. His wing was bitten this time, and with a furious side-blow, he caught the dog's nose. The dog dropped him with a yelp, and then, smarting, came on more warily, as Hook propped himself up from the ground again between his wings. Hook's artificial strength was waning, but his heart still stood to the battle, sustained by a fear of such dimension as he had never known before, but only anticipated when the arrogant young hawk had driven him to cover. The dog, unable to find any point at which the merciless, unwinking eye was not watching him, the parted beak waiting, paused and whimpered again.

"Oh, kill the poor thing," the woman begged.

The man, though, encouraged the dog again, saying, "Sick him; sick him."

The dog rushed bodily. Unable to avoid him, Hook was bowled down, snapping and raking. He left long slashes, as from the blade of a knife, on the dog's flank, but before he could right himself and assume guard again, was caught by the good wing and dragged, clattering, and seeking to make a good stroke from his back. The man followed them to keep the light on them, and the boy went with him, wetting his lips with his tongue and keeping his fists closed tightly. The woman remained behind, but could not help watching the diminished conclusion.

In the little, palely shining arena, the dog repeated his successful maneuver three times, growling but not barking, and when Hook thrashed up from the third blow, both wings were trailing, and dark, shining streams crept on his black-fretted breast from the shoulders. The great eye flashed more furiously than it ever had in victorious battle, and the beak still gaped, but there was no more clatter. He faltered when turning to keep front; the broken wings played him false even as props. He could not rise to use his talons.

The man had tired of holding the lantern up, and put it down to rub his arm. In the low, horizontal light, the dog charged again, this time throwing the weight of his forepaws against Hook's shoulder, so that Hook was crushed as he struck. With his talons up, Hook raked at the dog's belly, but the dog conceived the finish, and furiously worried the feathered bulk. Hook's neck went limp, and between his gaping clappers came only a faint chittering, as from some small kill of his own in the grasses.

In this last conflict, however, there had been minutes of the supreme fire of the hawk whose three hungers are fused in the one will; enough to burn off a year of shame.

Between the great sails the light body lay caved and perfectly still. The dog, smarting from his cuts, came to the master and was praised. The woman, joining them slowly, looked at the great wingspread, her husband raising the lantern that she might see it better.

"Oh, the brave bird," she said.

JOSEPHINE MILES

Miss Miles is a Professor of English at the University of
California (Berkeley), and is widely known as an editor
and critic of poetry. Volumes of her own poetry include
Line at Intersections (1939), *Poems on Several Occasions*
(1941), and *Local Measures* (1946). Miss Miles was born
in Chicago, and lived in Southern California before settling in Berkeley.

Project

The cathedral which rose up unfinished over San Francisco
Bore toward its eastern gate a front of stone,
Where in the times to be a rose window
Would shine for the eastern sun to shine upon.

Meanwhile the million windows of the city's
Traffic moving over Diamond Heights
Like bridges over slums, took in the rising
Sun in a battery of instant lights.

Wishing as well he might for both the colored
Window and two cars in every garage, the moving sun
Entered the choir loft by a side window
And sang aloud for the sparkling souls of the town.

Orderly

Hysteric sparks of self in the ward of night
Jangle their light to call their care's return.
In each nook and night, each flashing brain
Asserts itself's I want.

Then what is the self of the long orderly
Who all the shift strides to the crying signs,
Strides to the foglights and the needs' unneeds
To keep the blood in vein?

His is the fire of the open hearth
Tended and mended, till the stray sparks,
Blown almost away, he brings again
To its burning brand.

Message

Into the side aisle seats flicker the pony tails,
Then out to see the fights in the lobby,
Till the boys come back in too and sit down,
Heavy, angry for the popcorn.

Then out up the aisle like a troupe
Of spoon lipped bug eyed sky rimmed angels,
And damn your lip, and damn your dime that's my dime,
And shove—over on a bysitter's hippocket.

Then flock back again down the aisle to the seats, birds,
The usher patrol now working, flashing its lights
As club or illumination, to reinterpret
How love, on the steadying screen, is many-splendored.

Reception

When fate from its plane stepped down
And had its photo snapped for me in full color,
I did know it, but it had
The hundred faces of some Christmas cards.

The severe faces of five year old
Wilsons and Oppenheimers, and the Pandits, the round
Fortunes of immediate Presidents
Who will not read Pascal.

[367]

Also the crazy faces of leadership
That find their goodness in their morning cup.
To whom I said, Welcome ambassadors. And they,
Which of your hundred faces calls us home?

PART VIII

The Scene

The Scene

How Is It Possible To describe so multifarious and big a State, especially when it is all around you, impinging every hour and day upon your personality, directing most of your actions and many of your dreams and daydreams? Today's California is too large and close to the editors for them to pretend to a real knowledge of it, nor can either editor disassociate himself from that part of its literature which, best known or admired by him, has best managed to become a part of his own consciousness. To some extent the final selections in this book will show what they think of their own California. For the rest they can only pretend to an objectivity not really theirs, and speak (but timidly) as they believe some wandering stranger might speak, a Crespi, Sienkiewicz, or Zenas Leonard.

To such an outsider our geographical and meteorological arrangements would still seem extraordinarily varied and exciting. Our deserts are still the dryest, our mountains the highest, our interior valleys still acre for acre the most productive you can find. You can cross the oceans and deserts more quickly now, but the cost of this travel helps us to preserve a little of

[371]

our old isolation. Our water-engineering has increased the number of our lakes and partly regulated the flow of our rivers, but this ancient problem of water is still a major problem. Except for the Los Angeles area, cursed by the smog and soot of its industrial prosperity, the weather has not changed. There are still a dozen separate climates, each of them perfect in its way, each with its million or so loyal adherents. But our literature cares less than it did for these facts of nature. The life of a California writer is perhaps not more citified than before, but his literary backdrops tend more to be urban or suburban. Our foothill towns no longer have a Sam Clemens or Bret Harte, our sea cliffs no Jeffers, our valley ranches no Steinbeck. Future generations may think of our writers as a sedentary race, porchbound each in his city or street.

But the cities themselves offer plenty of variety. They differ from each other and differ within themselves. Accidents of water and geography seem likely to make a new Chicago out of the Sacramento-Stockton region, but that is in the future. At this writing the true cities are only two in number. Los Angeles spreads out mightily over its dryish plains and hillsides: forty towns and more, their citizens following forty separate and distinct modes of life. Los Angeles writers can depict all modes and types: kings of the world, the demoralized helots you find in James M. Cain and Gavin Lambert, Saxon, Mexican, and Negro slum-dwellers whose endemic disintegration has as yet inspired no good poetry or worthy prose. The image of Hollywood has changed little in the past forty years. Writers are still fascinated by the has-beens and would-be's of that place, the stars, directors, and writers floating on successes of the moment, the loss of self in an art-form created by masses for larger masses. For writers the total impression still seems one of rootlessness and disjunction, masses of integers, unrelated. Plotting the congress of northern towns running from San Jose to Santa Rosa, girdling the Bay and spilling over the

[372]

Berkeley Hills, a sociologist of San Francisco might derive the same impression. But in the literary image San Francisco stops within the narrow city limits. Brooklyn-Oakland, Connecticut-Marin, and the industrial Peninsula towns are fiefs of it, but not parts. Consequently its writers see it as an old, stable city, partly a museum, its contrasting types squeezed closely together—antiquely wicked, hustling in high life or low, full of degeneracy, ribaldry, and poetry—permanent and self-confident, built not on shifting sands but on its own proud ruins.

But who are the Californians now, what immigrants? The outsider is still impressed by their unusual and multifarious provenences. The immigrations no longer succeed each other chronologically: they are simultaneous now, everybody rushing in from everywhere. More often than not their hegiras began with trouble at home, the loss of a country, family, or job. Our dispossessed old White Russians are treated in this book by a dispossessed young ex-citizeness of Esthonia. San Francisco's hotels and cafes are increasingly staffed by Germans; four of the Hollywood writers represented in this book learned their art in the schools of Britain. The American immigration is always larger, of course. Much of it is still from the older, less promising states of the south and southwest—"some white, some black," as John Phoenix wrote a century ago, "and some kinder speckled." They come in all hues and and trades: millionaires from Brazil and Louisiana, crooks from the Bronx and Harlem syndicates, queens of beauty, factory hands, artists, professors. Everybody comes. In 1964 our population will exceed that of New York, and much more fairly will represent the populations of all the world.

These are the Californians, and always were. In other ways also they follow tradition. Their cynicism about hard work and the other abstract virtues will go on astonishing outsiders; they will give offense by their unconcern about political issues, their lack of enthusiasm for conventional morality, and

[373]

their abiding faith in cash and the cash nexus. Their enormous educational expenditures will astonish all hands, as will their inability to learn spelling and numbers. Europeans will be shocked by the glaring inequality with which they divide their wealth, gentle souls by the anarchy and violence of their social expressions, shown also in their literature. They will drink, party, gossip, knock or boost, and do their theft and sex bits with a lordly neglect of all consequences, still demanding the best bad things available, hardly abandoning a jot of the recklessness, violence, and illogicality hewn so deeply into the state's traditions. Appropriate are the three California headline-items of precisely today, February 16, 1960. One story concerns the sensational murder trial of a wealthy Los Angeles surgeon named Finch, accused with his mistress Carole Pappas (nee Tregoff) of murdering his wife to avoid a split of community property. The second concerns a San Francisco real-estate scandal: a firm called Fidelity Assurance, Incorporated, is accused of bilking some 284 Bay Area home-owners in a small-print confidence-style shuffling of mortgages. And third, a Navy jet-plane fell out of the sky, killing the pilot and one civilian, Mrs. Deszo Halmi of Mountain View. Mrs. Halmi, a Hungarian by birth, "broke through the Communist lines three years ago," seeking among Peninsula tract-homes her own better place. "There used to be a house next to mine," elegised her neighbor, "but when I went outside there wasn't a house there any more." The neighbor's name is Herbert Nishimura. By coincidence the pilot was also a close neighbor, one Lieutenant G. N. Blake, just back from sea duty, originally a South Carolinian.

The Californians were never much different from this. They are a cosmopolitan, widely-traveled, energetic, restless, curious, greedy, faddish, poetic, and violent people, not all wholly happy or safe, but lively, participating, deeply involved. One may love the state and still be awed by it, charmed and yet baffled. *Eureka*, "I have found it," is the antique motto of the State. In their wisdom the motto makers were silent as to just what had been found, but meant something rich, multifoliate, and strange. Confused by their history, caught in geographical tensions, stopped by the ocean at continent's end, the Californians go on with their finding.

America

By ALLEN GINSBERG

Born in New Jersey in 1925, a graduate of Columbia,
Ginsberg blossomed as a poet during the San Francisco
part of his wanderings. "America" was first printed in his
Howl and other Poems (San Francisco, 1957) with a
famous dedication to Jack Kerouac.

America I've given you all and now I'm nothing.
America two dollars and twentyseven cents January 17, 1956.
I can't stand on my own mind.
America when will we end the human war?
Go ---- yourself with your atom bomb.
I don't feel good don't bother me.
I won't write my poem till I'm in my right mind.
America when will you be angelic?
When will you take off your clothes?
When will you look at yourself through the grave?
When will you be worthy of your million Trotskyites?
America why are your libraries full of tears?
America when will you send your eggs to India?
I'm sick of your insane demands.
When can I go into the supermarket and buy what I need
  with my good looks?
America after all it is you and I who are perfect not the next
  world.
Your machinery is too much for me.
You made me want to be a saint.
There must be some other way to settle this argument.
Burroughs is in Tangiers I don't think he'll come back it's
  sinister.
Are you being sinister or is this some form of practical joke?
I'm trying to come to the point.

[376]

I refuse to give up my obsession.
America stop pushing I know what I'm doing.
America the plum blossoms are falling.
I haven't read the newspapers for months, every day some-
    body goes on trial for murder.
America I feel sentimental about the Wobblies.
America I used to be a communist when I was a kid I'm not
    sorry.
I smoke marijuana every chance I get.
I sit in my house for days on end and stare at the roses in the
    closet.
When I go to Chinatown I get drunk and never get laid.
My mind is made up there's going to be trouble.
You should have seen me reading Marx.
My psychoanalyst thinks I'm perfectly right.
I won't say the Lord's Prayer.
I have mystical visions and cosmic vibrations.
America I still haven't told you what you did to Uncle Max
    after he came over from Russia.

I'm addressing you.
Are you going to let your emotional life be run by Time
    Magazine?
I'm obsessed by Time Magazine.
I read it every week.
Its cover stares at me every time I slink past the corner
    candystore.
I read it in the basement of the Berkeley Public Library.
It's always telling me about responsibility. Businessmen are
    serious.
Movie producers are serious. Everybody's serious but me.
It occurs to me that I am America.
I am talking to myself again.
Asia is rising against me.

[377]

I haven't got a chinaman's chance.
I'd better consider my national resources.
My national resources consist of two joints of marijuana
    millions of genitals an unpublishable private literature
    that goes 1400 miles an hour and twentyfive-thousand
    mental institutions.
I say nothing about my prisons nor the millions of under-
    privileged who live in my flowerpots under the light of
    five hundred suns.
I have abolished the whorehouses of France, Tangiers is the
    next to go.
My ambition is to be President despite the fact that I'm a
    Catholic.

America how can I write a holy litany in your silly mood?
I will continue like Henry Ford my strophes are as individual
    as his automobiles more so they're all different sexes.
America I will sell you strophes $2500 apiece $500 down on
    your old strophe
America free Tom Mooney
America save the Spanish Loyalists
America Sacco & Vanzetti must not die
America I am the Scottsboro boys.
America when I was seven momma took me to Communist Cell
    meetings they sold us garbanzos a handful per ticket
    a ticket costs a nickel and the speeches were free everybody
    was angelic and sentimental about the workers it was all
    so sincere you have no idea what a good thing the party
    was in 1835 Scott Nearing was a grand old man a real
    mensch Mother Bloor made me cry I once saw Israel
    Amter plain. Everybody must have been a spy.
America you don't really want to go to war.
America it's them bad Russians.

[378]

Them Russians them Russians and them Chinamen. And them
Russians.

The Russia wants to eat us alive. The Russia's power mad. She
wants to take our cars from out our garages.

Her wants to grab Chicago. Her needs a Red Readers' Digest.
Her wants our auto plants in Siberia. Him big bureau-
cracy running our fillingstations.

That no good. Ugh. Him make Indians learn read. Him need
big black niggers. Hah. Her make us all work sixteen
hours a day. Help.

America this is quite serious.

America this is the impression I get from looking in the television set.

America is this correct?

I'd better get right down to the job.

It's true I don't want to join the Army or turn lathes in precision parts factories, I'm nearsighted and psychopathic
anyway.

America I'm putting my queer shoulder to the wheel.

The Fall of Mardou

By JACK KEROUAC

Although he was born in Massachusetts in 1922, and is now living in New York, Jack Kerouac remains one of the biggest figures in modern West Coast literature. After an apprenticeship with the conventional novel, Kerouac hunted his own style in *On the Road* (1957) and brought it to unique culmination in the two California books *The Dharma Bums* (1958) and *The Subterraneans* (1958), from which this selection is taken.

The pushcart incident not important in itself, but what I saw, what my quick eye and hungry paranoia ate—a gesture of Mardou's that made my heart sink even as I doubted maybe I wasn't seeing, interpreting right, as so oft I do.—We'd come in and run upstairs and jumped on the big double bed waking Adam up and yelling and tousling and Carmody too sitting on the edge as if to say "Now children now children," just a lot of drunken lushes—at one time in the play back and forth between the rooms Mardou and Yuri ended on the couch together in front, where I think all three of us had flopped—but I ran to the bedroom for further business, talking, coming back I saw Yuri who knew I was coming flop off the couch onto the floor and as he did so Mardou (who probably didn't know I was coming) shot out her hand at him as if to say OH YOU RASCAL as if almost he'd before rolling off the couch goosed her or done something playful—I saw for the first time their youthful playfulness which I in my scowlingness and writer-ness had not participated in and my old man-ness about which I kept telling myself "You're old you old sonofabitch you're lucky to have such a young sweet thing" (while nevertheless at the same time plotting, as I'd been doing for about three weeks now, to get rid of Mardou, without her being hurt, even if

possible "without her noticing" so as to get back to more comfortable modes of life, like say, stay at home all week and write
and work on the three novels to make a lot of money and come
in to town only for good times if not to see Mardou then any
other chick will do, this was my three week thought and really
the energy behind or the surface one behind the creation of
the Jealousy Phantasy in the Gray Guilt dream of the World
Around Our Bed)—now I saw Mardou pushing Yuri with a
O H Y O U and I shuddered to think something maybe
was going on behind my back—felt warned too by the quick
and immediate manner Yuri heard me coming and rolled off
but as if guiltily as I say after some kind of goose or feel up
some illegal touch of Mardou which made her purse little
love loff lips at him and push at him and like kids.—Mardou
was just like a kid I remember the first night I met her when
Julien, rolling joints on the floor, she behind him hunched, I'd
explained to them why that week I wasn't drinking at all (true
at the time, and due to events on the ship in New York, scaring
me, saying to myself "If you keep on drinking like that you'll
die you can't even hold a simple job any more," so returning
to Frisco and not drinking at all and everybody exclaiming "O
you look wonderful"), telling that first night almost heads
together with Mardou and Julien, they so kidlike in their naive
WHY when I told them I wasn't drinking any more, so kidlike
listening to my explanation about the one can of beer leading
to the second, the sudden gut explosions and glitters, the third
can, the fourth, "And then I go off and drink for days and I'm
gone man, like, I'm afraid I'm an alcoholic" and they kidlike
and othergenerationey making no comment, but awed, curious—
in the same rapport with young Yuri here (her age) pushing at
him, Oh You, which in drunkenness I paid not too much attention to, and we slept, Mardou and I on the floor, Yuri on the
couch (so kidlike, indulgent, funny of him, all that)—this
first exposure of the realization of the mysteries of the guilt

[381]

jealousy dream leading, from the pushcart time, to the night we went to Bromberg's, most awful of all.

Beginning as usual in the Mask.

Nights that begin so glitter clear with hope, let's go see our friends, things, phones ring, people come and go, coats, hats, statements, bright reports, metropolitan excitements, a round of beers, another round of beers, the talk gets more beautiful, more excited, flushed, another round, the midnight hour, later, the flushed happy faces are now wild and soon there's the swaying buddy da day oobab bab smash smoke drunken latenight goof leading finally to the bartender, like a seer in Eliot, TIME TO CLOSE UP—in this manner more or less arriving at the Mask where a kid called Harold Sand came in, a chance acquaintance of Mardou's from a year ago, a young novelist looking like Leslie Howard who'd just had a manuscript accepted and so acquired a strange grace in my eyes I wanted to devour—interested in him for same reasons as Lavalina, literary avidity, envy—as usual paying less attention therefore to Mardou (at table) than Yuri whose continual presence with us now did not raise my suspicions, whose complaints "I don't have a place to stay—do you realize Percepied what it is not to even have a place to write? I have not girls, nothing, Carmody and Moorad won't let me stay up there any more, they're a couple of old sisters," not sinking in, and already the only comment I'd made to Mardou about Yuri had been, after his leaving, "He's just like that Mexican stud comes up here and grabs up your last cigarettes," both of us laughing because whenever she was at her lowest financial ebb, bang, somebody who needed a "mooch" was there—not that I would call Yuri a mooch in the least (I'll tread lightly on him on this point, for obvious reasons).—(Yuri and I'd had a long talk that week in a bar, over port wines, he claimed everything was poetry, I tried to make the common old distinction between verse and prose, he said, "Lissen Percepied do you believe in freedom?—

then say what you want, it's poetry, poetry, all of it is poetry,
great prose is poetry, great verse is poetry."—"Yes" I said "but
verse is verse and prose is prose."—"No no" he yelled "it's
all poetry."—"Okay," I said, "I believe in you believing in
freedom and maybe you're right, have another wine." And he
read me his "best line" which was something to do with
"seldom nocturne" that I said sounded like small magazine
poetry and wasn't his best—as already I'd seen some much
better poetry by him concerning his tough boyhood, about
cats, mothers in gutters, Jesus striding in the ashcan, appear-
ing incarnate shining on the blowers of slum tenements or that
is making great steps across the light—the sum of it something
he could do, and did, well—"No, seldom nocturne isn't your
meat" but he claimed it was great, "I would say rather it was
great if you'd written it suddenly on the spur of the moment."
—"But I did—right out of my mind it flowed and I threw it
down, it sounds like it's been planned but it wasn't, it was
bang! just like you say, spontaneous vision!"—Which I now
doubt tho his saying "seldom nocturne" came to him spon-
taneously made me suddenly respect it more, some falsehood
hiding beneath our wine yells in a saloon on Kearney.) Yuri
hanging out with Mardou and me every night almost—like a
shadow—and knowing Sand himself from before, so he, Sand,
walking into the Mask, flushed successful young author but
"ironic" looking and with a big parkingticket sticking out of
his coat lapel, was set upon by the three of us with avidity,
made to sit at our table—made to talk.—Around the corner
from Mask to 13 Pater thence the lot of us going, and en route
(reminiscent now more strongly and now with hints of pain of
the pushcart night and Mardou's OH YOU) Yuri and Mardou
start racing, pushing, shoving, wrestling on the sidewalk and
finally she lofts a big empty cardboard box and throws it at
him and he throws it back, they're like kids again—I walk on
ahead in serious tone conversation with Sand tho—he too has

eyes for Mardou—somehow I'm not able (at least haven't
tried) to communicate to him that she is my love and I would
prefer if he didn't have eyes for her so obviously, just as Jimmy
Lowell, a colored seaman who'd suddenly phoned in the midst
of an Adam party, and came, with a Scandinavian shipmate,
looking at Mardou and me wondering, asking me "Do you
make it with her sex?" and I saying yes and the night after the
Red Drum session where Art Blakey was whaling like mad and
Thelonious Monk sweating leading the generation with his
elbow chords, eying the band madly to lead them on, *the
monk and saint of bop* I kept telling Yuri, smooth sharp hep
Jimmy Lowell leans to me and says "I would like to make it
with your chick," (like in the old days Leroy and I always
swapping so I'm not shocked), "would it be okay if I asked
her?" and I saying "She's not that kind of girl, I'm sure she
believes in one at a time, if you ask her that's what she'll tell
you man" (at that time still feeling no pain or jealousy, this
incidentally the night before the Jealousy Dream)—not able to
communicate to Lowell that's—that I wanted her—to stay—
to be stammer stammer be mine—not being able to come right
out and say, "Lissen this is my girl, what are you talking about,
if you want to try to make her you'll have to tangle with
me, you understand that pops as well as I do."—In that
way with a stud, in another way with polite dignified Sand a
very interesting young fellow, like, "Sand, Mardou is my girl
and I would prefer, etc."—but he has eyes for her and the
reason he stays with us and goes around the corner to 13 Pater,
but it's Yuri starts wrestling with her and goofing in the streets—
so when we leave 13 Pater later on (a dike bar slummish now
and nothing to it, where a year ago there were angels in red
shirts straight out of Genet and Djuna Barnes) I get in the
front seat of Sand's old car, he's going at least to drive us
home, I sit next to him at the clutch in front for purposes of
talking better and in drunkenness again avoiding Mardou's

womanness, leaving room for her to sit beside me at front window—instead of which, no sooner plops her ass behind me, jumps over seat and dives into backseat with Yuri who is alone back there, to wrestle again and goof with him and now with such intensity I'm afraid to look back and see with my own eyes what's happening and how the dream (the dream I announced to everyone and made big issues of and told even Yuri about) is coming true.

We pull up at Mardou's door at Heavenly Lane and drunkly now she says (Sand and I having decided drunkenly to drive down to Los Altos the lot of us and crash in on old Austin Bromberg and have big further parties) "If you're going down to Bromberg's in Los Altos you two go out, Yuri and I'll stay here"—my heart sank deep—it sank so I gloated to hear it for the first time and the confirmation of it crowned me and blessed me.

And I thought, "Well boy here's your chance to get rid of her" (which I'd plotted for three weeks now) but the sound of this in my own ears sounded awfully false, I didn't believe it, myself, any more.

But on the sidewalk going in flushed Yuri takes my arm as Mardou and Sand go on ahead up the fish head stairs, "Lissen, Leo I don't want to make Mardou at all, she's all over me, I want you to know that I don't want to make her, all I want to do if you're going out there is go to sleep in your bed because I have an appointment tomorrow."—But now I myself feel reluctant to stay in Heavenly Lane for the night because Yuri will be there, in fact now is already on the bed tacitly as if, one would have to say, "Get off the bed so we can get in, go to that uncomfortable chair for the night."—So this more than anything else (in my tiredness and growing wisdom and patience) makes me agree with Sand (also reluctant) that we might as well drive down to Los Altos and wake up good old Bromberg, and I turn to Mardou with eyes saying or suggesting, "You can

[385]

stay with Yuri you bitch" but she's already got her little
traveling basket or weekend bag and is putting my toothbrush
hairbrush and her things in and the idea is we three drive out—
which we do, leaving Yuri in the bed.—En route, at near Bayshore in the great highway roadlamp night, which is now
nothing but a bleakness for me and the prospect of the "weekend" at Bromberg's a horror of shame, I can't stand it any
more and look at Mardou as soon as Sand gets out to buy
hamburgs in the diner, "You jumped in the backseat with
Yuri why'd you do that? and why'd you say you wanted to stay
with him?"—"It was silly of me, I was just high baby."
But I don't darkly any more now want to believe her—art is
short, life is long—now I've got in full dragon bloom the
monster of jealousy as green as in any cliché cartoon rising
in my being, "You and Yuri play together all the time,
it's just like the dream I told you about, that's what's
horrible—O I'll never believe in dreams come true again."
—"But baby it isn't anything like that" but I don't believe
her—I can tell by looking at her she's got eyes for the youth
—you can't fool an old hand who at the age of sixteen
before even the juice was wiped off his heart by the Great
Imperial World Wiper with Sadcloth fell in love with an
impossible flirt and cheater, this is a boast—I feel so sick I
can't stand it, curl up in the back seat, alone—they drive on,
and Sand having anticipated a gay talkative weekend now
finds himself with a couple of grim lover worriers, hears in
fact the fragment "But I didn't mean you to think that baby"
so obviously harkening to his mind the Yuri incident—finds
himself with this pair of bores and has to drive all the way
down to Los Altos, and so with the same grit that made him
write the half million words of his novel bends to it and pushes
the car through the Peninsula night and on into the dawn.
    Arriving at Bromberg's house in Los Altos at gray dawn,
parking, and ringing the doorbell the three of us sheepishly I

[386]

most sheepish of all—and Bromberg comes right down, at
once, with great roars of approval cries "Leo I didn't know
you knew each other" (meaning Sand, whom Bromberg admired very much) and in we go to rum and coffee in the crazy
famous Bromberg kitchen.—You might say, Bromberg the
most amazing guy in the world with small dark curly hair like
the hip girl Roxanne making little garter snakes over his brow
and his great really angelic eyes shining, rolling, a big burbling
baby, a great genius of talk really, wrote research and essays
and has (and is famous for) the greatest possible private library
in the world, right there in that house, library due to his erudi-
tion and this no reflection also on his big income—the house
inherited from father—was also the sudden new bosom friend
of Carmody and about to go to Peru with him, they'd go dig
Indian boys and talk about it and discuss art and visit literaries
and things of that nature, all matters so much had been din-
ning in Mardou's ear (queer, cultured matters) in her love
affair with me that by now she was quite tired of cultured
tones and fancy explicity, emphatic daintiness of expression, of
which roll-eyed ecstatic almost spastic big Bromberg almost
the pastmaster, "O my dear it's such a charming thing and I
think much MUCH better than the Gascoyne translation tho I
do believe—" and Sand imitating him to a T, from some recent
great meeting and mutual admiration—so the two of them
there in the once-to-me adventurous gray dawn of the Metropolitan Great-Rome Frisco talking of literary and musical and
artistic matters, the kitchen littered, Bromberg rushing up
(in pajamas) to fetch three-inch thick French editions of Genet
or old editions of Chaucer or whatever he and Sand'd come to,
Mardou darklashed and still thinking of Yuri (as I'm thinking
to myself) sitting at the corner of the kitchen table, with her
getting-cold rum and coffee—O I on a stool, hurt, broken,
injured, about to get worse, drinking cup after cup and loading up on the great heavy brew—the birds beginning to sing

[387]

finally at about eight and Bromberg's great voice, one of the mightiest you can hear, making the walls of the kitchen throw back great shudders of deep ecstatic sound—turning on the phonograph, an expensive well-furnished completely appointed house, with French wine, refrigerators, three-speed machines with speakers, cellar, etc.—I want to look at Mardou I don't know with what expression—I am afraid in fact to look only to find there the supplication in her eyes saying "Don't worry baby, I told you, I confessed to you I was silly, I'm sorry sorry sorry—" that "I'm-sorry" look hurting me the most as I glance side eyes to see it. . . .

It won't do when the very bluebirds are bleak, which I mention to Bromberg, he asking, "Whatsamatter with you this morning Leo?" (with burbling peek under eyebrows to see me better and make me laugh).—"Nothing, Austin, just that when I look out the window this morning the birds are bleak."—(And earlier when Mardou went upstairs to toilet I did mention, bearded, gaunt, foolish drunkard, to these erudite gentlemen, something about 'inconstancy,' which must have surprised them tho)—O inconstancy!

So they try anyway to make the best of it in spite of my palpable unhappy brooding all over the place, while listening to Verdi and Puccini opera recordings in the great upstairs library (four walls from rug to ceiling with things like *The Explanation of the Apocalypse* in three volumes, the complete works and poems of Chris Smart, the complete this and that, the apology of so-and-so written obscurely to you-know-who in 1839, in 1638—). I jump at the chance to say, "I'm going to sleep," it's now eleven, I have a right to be tired, been sitting on the floor and Mardou with dame-like majesty all this time in the easy chair in the corner of the library (where once I'd seen the famous one-armed Nick Spain sit when Bromberg on a happier early time in the year played for us the original recording of *The Rake's Progress*) and looking so, herself, tragic, lost—hurt so much by my hurt—by my sorriness from her sorriness borrowing—I think sensitive—that at one point in a burst of forgiveness, need, I run and sit at her feet and lean head on her knee in front of the others who by now don't care any more, that is Sand does not care about these things now, deeply engrossed in the music, the books, the brilliant conversation (the likes of which cannot be surpassed anywhere in the world, incidentally, and this too, tho now tiredly, crosses by my epic-wanting brain and I see the scheme of all my life, all acquaintances, loves, worries, travels rising again in a big symphonic mass but now I'm beginning not to care so much any more because of this 105 pounds of woman and brown at that whose little toenails, red in the thonged sandals, make my throat gulp)—"O dear Leo, you DO seem to be bored."—"Not bored! how could I be bored here!"—I wish I had some sympathetic way to tell Bromberg, "Every time I come here there's something wrong with me, it must seem like some awful comment on your house and hospitality and it isn't at all, can't you understand that this morning my heart is broken and out the window is bleak" (and how explain to him the other time I was a guest at his place, again uninvited but breaking in at gray dawn with Charley Krasner and the kids were there, and Mary, and the others came, gin and Schweppes, I became so drunk, disorderly, lost, I then too brooded and slept in fact on the floor in the middle of the room in front of everybody in the height of day—and for reasons so far removed from now, tho still as tho an adverse comment on the quality of Bromberg's weekend)—"No Austin I'm just sick—." No doubt, too, Sand must have hipped him quietly in a whisper somewhere what was happening with the lovers, Mardou also being silent—one of the strangest guests ever to hit Bromberg's, a poor subterranean beat Negro girl with no clothes on her back worth a twopenny (I saw to that generously), and yet so strange faced, solemn, serious, like a

[389]

funny solemn unwanted probably angel in the house—feeling,
as she told me, later, really unwanted because of the circumstances.—So I cop out, from the lot, from life, all of it, go to
sleep in the bedroom (where Charley and I that earlier time
had danced the mambo naked with Mary) and fall exhausted
into new nightmares waking up about three hours later, in the
heartbreakingly pure, clear, sane, happy afternoon, birds still
singing, now kids singing, as if I was a spider waking up in a
dusty bin and the world wasn't for me but for other airier
creatures and more constant themselves and also less liable to
the stains of inconstancy too—

While sleeping they three get in Sand's car and (properly)
drive out to the beach, twenty miles, the boys jump in, swim,
Mardou wanders on the shores of eternity her toes and feet
that I love pressing down in the pale sand against the little
shells and anemones and paupered dry seaweed long washed
up and the wind blowing back her short haircut, as if
Eternity'd met Heavenly Lane (as I thought of it in my bed)
(seeing her also wandering around pouting, not knowing what
to do next, abandoned by Suffering Leo and really alone and
incapable of chatting about every tom dick and harry in art
with Bromberg and Sand, what to do?)—So when they return
she comes to the bed (after Bromberg's preliminary wild
bound up the stairs and bursting in of door and "WAKE up
Leo you don't want to sleep all day we've been to the beach,
really it's not fair!")—"Leo," says Mardou, "I didn't want to
sleep with you because I didn't want to wake up in Bromberg's
bed at seven o'clock in the evening, it would be too much to
cope with, I can't—" meaning her therapy (which she hadn't
been going to any more out of sheer paralysis with me and my
gang and cups), her inadequacy, the great now-crushing
weight and fear of madness increasing in this disorderly awful
life and unloved affair with me, to wake up horrified from
hangover in a stranger's (a kind but nevertheless not altogether

[390]

wholeheartedwelcoming stranger's) bed, with poor incapable Leo.—I suddenly looked at her, listening not to these real poor pleas so much as digging in her eyes that light that had shined on Yuri and it wasn't her fault it could shine on all the world all the time, my light o love—

"Are you sincere?"—("God you frighten me," she said later, "you make me think suddenly I've been two people and betrayed you in one way, with one person, and this other person—it really frightened me—") but as I ask that, "Are you sincere?" the pain I feel is so great, it has just risen fresh from that disordered roaring dream ("God is so disposed as to make our lives less cruel than our dreams," is a quote I saw the other day God knows where)—feeling all that and harkening to other horrified hangover awakenings in Bromberg's and all the hangover awakenings in my life, feeling now, "Boy, this is the real real beginning of the end, you can't go on much further, how much more vagueness can your positive flesh take and how long will it stay positive if your psyche keeps blamming on it—boy, you are going to die, when birds get bleak—that's the sign—." But thinking more roars than that, visions of my work neglected, my well-being (so-called old well-being again) smashed, brain permanently injured now—ideas for working on the railroad—O God the whole host and foolish illusion and entire rigamarole and madness that we erect in the place of onelove, in our sadness—but now with Mardou leaning over me, tired, solemn, somber, capable as she played with the little unshaven uglies of my chin of seeing right through my flesh into my horror and capable of feeling every vibration of pain and futility I could send, as, too, attested by her recognition of "Are you sincere?" as the deepwell sounded call from the bottom—"Baby, let's go home."

"We'll have to wait till Bromberg goes, take the train with him—I guess—." So I get up, go into the bathroom (where I'd been earlier while they were at the beach and sex-

[391]

phantasized in remembrance of the time, on another even wilder and further back Bromberg weekend, poor Annie with her hair done up in curlers and her face no makeup and Leroy poor Leroy in the other room wondering what his wife's doing in there, and Leroy later driving off desperately into the night realizing we were up to something in the bathroom and so remembering myself now the pain I had caused Leroy that morning just for the sake of a little bit of sate for that worm and snake called sex)—I go into the bathroom and wash up and come down, trying to be cheerful.

Still I can't look at Mardou straight in the eye—in my heart, "O why did you do it?"—sensing, in my desperation, the prophecy of what's to come.

As if not enough this was the day of the night of the great Jones party, which was the night I jumped out of Mardou's cab and abandoned her to the dogs of war—the war man Yuri wages gainst man Leo, each one.—Beginning, Bromberg making phonecalls and gathering birthday gifts and getting ready to take the bus to make old 151 at 4:47 for the city, Sand driving us (a sorry lot indeed) to bus stop, where we have quick one in bar across street while Mardou by now ashamed not only of herself but me too stays in back seat of car (tho exhausted) but in broad daylight, trying to catch a wink— really trying to think her way out of trap only I could help her out of if I'm given one more chance—in the bar, parenthetically amazed I am to hear Bromberg going right on with big booming burbling comments on art and literature and even in fact by God queer anecdotes as sullen Santa Clara Valley farmers guzzle at rail, Bromberg doesn't even have consciousness of his fantastic impact on the ordinary—and Sand enjoying, himself in fact also weird—but minor details.—I come out to tell Mardou we have decided to take later train in order to go back to house to pick up forgotten package which is just another ringaroundtherosy of futility for her, she receives this news with solemn lips—ah my love and lost darling (out of date word)—if then I'd known what I know now, instead of returning to bar, for further talks, and looking at her with hurt eyes, etc., and let her lay there in the bleak sea of time untended and unsolaced and unforgiven for the sin of the sea time I'd have gone in and sat down with her, taken her hand, promised her my life and protection—"Because I love you and there's no reason"—but then far from having completely successfully realized this love, I was still in the act of thinking I was climbing out of my doubt about her—but the train came, finally, 153 at 5:31 after all our delays, we got in, and rode to the city—through South San Francisco and past my house, facing one another in coach seats, riding by the big yards in Bayshore and I gleefully (trying to be gleeful) point out a kicked boxcar ramming a hopper and you see the tinscrap shuddering far off, wow—but most of the time sitting bleakly under either stare and saying, finally, "I really do feel I must be getting a rummy nose"—anything I could think of saying to ease the pressure of what I really wanted to weep about—but in the main the three of us really sad, riding together on a train to gayety, horror, the eventual H bomb.

—Bidding Austin adieu finally at some teeming corner on Market where Mardou and I wandered among great sad sullen crowds in a confusion mass, as if we were suddenly lost in the actual physical manifestation of the mental condition we'd been in now together for two months, not even holding hands but I anxiously leading the way through crowds (so's to get out fast, hated it) but really because I was too "hurt" to hold her hand and remembering (now with greater pain) her usual insistence that I not hold her in the street or people'll think she's a hustler—ending up, in bright lost sad afternoon, down Price Street (O fated Price Street) towards Heavenly Lane, among the children, the young good-looking Mex chicks each one making me say to myself with contempt "Ah they're al-

[393]

most all of 'em better than Mardou, all I gotta do is get one of them...but O, but O"—neither one of us speaking much, and such chagrin in her eyes that in the original place where I had seen that Indian warmth which had originally prompted me to say to her, on some happy candlelit night, "Honey what I see in your eyes is a lifetime of affection not only from the Indian in you but because as part Negro somehow you are the first, the essential woman, and therefore the most, most originally most fully affectionate and maternal"—there now is the chagrin too, some lost American addition and mood with it— "Eden's in Africa," I'd added one time—but now in my hurt hate turning the other way and so walking down Price with her every time I see a Mexican gal or Negress I say to myself, "hustlers," they're all the same, always trying to cheat and rob you—harking back to all relations in the past with them— Mardou sensing these waves of hostility from me and silent.

And who's in our bed in Heavenly Lane but Yuri—cheerful—"hey I been workin' all day, so tired I had to come back and get some more rest."—I decide to tell him everything, try to form the words in my mouth, Yuri sees my eyes, senses the tenseness, Mardou senses the tenseness, a knock on the door brings in John Golz (always romantically interested in Mardou in a naiver way), he senses the tenseness, "I've come to borrow a book"—grim expression on his face and remembering how I'd put him down about selectivity—so leaves at once, with book, and Yuri in getting up from bed (while Mardou hides behind screen to change from party dress to home jeans)—"Leo hand me my pants."—"Get up and get 'em yourself, they're right there on the chair, she can't see you"—a funny statement, and my mind feels funny and I look at Mardou who is silent and inward.

The moment she goes to the bathroom I say to Yuri "I'm very jealous about you and Mardou in the backseat last night man, I really am."—"It's not my fault, it was her started it."

[394]

—"Lissen, you're such—like don't let her, keep away—you're such a lady-killer they all fail for you"—saying this just as Mardou returns, looking up sharply not hearing the words but seeing them in the air, and Yuri at once grabs the still open door and says "Well anyway I'm going to Adam's I'll see you there later."

"What did you tell Yuri—?" —I tell her word for word— "God the tenseness in here was unbearable"—(sheepishly I review the fact that instead of being stern and Moses-like in my jealousy and position I'd instead chatted with nervous "poet" talk with Yuri, as always, giving him the tension but not the positiveness of my feelings in words—sheepishly I review my sheepishness—I get sad to see old Carmody somehow—

"Baby I'm gonna—you think they got chickens on Columbus?—I've seen some—And cook it, see, we'll have a nice chicken supper."—"And," I say to myself, "what good is a nice domestic chicken supper when you love Yuri so much he has to leave the moment you walk in because of the pressure of my jealousy and your possibility as prophesied in a dream?" "I want" (out loud) "to see Carmody, I'm sad—you stay here, cook the chicken, eat—alone—I'll come back later and get you."—"But it always starts off like this, we always go away, we never stay alone."—"I know but tonight I'm sad I gotta see Carmody, for some reason don't ask me I have a tremendous sad desire and reason just to—after all I drew his picture the other day" (I had drawn my first pencil sketches of human figures reclining and they were greeted with amazement by Carmody and Adam and so I was proud) "and after all in drawing those shots of Frank the other day I saw such great sadness in the lines under his eyes that I know he—" (to myself: I know he'll understand how sad I am now, I know he has suffered on four continents this way).—Pondering Mardou does not know which way to turn but suddenly I tell

[395]

her of my quick talk with Yuri the part I'd forgotten in the first report (and here too) "He said to me 'Leo I don't want to make your girl Mardou, after all I have no eyes—'." "Oh, so he has no eyes! A hell of a thing to say!" (the same teeth of glee now the portals where pass angry winds, and her eyes glitter) and I hear that junkey-like emphasis on the *ings* where she presses down on her *ings* like many junkies I know, from some inside heavy somnolent reason, which in Mardou I'd attributed to her amazing modernness culled (as I once asked her) "From where? where did you learn all you know and that amazing way you speak?" but now to hear that interesting *ing* only makes me mad as it's coming in a transparent speech about Yuri where she shows she's not really against seeing Yuri again at party or otherwise, "if he's gonna talk like that about no eyes," she's gonna tell him.—"O," I say, "now you WANT to come to the party at Adam's, because there you can get even with Yuri and tell him off—you're so transparent."

"Jesus," as we're walking along the benches of the church park sad park of the whole summer season, "now you're calling me names, transparent."

"Well that's what it is, you think I can't see through that, at first you didn't want to go to Adam's at all and now that you hear—well the hell with that if it ain't transparent I don't know what is."—"Calling me names, Jesus" (shnuffling to laugh) and both of us actually hysterically smiling and as tho nothing had happened at all and in fact like happy unconcerned people you see in newsreels busy going down the street to their chores and where-go's and we're in the same rainy newsreel mystery sad but inside of us (as must then be so inside the puppet filmdolls of screen) the great tumescent turbulent turmoil alliterative as a hammer on the brain bone bag and balls, bang I'm sorry I was ever born. . . .

To cap everything, as if it wasn't enough, the whole world opens up as Adam opens the door bowing solemnly but

[396]

with a glint and secret in his eye and some kind of unwelcome-
ness I bristle at the sight of—"What's the matter?" Then I
sense the presence of more people in there than Frank and
Adam and Yuri.—"We have visitors."—"Oh," I say, "distinguished visitors?"—"I think so."—"Who?"—"Mac Jones
and Phyllis."—"What?" (the great moment has come when
I'm to come face to face, or leave, with my arch literary enemy
Balliol Mac-Jones erstwhile so close to me we used to slop beer
on each other's knees in leaning-over talk excitement, we'd
talked and exchanged and borrowed and read books and lit-
erarized so much the poor innocent had actually come under
some kind of influence from me, that is, in the sense, only, that
he learned the talk and style, mainly the history of the hip or
beat generation or subterranean generation and I'd told him
"Mac, write a great book about everything that happened
when Leroy came to New York in 1949 and don't leave a word
out and blow, go!" which he did, and I read it, critically
Adam and I in visits to his place both critical of the manuscript but when it came out they guarantee him 20,000 dollars
an unheard of sum and all of us beat types wandering the
Beach and Market Street and Times Square when in New
York, tho Adam and I had solemnly admitted, quote, "Jones
is not of us—but from another world—the midtown sillies
world" (an Adamism). And so his great success coming at the
moment when I was poorest and most neglected by publishers
and worse than that hung-up on paranoiac drug habits I became incensed but I didn't get too mad, but stayed black
about it, changing my mind after father time's few local
scythes and various misfortunes and trips around, writing him
apologetic letters on ships which I tore up, he too writing
them meanwhile, and then, Adam acting a year later as some
kind of saint and mediator reported favorable inclinations on
both our parts, to both parties—the great moment when I
would have to face old Mac and shake with him and call it

quits, let go all the rancor—making as little impression on Mardou, who is so independent and unavailable in that new heartbreaking way. Anyway MacJones was there, immediately I said out loud "Good, great, I been wantin' to see him," and I rushed into the living-room and over someone's head who was getting up (Yuri it was) I shook hands firmly with Balliol, sat brooding awhile, didn't even notice how poor Mardou had managed to position herself (here as at Bromberg's as everywhere poor dark angel)—finally going to the bedroom unable to bear the polite conversation under which not only Yuri but Jones (and also Phyllis his woman who kept staring at me to see if it was still crazy) rumbled, I ran to the bedroom and lay in the dark and at the first opportunity tried to get Mardou to lie down with me but she said "Leo I don't want to lay around in here in the dark."—Yuri then coming over, putting on one of Adam's ties, saying, "I'm going out and find me a girl," and we have a kind of whispering rapport now away from them in the parlor—all's forgiven.—But I feel that because Jones does not move from his couch he really doesn't want to talk to me and probably wishes secretly I'd leave, when Mardou roams back again to my bed of shame and sorrow and hidingplace, I say, "What are you talking about in there, bop? Don't tell *him* anything about music."—(Let him find out for himself! I say to myself pettishly)—*I'm* the bop writer!—But as I'm commissioned to get the beer downstairs, when I come in again with beer in arms they're all in the kitchen, Mac foremost, smiling, and saying, "Leo! let me see those drawings they told me you did, I want to see them." —So we become friends again bending over drawings and Yuri has to be showing his too (he draws) and Mardou is in the other room, again forgotten—but it is a historic moment and as we also, with Carmody, study Carmody's South American bleak pictures of high jungle villages and Andean towns where you can see the clouds pass, I notice Mac's ex-

[398]

pensive good-looking clothes, wrist watch, I feel proud of him and now he has an attractive little mustache that makes his maturity—which I announce to everyone—the beer by now warming us all up, and then his wife Phyllis begins a supper and the conviviality flows back and forth—

In the red bulblight parlor in fact I see Jones alone with Mardou questioning, as if interviewing her, I see that he's grinning and saying to himself 'Old Percepied's got himself another amazing doll' and I inside yearn to myself, "Yeah, for how long"—and he's listening to Mardou, who, impressed, forewarned, understanding everything, makes solemn statements about bop, like, "I don't like bop, I really don't, it's like junk to me, too many junkies are bop men and I hear the junk in it."—"Well," Mac adjusting glasses, "that's interesting."—And I go up and say, "But you never like what you come from" (looking at Mardou).—"What do you mean?"—"You're the child of Bop," or the children of bop, some such statement, which Mac and I agree on—so that later when we all the whole gang troop out to further festivities of the night, and Mardou, wearing Adam's long black velvet jacket (for her long) and a mad long scarf too, looking like a little Polish underground girl or boy in a sewer beneath the city and cute and hip, and in the street rushes up from one group to the one I'm in, and I reach out as she reaches me (I'm wearing Carmody's felt hat straight on my head like hipster for joke and my red shirt still, now defunct from weekends) and sweep her littleness off her feet and up against me and go on walking carrying her, I hear Mac's appreciative "Wow" and "Go" laugh in the background and I think proudly "He sees now that I have a real great chick—that I am not dead but going on—old continuous Percepied—never getting older, always in there, always with the young, the new generations—." A motley group in any case going down the street what with Adam Moorad wearing a full tuxedo borrowed from Sam the

[399]

night before so he could attend some opening with tickets free from his office—trooping down to Dante's and Mask again —that Mask, that old po mask all the time—Dante's where in the rise and roar of the social and gab excitement I looked up many times to catch Mardou's eyes and play eyes with her but she seemed reluctant, abstract, brooding—no longer affectionate of me—sick of all our talk, with Bromberg re-arriving and great further discourses and that particular noxious group-enthusiasm that you're supposed to feel when like Mardou you're with a star of the group or even I mean just a member of that constellation, how noisome, tiresome it must have been to her to have to appreciate all we were saying, to be amazed by the latest quip from the lips of the one and only, the newest manifestation of the same old dreary mystery of personality in KaJa the great—disgusted she seemed indeed, and looking into space.

So later when in my drunkenness I managed to get Paddy Cordavan over to our table and he invited us all to his place for further drinking (the usually unattainable social Paddy Cordavan due to his woman who always wanted to go home alone with him, Paddy Cordavan of whom Buddy Pond had said, "He's too beautiful I can't look," tall, blond, big-jawed somber Montana cowboy slowmoving, slow talking, slow shouldered) Mardou wasn't impressed, as she wanted to get away from Paddy and all the other subterraneans of Dante's anyway, whom I had just freshly annoyed by yelling again at Julien, "Come here, we're all going to Paddy's party and Julien's coming," at which Julien immediately leaped up and rushed back to Ross Wallenstein and the others at their own booth, thinking, "God that awful Percepied is screaming at me and trying to drag me to his silly places again, I wish some-one would do something about him." And Mardou wasn't any further impressed when, at Yuri's insistence, I went to the phone and spoke to Sam (calling from work) and agreed to meet him later at the bar across from the office—"We'll all go! we'll all go!" I'm screaming by now and even Adam and Frank are yawning ready to go home and Jones is long gone—rushing around up and down Paddy's stairs for further calls with Sam and at one point here I am rushing into Paddy's kitchen to get Mardou to come meet Sam with me and Ross Wallenstein having arrived while I was in the bar calling says, looking up, "Who let this guy in, hey, who is this? how'd you get in here! Hey Paddy!" in serious continuation of his original dislike and "are-you-a-fag" come-on, which I ignored, saying, "Brother I'll take the fuzz off your peach if you don't shut up," or some such putdown, can't remember, strong enough to make him swivel like a soldier, the way he does, stiff necked, and retire— I dragging Mardou down to a cab to rush to Sam's and all this wild world swirling night and she in her little voice I hear protesting from far away, "But Leo, dear Leo, I want to go home and sleep."—"Ah hell!" and I give Sam's address to the taxidriver, she says NO, insists, gives Heavenly Lane, "Take me there first and then go to Sam's" but I'm really seriously hung-up on the undeniable fact that if I take her to Heavenly Lane first the cab will never make it to Sam's waiting bar before closing time, so I argue, we harangue hurling different addresses at the cab driver who like in a movie waits, but suddenly, with that red flame that same red flame (for want of a better image) I leap out of the cab and rush out and there's another one, I jump in, give Sam's address and off he guns her —Mardou left in the night, in a cab, sick, and tired, and me intending to pay the second cab with the buck she'd entrusted to Adam to get her a sandwich but which in the turmoil had been forgotten but he gave it to me for her—poor Mardou going home alone, again, and drunken maniac was gone.

Well, I thought, this is the end—I finally made the step and by God I paid her back for what she done to me—it had to come and this is it—ploop.

Isn't it good to know winter is coming—
and that life will be a little
more quiet—and you will be home
writing and eating well and we will
be spending pleasant nights wrapped
round one another—and you are home
now, rested and eating well because you
should not become too sad—and I feel
better when I know you are well.

and

Write to me   Anything.
Please stay well
Your Freind
And my love
And Oh
And Love for You
MARDOU
Please

BUT THE DEEPEST premonition and prophesy of all had always been, that when I walked into Heavenly Lane, cutting in sharply from sidewalk, I'd look up, and if Mardou's light was on Mardou's light was on—"But some day, dear Leo, that light will not shine for you"—this a prophesy irrespective of all your Yuris and attenuations in the snake of time.— "Someday she won't be there when you want her to be there, the light'll be out and you'll be looking up and it will be dark in Heavenly Lane and Mardou'll be gone, and it'll be when you least expect it and want it."—Always I knew this—it crossed my mind that night when I ran up, met Sam in the bar, he was with two newspapermen, we bought drinks, I spilled money on the floor, I hurried to get drunk (through with my baby!), rushed up to Adam and Frank's, woke them up again, wrestled on the floor, made noise, Sam tore my

[402]

T-shirt off, bashed the lamp in, drank a fifth of bourbon as of old in our tremendous days together, it was just another big downcrashing in the night and all for nothing... waking up, I, in the morning with the final hangover that said to me, "Too late"—and got up and staggered to the door through the debris, and opened it, and went home, Adam saying to me as he heard me fiddle with the groaning faucet, "Leo go home and recuperate well," sensing how sick I was tho not knowing about Mardou and me—and at home I wandered around, couldn't stay in the house, couldn't stop, had to walk, as if someone was going to die soon, as if I could smell the flowers of death in the air, and I went in the South San Francisco railyard and cried.

GIL ORLOVITZ

A confirmed wanderer between the two coasts, Orlovitz has contributed poetry, prose, and drama to many avant-garde journals and presses. These selections are from his *Diary of Alexander Patience* (Inferno Press, San Francisco, 1958).

29 *March, 10:20 p.m.*

It is said by the wealthy West Coast
Americans that the sun in dark glasses
drives a foreign-make car through the heavens.
The East Coast, less critical, lives
in the slums of the moon. It is hard
to choose between the oranges soaring
the high colonic irrigation of the former,
and the vitreous vandyked brains of the latter.
The farmers, and their tractor cerebration,
connect us both. Lincoln might have said
that a civil war is further off than ever.

4 *April, 1:45 a.m.*

There are in the advertisements the chatter
of the little mythmakers, like that Princeton
lad who whittled out the magic car
where rain fell in harmless hypotenuse.
Or that graying boy, Yale '40, who
comforted thousands with the Savings Plan,
in which Mother reached for the skillet
as Dad, in a hat of battered tenderness,
brought home a mess of trout. Electric
this and atomic that; no sooner one
vacation ends, another must begin,

[404]

while lurks the little boy who will draw
a mustache on a stained-glass christ.

5 June, 10 a.m.

    "Try the longshot in the 4th"
Al said, picking the snot from
his eyes with the racing form.
Outside the candystore two old
things hauled a cartful of wash
between them as a wobbling idiot
son from the laundromat
under the jellyfish sun.
They turned the corner and never
said a word that a plateglass
window forehead couldve heard.

A postman felt for his oats.
"Went to Vegas over the weekend
with three hundred and came back
with four. Not bad" Al said;
"caught the Rosemary Clooney show
too. Terrific. They were standing
five deep at the bar."
I worried a little about
the two old things hauling the wash,
that man and woman with two
humps of fat on the backs of their
necks, pommels age rode on.
I worried, but not for long: they
have cemetaries in California, too.
So, free of charge, here's an
idea: how about a chain of
cemetaries, like hotels, or supermarkets,

[405]

with travelling salesmen, and Executive
Offices where most deaths occur,
and a Wire Service with a
slogan, say, "Telegraph Her
Your Dust" and "We Bury
Anywhere" and "Free Pickup
And Delivery". Because death in
America ought to be dynamic
too, with a streamlined advertising
campaign to sell it, like "Die
Now—Why Wait" or "Your
Best Friend Wont Tell You—Have
You got C.O.?† (†Cadaver Odor)".
Better yet, "Be The Death Of
The Party". Like I say, the possibilities
are limitless under an Expanding
Dichotomy, as the economists say.

The Bull Market in Rebellion

By JAMES LEIGH

James Leigh, whose "Los Angeles at War" appeared on page 271 contributes an equally laconic article on the San Francisco literary scene as affected by the goings and comings of the Beat Generation.

In the early Fifties, when I lived for a year on San Francisco's North Beach, Upper Grant Avenue was unmistakably Bohemian, in an artsy-craftsy sort of way, but it was hardly a tourist attraction. By the autumn of 1958, when my wife and I lived for several months in an apartment exactly between The Co-existence Bagel Shop and The Place, all hell had broken loose. What had taken place in the interim had already been ambiguously chronicled at some length by the mass media. We might have been excusably bored, but for the fact that boredom is a fruit of leisure, and we couldn't even sleep. In Number One and Number Three, parties ran nonstop around the clock. We were in Number Two, and if we threw open the windows to let in air from Grant Avenue, it came in full of car exhaust, hi-fi jazz, bongo drumming, and the permanent shout, mutter and shuffle from the sidewalk below. As soon as we could, we moved.

Since then, so much has been talked and written about the *phenomenon* of the Beat Generation—so much from Inside, so much more from Outside—that I have to dig through it, dog-like, to unearth the memory of that autumn. It was literally a *scene*, and, quite as literally, *crazy*. Busy enough in the daytime, Grant teemed and twitched at night, the sidewalks full of people, the street a circling train of cars in second gear, and everyone looking. At the sandal shop across the Avenue there would be, dependably, a few of the real "denizens," as the papers like to call the stars of the show.

As a rule they inhabited an Olympian disdain for their audience, only breaking out from time to time to snarl at one "square," or, contemptuously, to "act crazy" for another. There were as well the "weekend Bohemians" from Marin County or the Peninsula, driving sports cars, wearing prescription dark glasses and faultlessly sloppy sweaters from Magnin's or Robert Kirk's. "If Brooks Brothers made sweatshirts," my wife said, "they'd clean up." There were tourists with cameras, hunting beards, and old ladies who had ditched the Gray Line tour to take a walk on the wild side. There were highschool boys and overage toughs in threes and fours, looking for someone to punch. There were lone office-looking young men, buttoned-down but interested. There were husbands and wives walking each other after the weekly dinner out. There were a lot of policemen, and more to come. The many Chinese who live along Grant stayed inside, except to shop or go to work, and they kept their children in. Outside on the street, everyone was looking, waiting for something to happen. And something may have, but it would have had to be something spectacular to satisfy the enormous itch of confused expectation which charged the air. The most violent act I witnessed was a fistfight over a parking place between two men in business suits, and shortly after that we moved, leaving our sleeping pills in the medicine cabinet.

We couldn't know it then, of course, but the avalanche of testimony, criticism and comment had only begun. No sooner had messianic primary sources like *Howl* and *On the Road* come out than they were almost buried, not only beneath imitations but beneath attacks, defenses, and "balanced judgments." As a literary movement, the Beat Generation was already something upon which professors had to "take a position," and writers—"serious," "popular," and all points in between—immediately broadened their pursuit of the Significance of it all. Psychologists and social historians, syndicated columnists and shoestring pamphleteers, ministers, magistrates and police chiefs—all had something to say, and said it as loud and· often as possible.

If only by the law of averages, there were lucid and literate observers of the Phenomenon. The novelist Norman Mailer qualifies as one of these, though his vision of It is aggressively apocalyptic. He notes the succession of descriptive words which came into use during the Fifties, from "Hipster" to "Beat Generation" to "Beatnik." The first of these was an insider's word of approval, denoting primarily the jazz *aficionado;* the second was a generic term used to refer to a group of writers, then to a social—or asocial—movement whose values they expressed and helped dictate; the last, coined by Mr. Herb Caem, a San Francisco columnist, came rapidly to be nothing more precise than a synonym for "nonconformist"

"The addition of 'nik' . . . a pejorative diminutive in Yiddish, gave the quality of condescension to the word which proved agreeable to the newspaper mentality," says Mailer, and he is exactly right. The subtle connotative downgrading from "Hipster" to "Beatnik" also made the mass promotion of the image attached to the latter distinctly less risky. Under the tutelage of the mass media, millions more people used the term "Beat Generation" than had ever used "Hipster." Then came "Beatnik," which *really* caught on. Linguistically it pretended to be more specific than the generic term which is succeeded, but in actuality it was even less so, and hence was suitable for the widest manipulation.

For the fad-bound it now became possible to *be*—or to play at being—a Beatnik without leaving the comfort of home. For how many vaguely dissatisfied adolescents was it no more than a novel posture in which sulk around the house, "rejecting" Mama and Daddy as "square" with still no better notion of Why? Every drugstore in America had a rack of dark glasses, and the clothes called for by the mass image might be bought at the best shops, or through the mail; for the really serious, there were paperback books, which might be read or worn. LIFE had a picture spread of midwestern highschool girls (minus boys) enjoying a Beatnik party, but Hollywood reinforced the nation's moral structure with an epic about a Beatnik sculptor-murderer who coated his victims in hot metal and sold them for *objets d'art.* The anti-commercial rebellion had first become news, then a marketable commodity, and at last a thumping commercial success for a number of industries. Whatever philosophic or artistic content it had once—and perhaps still—contained was lost in the shadows of mass-produced mannequins posed in black stockings, clutching bongo drums or empty wine bottles.

Recently, in that very newspaper whose most highly-paid columnist had invented the word, there appeared a front-page Farewell to the Beatniks in two installments. The burden of this thickly nostalgic valediction was that the "real" Beatniks were leaving the North Beach for happier haunts— Venice (California), New Orleans, Greenwich Village—and leaving behind only a glossily respectable commercial *doppelganger* to trap tourists. Those tourists, I suppose, who are not yet fed up with the endless accounts complete with Glossaries of Hip Talk—of cats with beards and chicks in shades making casual homo- and/or heterosexual love, drinking wine and smoking marijuana, playing bongos and holding séances with the spirit of Charlie Parker, professing Zen Buddhism or Existentialism, and being quoted, in words which almost everyone can almost understand, about their withdrawal, alienation, disaffiliation, and rejection of conformist middle-class morality. In short, the End of an Era.

I couldn't resist the suspicion that, having helped mightily to create the Phenomenon, having then milked it for all it was worth (including, at low ebb, some dirty tickling of the mass reflex with lip-smacking reports of winsome blonde secretaries supporting handsome young Negroes), the editors decided to give it one more good squeeze because it was no longer news. Quite naturally, their own part in publicizing the "spontaneous" rebellion could not be considered news. And how anticlimactic it seemed a few days later when the neologist himself mentioned that the heralded exodus had somehow reversed itself—the Beatniks were back! The whole affair smacked a little of Frankenstein and his unruly monster, except that the disobedient parties were simply people who happened, as people will, not to behave as a well-disciplined Phenomenon should.

I was on the scene briefly, though I didn't "make it." The testimonies of those who did are plentifully in print. Some are worth reading. I know, however, and not merely by conjecture, that there were people of talent and integrity, intelligence and imagination, in or of or about the movement for which we are now stuck with the sorry label Beat Generation. Some disaffiliated themselves further—from It; some stuck it out. A few found markets; many were swamped. Many of the patterns in American life which the best of them rejected plainly deserved rejection; at the very least they deserved hard examination. I doubt that these patterns have been seriously shaken by the Phenomenon; I suspect they may rather have been strengthened. At this point, meliorists who like to look on the sunny side of mass culture may say, "But look how many more people were exposed to *Howl* because of all the publicity." Yet for every person who read *Howl*, there were a hundred who simply equated Beards with Beatniks— probably a thousand for every one who read *Howl* thoughtfully. Exploitation seems to demand dilution, and diluted rebellion is worthless, or worse.

During World War II, Australian soldiers had a way of describing Americans which, bowdlerized in the middle, may

[411]

be repeated as follows: "If the Yanks can't fight it, they'll make love to it; if they can't make love to it, they'll make a sandwich of it." Some Americans took this as a grudging tribute to our spirit of pragmatic free enterprise, but I make a connection between it and what happened to the Beat Generation. What comes out seems to me a clear lesson for potential rebels:

If your line of thinking runs, even mildly, to political rebellion, it may be said with a great deal of security that the Federal Bureau of Investigation will take care of you. But if you are apolitical, subversive only of such comprehensive socio-economic ideals as the suburban tract home with two children or the centrifugal spiral of consumerism—watch out! Do your rebelling quietly, in ones and twos. If you must write books, don't become a Personality who gives interviews. Above all don't adhere to any duplicable style of speech, clothing, cosmetics or hairstyling—any pattern of behavior at all, however harmless and absurd, into which our gimmick-hungry culture-merchants, doubtless projecting their fantasies of delicious sin and rebellion, can turn into a marketable commodity. Otherwise, you may depend on it, they will not fight. Then they may or may not make love to you—on their own terms, in their own image—but they will certainly make a sandwich of you.

On Casting D. H. Lawrence

By HERBERT FEINSTEIN

Before coming to California in 1954, Feinstein practiced law in Massachusetts. Since then he has worked as a lawyer in Beverly Hills and San Francisco, taught at the University of California and San Francisco State College, and published film criticism in many journals, including *The Reporter, Film Quarterly,* etc.

On a recent field trip to Hollywood,[1] I ran into an old friend who works for what is humorously called a talent agency. My friend asked me what I think of all the legal fuss attending *Lady Chatterley's Lovers* [sic]. When I said that the lady's serious affair was solo, the agent, whose notions of prurience have been conditioned by *Playboy*, was surprised. "You mean to say," he wondered, "you mean to say, she had only one?" Again, inaccurately, my friend went on to say that Jerry Wald is preparing to film *Lady Chatterley's Lover*. The agent reported Wald is having a lot of trouble in casting the lead. About four years back, the agent said, Wald intended to star in the picture an alumnus of the Actor's Studio who has since plunged downhill into the bottle, baldness, automobile accidents, and the global courtship of a vintaged torch singer whose notoriety beats his own. The agent conceded, "The boy can still act, but who could take a chance on him?" Gone, then, was Wald's star of yesteryear, and his picture lacked a leading man.

I knew, of course, that Jerry Wald has been planning to film not D. H. Lawrence's *Lady Chatterley's Lover*, but his *Sons and Lovers*. Since our talk had already been strained by one correction, the professor in me pedagogically asked the agent what part the on-the-skids actor had been slated to play.

[1]The last week in July, 1959.

[413]

Surely the fellow's methodologized charm, even in its wispiest hour, never held the sturdier stuffs of Mellors or Chatterley. Trapped, my friend's wisecrack became inevitable: "Maybe he could play Lady Chatterley."

Next morning, some business carried me out to see Jerry Wald at his Company of Artists, an "indie"[2] whose presidential offices are lodged in Bungalow 10 at the Twentieth Century Fox Studios. When I arrived at that outer-office where mothers sit clutching their beribboned darlings, and where hopefuls burn to issue through the magic turnstile so that they may be born anew on screen, I was irritated to learn I could not walk in. Mr. Wald's office considerately had arranged a car pass for me; and, in Hollywood, tokens of prestige are not to be denied. I was obliged to retrace 100 yards in the oppressive heat in order to drive within the gates. Wald's air-conditioned bungalow shames its country cousins in either Far Rockaway or Capistrano. Its walls are adorned with splendidly framed posters which announce showings of Toulouse-Lautrec, Chagall, Picasso, etc.; but, strangely, the posters are clever imitations, not originals, of the work of the masters. The office furnishings are plush and comfortable, save for the larger-than-life ashtrays which gave me the guilty feeling I was flicking ashes into exotic, spic-and-span dinner plates. Two secretaries in the anteroom typed pleasantly. The factotum-in-chief was a marvel of efficiency. Based upon a two minute phone call she had figured out an impressive amount about my business purpose. In the short time I had to wait for Mr. Wald, I was again reminded of the importance of status in the film capital when the girl called to break her appointment at the beauty parlor: she did not give her own name, but identi-

[2]An "indie" is an independent film-making company which leases production facilities from a major studio. The independent company may release its pictures through the studio—in the way Company of Artists releases through Twentieth Century Fox.

fied herself as "Mr. Wald's secretary."

Some folklorists in Hollywood cast Jerry Wald as Budd Schulberg's sad portrait of Sammy in *What Makes Sammy Run?* Even reckoning Schulberg says that, in the years between, Sammy probably has had himself analyzed, I would deny that Wald is in any way recognizable as Schulberg's nasty makeout. Wald is short, heavy set, and twinkling. He lisps. Save for some natty white moccasins, the producer was dressed with all the sleekness of an undertaker. Throughout our long talk he was sweeter and more cordial than any mogul has the right to be.

Once our business was pleasantly dispatched, we settled down to talking about pictures, mainly Mr. Wald's pictures. Movies, one soon sees, are his life. In an industry where many of the big name producers make few films—David O. Selznick is as bleak a case in point as any—Wald is admired as a producer who produces. In the three years he has been at Fox (Wald transferred from Columbia in 1956) he has made eight pictures. In late 1957, there was the bonanza *Peyton Place;* next year, he made two prestige pictures putatively based upon the work of William Faulkner—a winner, *The Long Hot Summer,* and a loser, *The Sound and the Fury.* In midsummer 1959, he has at least five in the works. He is winding up *The Best of Everything* (wherein Joan Crawford comes back again); he is shooting *Beloved Infidel* (Gregory Peck in the last days of F. Scott Fitzgerald finds true love with Deborah Kerr's Sheilah Graham); he is starting *Story on Page One* and *Hound Dog Man* (more on these anon); and he is planning his "next" picture, the still embryonic *Sons and Lovers.*

Wald pays enormous respect to Lawrence's written word, perhaps more than any translator from the genre of the novel into the medium of celluloid should. In 1957, Satyajit Ray, the Indian film-maker, spoke of his problems in making a novel into a film—Mr. Ray was talking about *Pather Panchali*: "I made whatever changes I felt were demanded by the medium, departing, that is, only from the literary form, not from the truth. Cinema has its own way of telling the truth and it must be left free to function in its own right. I am interested first and last and only in the cinematic way of motion-picture making." Quite differently, Wald visualizes the screen player as a carbon copy of the character on Lawrence's printed page rather than as a viable, flesh-and-blood man or woman. Thus the producer imposes upon himself the impossible chore of carrying out Lawrence's *literal* description of a character, though Lawrence himself has bequeathed to us *three* different, shifting ladies Chatterley. Plato has adjudicated what should happen to those who seek to imitate an imitation: they are to be kicked out of the Republic, or as *Variety* might say, they are simply poison at the box office. Wald's reverence for Lawrence's expressed intention becomes a good thing, I think, when he wants to recreate the *mise en scène* of the novel. He has sent me a note which explains, "We plan to make this film in the real locations of this story in England." Then Wald goes on to give this as a reason why "it is most likely that an English actress will portray the role." Mrs. Morel is the role in question.

In Paul Morel, Lawrence created what he said was a largely autobiographical figure: a sensitive, artistic son of proletarian beginnings, strangled by the silver noose supplied by a dominant mother. (There is the important difference that Lawrence seems to have beaten the fix with his wife, Frieda, but that is beside the point here.)

The male lead of Paul Morel remains Wald's big problem. As Wald shrewdly observed, "I can't cast the parents till I know how old their son is." The dimmed star who would have been "great" four years back clearly is "out." In the relentless casting which takes place, say, in Schwab's drug-store on Sunset Boulevard, Lawrence Harvey already has the part. Mr. Harvey has just served one petulant turn as John Braine's pseudo-Lawrentian hero in *Room at the Top*. Harvey, in fact, this past summer visited Hollywood, where Jules Stein, the Chairman of the Boards at MCA (the world's biggest talent agency) feted Harvey in much the manner as of yore doled out to his slipped predecessor, the former inside trackman for Paul Morel. But Mr. Wald isn't saying.

In a town where charm is con, cash is king, and casting often a matter of contact and connive, Jerry Wald is brave in that he abides little by the need of a "star" in every big part—witness his plans for the beloveds of Paul Morel. Wald has only a Clara—Joan Collins, who should make a very good one. Miss Collins is tall, statuesque, and, at the same time, both sexual and cold. If her mannerisms are reminiscent of those of a bad actress, that seems precisely what Lawrence *intends* Clara to be. Miss Collins is a natural. Miriam presents a harder case. She is the intense girl whose consuming love Paul is never able to meet. Lawrence has Paul's mother say of Miriam: "She is one of those who will want to suck a man's soul out till he has none of his own left..." Again, Mrs. Morel: "I can't bear it. I could let another woman—but not her. She'd leave me no room, not a bit of room..." In the bygone time of four years ago, Elizabeth Taylor had been mentioned for dark, enticing Miriam; after all, she had played a similar girl in *A Place in the Sun*.[3] It should go without too much saying that the Hollywood wags claim Miss Taylor now requires a more youthful photographer in order to be Miriam. Wald does not abide that Miss Taylor's years (she is all of 27) preclude her playing the part: but, he says, "She is too sensual." Perhaps Miss Taylor's four husbands enjoin her chances; an actress' art, after all, must not deviate too far from her publicity. Wald maintains that Miriam should "present a conflict between the flesh and the spirit." He is, for that reason, considering for the

[3] *A Place in the Sun* (1951) was George Stevens' screen version of Theodore Dreiser's novel, *An American Tragedy*.

[417]

role Heather Sears, a demure British actress. Miss Sears, I must say, as the psychosomatically deaf, dumb, and blind girl in *The Story of Esther Costello* all but acted off the screen Joan Crawford, who was busy playing Movie Star. However, my reservations about Miss Sears stem from her performance in *Room at the Top*, in which she was nondescript, and was herself pushed around by another old cinema pro, Simone Signoret. About Miss Sears' demonstrable sexuality—to be quite ungentlemanly—there is a large question, a question one must never ask about Lawrence's Miriam who is by "love itself possessed."

Despite the tentativeness of their ages, Wald spoke at length about finding a suitable couple of Morels who might play Paul's parents. Exact chronology may not be all that important, since every Hollywood makeup artist and camera man has had plenty of practice in manipulating the middle years of a great many stars. Mrs. Morel dominates the novel in much the way she dominates her son; and it is her grim victory, his bad luck, that she continues to rule from beyond the grave. A tough part to fill. Wald is looking for someone small, sexual, powerful, and—preferably—English. The choice of his present star, Joan Crawford, seems to me inexorable. Though some of Miss Crawford's fans might deny the fact she looks old enough for the role—Mrs. Morel hovers around 53—surely the art of Westmore can fix *that*. When she has the right part, and the director manages to fight it out with her, I yield to none in my addiction to Miss Crawford's florid style of film necromancy. I have in mind three films of Miss Crawford's— all produced by Wald—*Possessed, Humoresque,* and *Mildred Pierce*; for the last role she won an Academy Award. Miss Crawford's extreme Americanism seems to count against her as Mrs. Morel. Mr. Wald somewhat inconsistently has tried to obtain the just as homegrown Helen Hayes: I take it Miss Hayes isn't available. Mr. Wald is also interested in Margaret Leighton who played *Separate Tables* on the stage, and who was the sex-craving Caddy in Wald's *The Sound and the Fury* (a bad part cagily refused by Lana Turner). But, worries Wald, Miss Leighton is "too tall. I need a *small* woman." Another British actress, Celia Johnson (*Brief Encounter, The Captain's Paradise*) figures as an alternative. "But she is too, too . . ." Wald groped for the word, and I supplied it—"fawnlike." And, in the last analysis, Jerry Wald means to have Vivien Leigh in the part.

Morel poses no less a casting problem than does his wife. Any actor who looks like a Nottinghamshire coal miner, mumbles his lines, and who especially combines bestiality with sweetness is hard to come by. The focus of sympathy in the novel lies with Paul's father. Despite Lawrence's expressed sympathy for the mother in her rough marriage, the lady comes across as a moral monster—one whose rigid and possessive love disables her son from ever loving anyone else. Most of Lawrence's unconscious admiration, at any rate, flows to the all-too-human, at times brutal, at times gentle, miner. Wald said Sir John Gielgud was first choice for Walter Morel, and added he was very sorry Gielgud's commitments in a play foreclosed that happy possibility. Mr. Wald brushed aside my doubts that Sir John is too identified with roles which have called for the most elegant of diction—with old man Barrett, with Cassius, with Hamlet himself. The producer rightly corrected the professor when he pointed out that a great actor should be judged by his capacities, not typed by the roles one has happened to see him play. Wald said he could get Jack Hawkins, who, he added, "more than looks the part." Hawkins seems to me the most cloddish of actors; for instance, his brainwasher in *The Prisoner* suffered from such stiffness of the upper lip that nothing which issued from under it resembled the speech of a man. Mr. Wald does not agree. "What scares me," Wald said, "What scares me is that Hawkins would be on the nose casting." Life, Jerry Wald imagines, need only imitate art, not trump it. Still, Hawkins seems set for Morel.

I should add that Mr. Wald refused to take seriously my own surprise casting of Noel Coward (beat, inarticulate, bittersweet) as Morel. I have had this sop from Wald's Executive Assistant: "Mr. Wald has asked me to thank you for...suggesting Mr. Noel Coward for the role of Morel in *Sons and Lovers*. I am sure he will give Mr. Coward every consideration when we cast the film." To cite the lesson Mr. Wald taught me: Coward's abilities impress me as great indeed; though I do admit one would be hard put to find a Paul who would seem a likely offspring of *both* Joan Crawford and Noel Coward.

Gross appearances continue as Hollywood's great realities, and a scintilla of the last tycoon flickered when Wald went into the matter of titles. "A title," he said, "is all important. A bad one can ruin a picture." He believes that his current handful (*The Best of Everything, Beloved Infidel, Hound Dog Man, Story on Page One,* and *Sons and Lovers*) "all have terrific titles." But he maintained my own title, "Dancing Is How Salome Ends" had better find its text in the Bible, and that something as abstruse as another in my file, "The Peloponnesian Actress," would never make its way either as a war or a Hollywood story. "That's all well and good," he interposed, "but that title would only confuse the audience." Mr. Wald seems always to envision an "audience" out there. He remembered warning a gifted young writer who persisted in calling his first novel *Lost Country*. This, said Wald, was a misnomer, for the book was neither about the jungle nor the Far West: it was about adolescence. Predictably, Wald regretted, "*Lost Country* got lost."

Enter pathos: Mr. Wald craves intellectual respectability. The *International Motion Picture Almanac* for 1959 lists, soon after Jerry Wald's name, "e. Columbia Univ. B.A." During Mr. Wald's early days in New York as a radio columnist for the *Daily Graphic* only the College at Columbia awarded the B.A. There is no record of Jerry Wald's having been graduated from any Columbia school. One Gerson E. Wald did attend the Extension at Morningside Heights in 1928–29.[4] Whenever Wald speaks of the Academy, one senses Jerry Wald's own lost country, the world he never made. The thing which seemed to impress Wald most about me is the fact I happen to earn my living as a teacher of literature. He reads *Partisan Review* and he reveres highbrows such as Lionel Trilling and Mark Schorer. "He does?" Wald wistfully asked when I said that Schorer teaches the D. H. Lawrence course in Berkeley. He went on, "I once sent Mark Schorer a fan letter." This was, to be sure, more of a form letter, the sort Wald dictates by the reel to recruit writers to write—on speculation—"treatments" of their work, a few of which he buys. Wald is no snob. A writer as lowbrow as the late, and lamented by a quantity of women, John McPartland, whose *No Down Payment* Wald did film, received some encouraging words to send on his ideas when Wald discovered McPartland in *Esquire*. The files in many Hollywood literary agencies (MCA, Famous Artists, Frank Cooper Associates) are crammed with form fan letters from Jerry Wald.

He does buy a lot. Among the skits at the last annual banquet of the Writers Guild of America, West (the old Screen Writers Guild), one sketch lampooned Jerry Wald's well known practice of acquiring film rights to more properties than any producer can possibly use. At the end of the skit, by prearrangement, and quite predictably, Wald rushed onstage to declaim, "I'd like to buy that!" It is the fact too that Wald promoted Rona Jaffee's *The Best of Everything* into a brief best seller. Before Miss Jaffee, then unknown, undertook to write the novel, Wald had had compiled a mass of sociological statistics on the emperiled, contemporary working girl; and he offered the idea of a novel about a bevy of career girls both in and out of the sack—a Grand Hotel from nine to five, so to

[4]The *1947–48 International Motion Picture Almanac* gives Jerry Wald's date of birth as September 16, 1911; by the 1959 edition, the date has become September 16, 1912. Of course, many people listed in the *Motion Picture Almanac* grow younger through the years.

[421]

speak—to several young Hollywood writers. On "spec." But the best is none too good for Wald's own grown-up love child. *The Best of Everything* will be reissued in paperback to promote the Big Picture which stars Joan Crawford as the Editor-in-Chief of a whole streetful of Big City Girls, played by Suzy Parker, Hope Lange, Diane Baker, Martha Hyer.

Moving deep into that house of intellect, Wald was proud to claim, "Clifford Odets has just finished writing an original screenplay for me. On what morality means in the modern world. We're not interested in making just any picture. Odets is directing too." Wald hopes Odets' *Story on Page One* "captures all the excitement of a regular play." Wald and Odets collaborated a dozen years ago in the filming of Fanny Hurst's *Humoresque*, in which John Garfield fiddled while Joan Crawford drowned. Expectably, Wald did not think much of Odets' *The Big Knife*, which became a movie too. *The Big Knife* is a grim exposé of the evils of a film titan who makes Sammy Glick look like a cub scout. Wald was also pleased that he has been working with Paul Bowles. Bowles is a writer whose smut (e.g., *The Sheltering Sky*) I find disgusting, though Mr. Wald assured me he has been able "to clean it up."

Time and again, Wald iterated he is interested in making pictures which are a "challenge." On the subject of "challenge" Mr. Wald did indulge in the spate of grim clichés which floods Hollywood: it goes something like this—"the public is growing up, and no producer can count any more on the average mentality of his audience as being that of a twelve year old." Opuses like *The Fly* and *The Return of the Fly* make me estimate it at a good deal under twelve. If Mr. Wald's are the clichés of progress, I grant they are a good deal easier to listen to than the idiocies uttered—forgive me for speaking ill of the dead and the venerable—idiocies uttered by old time bigwigs like the late Cecil B. DeMille and by Samuel Goldwyn.

Wald maintains that in addition to morality, he wants to

explore cinematically the issue of what is love. "Love," he laments, as imaged in the cinema, has become something even worse than the phenomenon which is many-splendored. Wald said, "Too often love means a four-letter word." Sure, it does: L-O-V-E. But Wald wants to explore the mystery of love; and he buzzed his secretary to remind him to take home his project book on Mark Schorer's novel which analyzes some of the subtler strategies of the grand passion, Schorer's brilliantly called, *The Wars of Love.*

During our talk several phone calls were put through to Wald, and I must say he handled all crises with aplomb. The first call concerned Suzy Parker, a Wald comer, who plays the moribund working girl in *The Best of Everything.* In real life the handsome, highstrung Miss Parker works as a model of high fashion. Not unreasonably, the studio asked her to pose for stills in order to sell the picture. The actress said she was willing, but claimed that Hollywood has no photographer who can do her justice: to make her look good, Miss Parker wanted her very special camera man (Richard Avedon, I think) flown in from New York. Mr. Wald magnanimously acceded. He comforted someone who had phoned, presumably to protest the expense. "On the subject of who can take her picture right," Wald said, "I can't argue with the girl...that's how she earns her living." Then resignedly, he sighed, "You and I can't always be fighting windmills."

Another request for special photography was raised by a picture service that wanted to hunt with camera Wald's hot new singing property, Fabian, age 16, who is, one gathers, an adolescent Elvis Presley. The service alleged it had once gotten Harry Truman into *Life.* Mr. Wald parried the request with his own question, "How do you get him?" It seems that Fabian has been spending his time out at the Studio Ranch in the San Fernando Valley where other livestock for outdoors pictures are kept. Wald announced that Fabian was about to star in

[423]

"Fred Gipson's American classic, *Hound Dog Man.*" Adroitly, Wald was figuring out a way to put the photographer at-home-on-the-range with Fabian.

A final call once more raised the art of casting. This involved the negotiations for the services of Rita Hayworth for the lead in *Story on Page One.* The part is in a state of flux, since it may have to be rewritten to fit Miss Hayworth's special talents. Mr. Wald, I take it, requires a beautiful ruin. Here, Wald's creative imagination, for once, failed him. He told his caller that if Miss Hayworth turned out to be available, then the character would have to be changed from that of a "pushover." Strangely, he added, "She can't play the mother of any ten year old kid." I should like to know why not; Miss Hayworth's younger daughter is now nine.[5]

Our conversation could have gone on, but another call reminded me of how busy a magnate Wald is. I asked him if he reads articles about making pictures. He smiled a friendly, "yeah." I shook Jerry Wald's hand, and searched for that car in which I might exit to the dull, tame world.

Postscript

Daily Variety, for Tuesday, February 9th, 1960, page four, reported that a rough cut of *Sons and Lovers* was being wound up in England. The director of the picture was Jack Cardiff and its scenarist was Gavin Lambert. The cast included Dean Stockwell as Paul Morel, Heather Sears as Miriam, Mary Ure as Clara, Trevor Howard as Walter Morel, and the *tall* Wendy Hiller as Mrs. Morel. Of all the actors Jerry Wald was considering in mid-summer 1959, Miss Sears alone got the part.

[5]Note, January, 1960. *Story on Page One*, as released, has Rita Hayworth, as a woman of great integrity, a model mother of a girl of about six. The lady, wrongly accused of the murder of her brutal cop of a husband, while on trial for her life, admits she slept with her lover "just once," and then under the most extenuating of circumstances. Further, the heroine testifies she is "ashamed" of having broken her marriage vows, as "what woman wouldn't be?"

[424]

Lenore and the Boys

By HAMILTON WRIGHT

Wright is a graduate of Choate and Yale, and now lives
in Connecticut, none of which obscures his insight into
things like the delicate relationships of resident Californians with tourists.

The first time Lenore ever saw Ray and Harry they were
driving down Sunset in a convertible with the boxer between
them, on their way to the market to buy broccoli. Then one
afternoon she heard loafers scuffing the sidewalk outside the
drape shop, and the same two strolled in out of the sunshine.

"Hello," Lenore said, pleasantly. Hard to tell, she
thought, how old they are.

"Do you carry seventy-two-inch antique white satin?"
asked the darker one. Both boys seemed to wait breathlessly
for her answer.

"I'm afraid not," Lenore replied, "I'm sorry." And she
decided, about my age, only they look younger. Twenty-four
maybe.

"Oh, no. This can't go on."

"We're decorating a bedroom," said Ray, emerging from
behind Harry. His hair was fair and fine, already getting scarce.

"I wish I could help," Lenore was really sorry, "but
seventy-*two*-inch——"

"I know. We simply cannot find any. And we've got to
have that amount of fullness to make our bedroom windows
look right."

There came a bark from the front seat of the convertible
outside.

"What a cute boxer," Lenore said. "What's she called?"

"Stella," said Ray.

"And she's pregnant," Harry told her.

[425]

"My," said Lenore, while Stella barked again.

"She's so loyal, that one. Refuses to have the puppies till we find our satin. She knows how hard we've tried." But Harry's glance, Lenore saw, had turned impatient. "Couldn't you possibly suggest anything?"

"Not so much for our sake," Ray put in, "as hers."

Lenore laughed. It began to feel more like a reunion than a first meeting. "Poor Stella." She looked sideways and down, rather sagely. "Give me a week. I've got antique white satin ideas."

Harry turned to the car, calling, "Stella, do you hear that, sweetie?"

"It may take longer, but I think."

"Wonderful."

"For Stella's sake," said Lenore archly.

"But naturally," Harry answered. The boys began scuffing toward the door. "Which means you'll be seeing us again soon. We'll even christen a puppy after you. What's your name?"

"She's nice," Ray said to Harry as they got back in the car, meaning she's not too bright and she's unselfish.

Lenore had changed her name from Lenora di Bianchi to Lenore White. She was a tall, auburn-haired Italian girl with pale skin, her slimness most striking in bright colors on black. A good girl, but a trifle absent-minded, she lived in the pink haze of lotus land among movie people—this suited her nature. She liked dreaming in the sun, earrings, Charles Boyer, and what she thought of as clever talk.

There had been none of this drifting-out-to-California for Lenore. She was a dark weary-faced child of four when her family settled in Los Angeles. The day after her papa saw Rod La Rocque cruising down Hollywood Boulevard in a Stutz with the top down, little Lenora was placed in a convent.

[426]

People weren't always aware of her charms until they saw her walk, and then they stared. It was just one of those things that happened as she grew up, and had nothing to do with Hollywood. An easy, slowish walk it was, much more assured than she felt on the inside. Her greatest asset was her greatest fraud.

Although aware of these assets, in private Lenore was puzzled; occasionally even unhappy. Things simply weren't going right between her and men; time was passing and she couldn't ever quite decide what to do, because Love and Pleasant Company—as she referred to them in her mind— refused to get together in her life. The two had never yet quite merged in one man. Again and again she found herself tossed back and forth between men who had little but their large, anxious hands to make love with—and boys like Harry and Ray, boys who were so much alert to things; pleasant company, yes; laughs, yes; but who remained far from impatient to settle down to love as Lenore thought of it.

"I'm straddling a fence that isn't there." It got said out loud one night after too many stingers.

Only the fence *was* there, and she could prove it.

On one side was an assured future: a healthy husband in prospect who might drink a bit too much perhaps, but proud he would be of her always. The younger she was than he, the more likely he was to speak of her as "my old lady" to his friends in the locker room at the golf club. He would provide, as they say; be faithful even; but somehow just not fun.

On the other side of the fence, there was no assurance— Lenore faced it—of anything. Simply a temporary invitation to a temporary world insulated against too much concern with what went on outside it. She didn't always understand the words to this world, but she liked the music of them; the meaning, like the rules, eluded her. It was a kind world, and it could be unkind; vague in its dimensions and at the same time

[427]

definitive; bold yet frightened.

Almost at once an impersonal affection sprang up around Lenore and the boys; quickly they were caught in the habit of being together. She was a need, though not a necessity, and she fitted easily into Stella's old place in the front seat of the convertible. Just how deep their feelings went, none of them really knew.

But after Lenore found the seventy-two-inch antique white satin at a wholesale place in downtown Los Angeles, the boys said she was wonderful.

"Doll," said Harry, "you are my dream."

Lenore laughed as she underwent a brief, sanitary hug.

That evening the boys invited her over to their apartment for dinner, and that same Sunday they all went to the beach; after which Sunday on the beach together was like a reflex. It worked out so nicely with the three of them that way, and it seemed to bring so many new friends from all sides.

The boys even got Lenore a new job, partly on account of that wonderful walk of hers. Almost overnight she had become a dinner hostess—gliding back and forth, and sort of purring at everyone—at the Bronze Room, a hushed, dimly lit restaurant in Beverly Hills where Harry and Ray ate on occasional week nights.

But even the new job didn't matter to her as much as the boys. Nothing else seemed as important. It was the beach, or the theater, or ballet, or Laguna on week ends—anywhere the three of them could go for amusement, with all her decisions made for her. She even dressed the way they wanted her to, although there were times when she scarcely knew the girl in the mirror. Always, Lenore tried to look at things as they did, to laugh when they laughed; tried very hard not to mind when, at the end of the day's fun, the boys stepped off into the night together, leaving her at the door of her apartment with that moment's wonder, right after they had gone, if she would ever see them again.

But she did, of course. And Harry got a promotion at Sloane's just as an aunt of Ray's died, leaving him a few thousand dollars. All of which meant they could make a down payment on a beach bungalow at Laguna, go straight there after Harry finished work on week ends, the three of them, with Stella and her pups, and almost live on the beach until Monday morning. It was perfect.

"At last I'm getting practically enough sun," Harry said, and Lenore agreed.

Joe Marzano was different, in a way, from the rest of the Los Angeles men Lenore had attracted to date. He was good-looking without being too sleek, and he hadn't started off with his hands, not the first night at least. He read books quite a lot and his shoulders were not entirely due to the skillful padding of his tailor. He had a good job. He wasn't kidding.

There had been other admirers since Lenore began seeing so much of Harry and Ray, but these she never introduced to the boys. Some instinct, some psychic warning, told her that the boys and such men wouldn't get along. Their interests, their outlooks, were just not the same. Talk would get difficult; yes. All she had to do was think about it happening, and the tightness in her stomach told her so.

But she couldn't put Joe off like the others. Joe was so good-natured he wanted to meet every one of her friends; and she wanted him to, because there was something about him she liked better than all the previous Joes of her life. From any angle she felt attracted to him—any. He was such a good businessman too, yet he never talked business when they were alone. And when he looked at her and said softly, "You look tired, baby, you shouldn't work so hard, you're too pretty to look tired," it made her feel dizzy, she would have to shut her eyes; and when she opened them, she was usually in his arms.

But what about the boys?

She would miss them an awful lot once she said yes to Joe. Married life with Joe would be so different, mostly in little things. With the boys the days were made up of so many of the little things. That was one of their chief faults, and comforts.

"But, my goodness, I'm twenty-eight already."

Listening to herself say it put her right back on that fence that wasn't there again, more certain than ever that it was, though.

Casually, at first, she dropped a hint about Joe to the boys. But she said it wasn't serious when they asked her once, and they chose, it appeared, to believe that. So she dropped a pebble, a stone, a boulder.

"I think maybe I'm in love with Joe Marzano, kids. Isn't that something?"

The Bronze Room was empty except for the three of them, seated over coffee.

"Then why," said Ray finally, reaching for his comb, "don't you invite him down to Laguna next week end?"

But suppose the boys couldn't stand Joe and that influenced her feelings for him?

"Well," Lenore said.

Suppose she couldn't help agreeing? It might be her love against their derision, once the boys got started. Even so, it might be the easiest way.

"Could we?"

Yes. Introduce them down at Laguna where it was bound to be more relaxed. Then if one didn't like the other, someone could go in swimming.

"If we don't like him," she heard Harry say, "we'll push him in the ocean. Or he can push us." Ray snickered.

She looked up quickly from her coffee, but neither of their faces wore even the memory of a smile. That was the boys for you—the most peculiar things amused them. She couldn't always hear or even see it, she could just tell by feel.

Much later that night she passed the invitation on to Joe. They were seated in his car outside her apartment house.

"You'll come, won't you, Joe?"

His dark eyes were on her with the look of a lover. "Sure," he said. "Mind if I bring Cora, my sister?"

"Cora?" She emerged from a tangle of arms.

"My older sister. The only relative."

"I didn't know you had a sister."

"Cora can't see living anywhere but New York. But she's flying out Friday."

"What's she coming for, then?"

"I asked her to."

"To meet me?"

"As well as your friends, baby."

"All that way, Joe, just to meet me?"

"And your friends."

Why certainly, she told herself, men like Joe always had sisters. Sooner or later. "How very interesting," she tried to sound calm. "And what does Cora do?"

Joe gathered her in his arms again, sighing comfortably. "She's big guns in real estate." His lips began to lower to hers.

"So. You love me, baby?"

For the first time kissing Joe her eyes weren't closed.

In the patio back of the house overlooking Laguna's share of ocean, Lenore sat with the unread Sunday papers in her lap, waiting.

It was the bright kind of day that is a little cool. The few clouds rushing along knew obviously where they were going, even where they had been. There was that tenseness in her middle, but Lenore was ready.

[431]

Ray she could hear in the kitchen, preparing lunch for the five of them. By trial and error she had learned to let him do the cooking alone; over a hot stove Ray, a thin, quiet boy, grew preferences that reached up into temper. Sometimes he simply pursed his lips and wouldn't speak at all.

She could not only hear, she could see Harry. He was hammering at a hinge on one of the garage doors; quite an unusual undertaking for Harry. The sight of it made her wish that Joe and his sister would drive up that very instant so they could see Harry being so—well, manly about the house.

Instead, Lenore found a rip in the hem of her skirt and Harry seated himself at her feet to sew it up. Cars going by on Highway 101 were making such a noise that they had no warning. Harry was still sewing when the patio gate swung open, revealing Joe with Cora. All at the same time Lenore jumped up, jerking her skirt in a way that made Harry stick his thumb with the needle, Stella, meanwhile, trying to convince Laguna that her children were about to be abducted.

Harry uttered a short word much too loudly, though it had no effect on Cora's advance.

"Please," she said to him, "don't get up." Her voice was like an oddly attractive bark. "You remind me of Ethel, my old nurse."

Harry wasn't trying to get up. After a quick glance at Joe, he wasn't doing anything, in fact, except stare at Cora.

She was extremely thin. Her complexion was pasty, with her dark hair parted in the middle and pulled back, straight. She wore a yellow turtle-neck sweater with gray slacks, and a huge amethyst ring. Her wrists were crowded with jingling bracelets. Overhead, somewhat unexpectedly, was a white parasol.

Cora twirled it a little and said, "Shubert Alley's answer to dark glasses, hello, everyone." She brushed a bug off her sleeve. "How lovely here. Where did Bette Davis live?" She crossed the patio, peering out to sea.

"We don't know Bette Davis," Harry said, getting to his feet.

"Doesn't her ex-husband live here and paint or something?"

Just like an Easterner to think the entire West Coast throbbed to the doings of movie stars. "Does he?" Harry opened his mouth to say it, then heard it said with his very own languor. Ray, having come around from the kitchen with drinks, had already inspected Joe.

"I know." Cora flicked Ray with a glance. "You're the boy friend."

"I guess Joe must have told you lots about us," Lenore said, "from what I've told him."

"Just about you." Cora plucked a drink from the tray. "I should think everyone in Laguna would know where Bette Davis lived."

The boys exchanged a glance.

"We're just unusually stupid." Ray extended a not very firm hand to Joe.

Joe said, pleasantly, "Wish I had your tan. Terrific."

Lenore could tell already that the tense feeling was not going away. So far Joe hadn't said anything special to her or looked his special look. Today there was space between them; it had set in somehow since the last time they had been together, just two days ago. Today he was acting nervous, talkative: Joe, who generally just agreed and let you do the talking.

"You ought to come out here and settle down, Cora," he was saying. "No kidding. Feel that sun. It's got iodine in it the year round."

"I don't care if it's got uranium, you know what sun does to my skin." She turned seaward again. "Say, how about that house on the cliff down there? That looks like a six-figure Warner Brothers' pay check."

"It isn't, however," said Harry.

"Whose is it?"

"I don't know. No one ever asked before."

"But nice despite," Lenore said, listening for a laugh.

Cora wheeled and took two strides inland, reaching the center of the patio. "What did you have to pay for this house?"

"Oh—" Lenore saw that she was being addressed "—not me. It belongs to just the boys."

"Honest? I thought maybe you all did everything in threes."

"Not everything," Harry said.

"I suppose," Cora agreed. As she offered her cocktail glass for a refill, she looked at Lenore again. "No real estate?" She wiggled the finger with the amethyst. "No jewelry?"

Lenore shook her head.

"Big salary, maybe?"

"Nothing," Lenore said, glancing hopefully at Joe. But he was watching his sister.

Cora placed a hand on her hip. "Honey, doesn't anything around here belong to you?"

Lenore didn't answer. A heavy wave pounded the beach just below them, rolling in, curling under. It was washing out again, sucking loudly at the pebbles—at the very roots, it seemed, of the silence.

"Not a thing," said Harry, "except Joe."

Harry certainly is loyal, thought Lenore.

It sounded that way, and Harry meant it to sound that way; but the reason he had said it was not as nice. It was a deeper thing, an instinctive part of the cold war on Cora. Victory, only victory, counted now.

Yet lunch, which was served in the patio, was clearly Cora's scene. Her interest in the Bette Davis house was not merely professional, here was her Subject. She tossed it to

[434]

them and kept them at it—her thumb pushing the big amethyst round her finger, her mind busied exclusively with her own thoughts, whether she was talking or, supposedly, listening. Some women got this way from gambling. Cora reacted to quoting the price of some house, then impressively quoting another price, much larger or smaller, the difference between the two being the huge profit or loss in the case involved; all the while nervously nudging that amethyst over and under, till she made them feel that she had personally handled every dollar in the transaction.

This might have lasted through dessert if she hadn't carelessly begun to appraise some New York frontage belonging to a girl named Martha Russell that Joe had once gone around with.

"Nix on that, Cora," Joe said at once.

"Why not?"

"I just said nix, it's not for now."

"Got in all the columns, didn't it? Anyone could read it for themselves."

"Sure," said Joe, "because you told them, it did."

"Listen. Anything Martha Russell did with all that money she had was bound to get written up." Cora turned to Lenore. "Had a fortune in her own name. Gorgeous blonde. Quite definitely pretty, with this lovely house and such furs."

"Also a bitch," said Joe. "She didn't like men anyhow."

"Joe."

"Sure she was."

"Do you always have to say something stupid once you've stopped going with them?"

To Lenore it felt as if she were just human edging now around the big knot in her middle. One of many, I'm really just one of many, she thought; we haven't a chance. It's over. He hasn't looked at me all day.

"What happened?" said Ray.

[435]

Cora shrugged aside the Russell mint. "I wouldn't know. Joe was engaged to her, honey, not me."

"Would you care to swear to that?"

Harry's eyes stayed serious; that's what made Ray laugh.

"If that's supposed to be funny," Cora's voice got abruptly deeper, "I might be able to be even funnier."

Joe stood up.

"God." He rubbed his head where he had hit it on the umbrella that shaded the long wooden table they were eating at. "Anybody going swimming?"

"You've just finished lunch, you'll get cramps, Joe," Cora said. "Take it easy for a while, why don't you?"

He rumbled slightly and said nothing, having already lit up a cigar. On Joe even cigars looked good, Lenore noted, as she helped the boys clear away the dishes. And she thought: how can things end so suddenly?

Cora had settled back on a low, canvas-cushioned settee. Under her parasol was a face with not a worry beyond who would light the next cigarette.

"Well, Cora," Joe said gradually, around his cigar, "how do you think you'll like it?"

"Like what?"

"Having Lenore for a sister-in-law."

Lenore turned in the doorway. She could feel now how warm the sun really was.

"Why—" began Cora, and might as well have said, Joe, how could you be so tactless? "Fine. Only I haven't had a chance, it won't be necessary."

Ray snickered. "It couldn't be that Lenore isn't rich enough, could it?"

Cora sat up. "Rich enough? For me? What difference does that make? I don't care anything about money."

"Prove it," said Harry.

"Well, I don't!"

"Or at least be a little less obvious about it."

Today was for us, Lenore was thinking, it was all about us; yet, it's funny, we hardly seem to count any more.

"Money is just—money," Cora said it with a gesture. "You can have it for all I care."

"Me and Bette Davis?"

"Oh, we'll show you where she lives," Ray said, with a kind of exasperation.

But Cora hadn't heard. Slowly she lowered her parasol. "By the way," she eyed Harry, "just what the hell part do you think you're playing, anyway? *Pimp*?"

Harry was standing beside the settee just then, with some dishes in his hand. He looked down at Cora, his glance moving coolly from her face to her forehead, to her hair, to a certain streak on top.

"You'd better watch out for *your* part, dear, it's beginning to show."

He turned toward the house, the stack of dishes against his chest. There was a slight sound from Cora, as if she were clearing her throat, and after it several sounds: a scream from Ray, an equivalent from Stella, and the crash of china. Joe watched his sister withdraw the parasol from the small of Harry's back and replace it innocently against the heavens.

"Cora!"

For the others it was confusion, but for Lenore it was just to get away. Suddenly. Anywhere away, so long as she was beyond that feeling of smothering, of being ashamed almost of wanting to get married; of knowing now that for months what she had really been laughing at was herself.

It was Cora who was laughing this time, though. Lenore hurried down the brick steps to the sand, into the sound of the surf and the mercy of its deafening roar. She remembered half-running down the beach a few yards before sensing that Joe was right behind her. Stella too, letting off happy, witless noises and bounding by them, glad to be free of her hungry pups. Lenore even remembered thinking how she would like to run (well, walk) the beach on and on this way, listening to the voice of the sea; just that and Joe, and never going back to those other voices. And Stella, mustn't forget Stella. There always had to be pets, or children.

Yet, once started, she could never quite remember the walk down the beach itself, not the first part. It must have been that they didn't say much and that she was thinking too hard. Or just how they got to where they stopped, turned around, and looked back, way back to where they had come from.

At first there was the long white slash of sand, that only. Then, far down at the other end, beyond the boys' bungalow, she could see three figures climbing out among the rocks overhanging the ocean. Her eyes were watering so from the wind that it was hard to make sure. Yes; it was Cora's yellow sweater all right.

Joe took her hand. "Where are those dopes headed for?"

"You can see Bette Davis' house from that point way out there," Lenore yelled into the wind.

"I thought the boys didn't know."

"Oh, they know. They just don't like people to think they care." She yelled once more, "And they don't like Cora."

Joe shaded his eyes. "Looks from here like they must've kissed and made up. Cora must've apologized."

"Oh—well—"

"She can afford to. She could set 'em up in a whole brand-new batch of china, for that matter."

The three climbing figures were nearing the point. It was high and exposed on three sides, with the waves pounding from just below. An absurd scramble, it looked, yet they kept right at it.

"That looks kind of dangerous, you know." Joe shook

his head. "What do you suppose they're doing it for?"

Cora is his problem just like the boys are mine, Lenore thought, proud of such insight. She moved closer to him in the wind. Then she said "I hope—" and stopped.

"What?"

She didn't answer.

"Hope what, baby?"

"Joe," she yelled, "can Cora swim?"

"I guess so, why? I forget."

"Are you sure?"

He looked at her carefully before speaking. "You mean
He looked at her carefully before speaking. "You mean—?"

Lenore stared back.

"You actually think the boys would push her off those rocks into the water?"

"I don't know."

"Look where they are now. No kidding, do you think they *might*, baby?"

"Oh, Joe, I don't know." It wasn't always fun, Lenore knew, being a loyal friend to the boys. It made her afraid sometimes; could make her say things she didn't want to say at all. "But we'd better go back."

The wind, responding like fate, seemed intent on driving her back. She swayed away from him.

To go back to them, she realized, meant she might lose Joe for good; if she hadn't already. She might lose herself as well. And the worst of it is, I love him. She knew now. I love him.

"Because the boys can get awfully mad," she heard herself speaking again, "so fast."

Yet she wondered for a moment if Joe were really listening. He showed no sign, standing there, staring out at the ocean over her shoulder, not quite smiling at some private vision.

[439]

She waited.

All at once the wind died for him.

"So can Cora get mad," he said. "She might push first."

From way up the beach came Stella's tidings of new finds.

Lenore felt the strength of Joe's arm as it turned her gently around toward the barking and away from Cora and the boys. The knot in her middle was gone, the sun seemed warm and comforting. Joe was smiling at her, though she could hardly see, with the wind against her face, and her hair was coming down. Stumbling along the hard white sand at his side, she probably looked foolish. But, she thought, the boys can't make me feel it; not any more they can't; nobody can.

The Fisherman from Chihuahua

By EVAN S. CONNELL, JR.

Connell was born in Kansas City in 1924, studied at Dartmouth, Kansas University, and Columbia, and now lives in San Francisco. He is the author of *Mrs. Bridge* (1959) and *The Anatomy Lesson and Other Stories* (1957), from which "The Fisherman from Chihuahua" is taken.

Santa Cruz is at the top of Monterey Bay, which is about a hundred miles below San Francisco, and in the winter there are not many people in Santa Cruz. The boardwalk concessions are shuttered except for one counter-and-booth restaurant, the Ferris-wheel seats are hooded with olive green canvas and the powerhouse padlocked, and the rococo doors of the carousel are boarded over and if one peers through a knothole into its gloom the horses which buck and plunge through summer prosperity seem like animals touched by a magic wand that they may never move again. Dust dims the gilt of their saddles and sifts through cracks into their bold nostrils. About the only sounds to be heard around the water front in Santa Cruz during winter are the voices of Italian fishermen hidden by mist as they work against the long pier, and the slap of waves against the pilings of the cement dance pavilion when tide runs high, or the squeak of a gull, or once in a long time bootsteps on the slippery boards as some person comes quite alone and usually slowly to the edge of the gray and fogbound ocean.

The restaurant is Pendleton's and white brush strokes on the glass announce *tacos, frijoles,* and *enchiladas* as house specialties, these being mostly greens and beans and fried meat made arrogant with pepper. Smaller letters in pseudo-Gothic script say *Se Habla Espanol* but this is not true; it was the man who owned the place before Pendleton who could speak Spanish. From him, though, Pendleton did learn how to make

[441]

the food and this is the reason a short fat Mexican who worked as a mechanic at Ace Dillon's Texaco station continued eating his suppers there. He came in every night just after eight o'clock and sat at the counter, ate an astounding amount of this food, which he first splattered with tabasco sauce as casually as though it were ketchup, and then washed it farther down with beer. After that he would feel a little drunk and would spend as much as two or even three dollars playing the pinball machine and the great nickelodeon and dancing by himself, but inoffensively, contentedly, just snapping his fingers and shuffling across the warped boards often until Pendleton began pulling in the shutters. Then, having had a suitable evening, he would half-dance his way home, or at least back in the direction of town. He was a squat little man who waddled like a duck full of eggs and he had a face like a blunt arrowhead or a Toltec idol, and he was about the color of hot sand. His fingers were much too thick for their length, seemingly without joints, only creases where it was necessary for them to bend. He smelled principally of cold grease and of urine as though his pants needed some air, but Pendleton who did not smell very good himself did not mind and besides there were not many customers during these winter months.

So every evening shortly after dark he entered for his food and some amusement, and as he appeared to contain all God's world within his own self Pendleton was not disinterested when another Mexican came in directly behind him like a long shadow. This new man was tall, very tall, possibly six feet or more, and much darker, almost black in the manner of a sweat-stained saddle. He was handsome, silent, and perhaps forty years of age. Also he was something of a dandy; his trousers, which were long and quite tight, revealed the fact that he was bowlegged, as befits certain types of men, and made one think of him easily riding a large fast horse, not necessarily toward a woman but in the direction of something more remote and mysterious—bearing a significant message or something like that. Exceedingly short black boots of finest leather took in his narrow trouser bottoms. For a shirt he wore long-sleeved white silk unbuttoned to below the level of his nipples which themselves were vaguely visible. The hair of his chest was so luxuriant that an enameled crucifix there did not even rest on the skin.

These two men sat at the counter side by side. The tall one lifted off his sombrero as if afraid of mussing his hair and he placed it on the third stool. His hair was deeply oiled, and comb tracks went all the way from his temples to the back of his thin black neck, and he gave out a scent of green perfume. He had a mustache that consisted of nothing but two black strings hanging across the corners of his unforgiving mouth and ending in soft points about an inch below his chin. He seemed to think himself alone in the restaurant because, after slowly licking his lips and interlacing his fingers, he just sat looking somberly ahead. The small man ordered for them both.

After they had eaten supper the little one played the pinball machine while this strange man took from his shirt pocket a cigarillo only a little bigger than his mustache and smoked it with care; that is, he would take it from his mouth between his thumb and one finger as if he were afraid of crushing it, and after releasing the smoke he would replace it with the same care in the exact center of his mouth. It never dangled or rolled; he respected it. Nor was it a cheap piece of tobacco; its smoke ascended heavily, moist and sweet.

Suddenly the fat Mexican kicked the pinball game and with a surly expression walked over to drop a coin into the nickelodeon. The tall man had remained all this time at the counter with his long savage eyes half-shut, smoking and smoking the fragrant cigarillo. Now he did not turn around—in fact his single movement was to remove the stump from his lips—but clearly he was disturbed. When the music ended he sat totally motionless for several minutes. Then he lifted his head and his throat began to swell like that of a mating pigeon.

Pendleton, sponging an ash tray, staggered as if a knife had plunged through his ribs.

The Mexican's eyes were squeezed altogether shut. His lips had peeled back from his teeth like those of a jaguar tearing meat, and the veins of his neck looked ready to burst. In the shrill screams bursting from his throat was a memory of Moors, the ching of Arab cymbals, of rags and of running feet through all the market places of the East.

His song had no beginning; it had no end. All at once he was simply sitting on the stool looking miserably ahead.

After a while the small fat Mexican said to Pendleton "Be seeing you, man," and waddled through the door into darkness. A few seconds later the tall one's stool creaked. Without a sound he placed the high steepled sombrero like a crown on his hair and followed his friend through the door.

The next night there happened to be a pair of tourists eating in the back booth when the men entered. They were dressed as before except that the big one's shirt was lime green and Pendleton noticed his wrist watch, fastened not to his wrist actually but over the green cuff where it bulged like an oily bubble. They took the same stools and ate fried beans, tacos, and enchiladas for almost an hour, after which the short one who looked like his Toltec ancestors gently belched, smiled in a benign way, and moved over to his machine. Failing to win anything he cursed it and kicked it before selecting his favorite records.

This time Pendleton was alert; as the music ended he got ready for the first shriek. The tourists, caught unaware, thought their time had come. When they recovered from the shock they looked fearfully over the top of the booth and then the woman stood up in order to see better. After the black Mexican's song was finished they all could hear the incoming

[444]

tide, washing softly around the pillars of the pavilion.

Presently the two men paid their bill and went out, the short one leading, into the dirty yellow fog and the diving, squeaking gulls.

"Why, that's terrible," the woman laughed. "It wasn't musical." Anyone who looked at her would know she was still shuddering from the force of the ominous man.

Her husband too was frightened and laughed. "Somebody should play a little drum behind that fellow." Unaware of what a peculiar statement he had made he formed a circle of his thumb and forefinger to show how big the drum should be.

She was watching the door, trying to frown compassionately. "I wonder what's the matter with that poor man. Some woman must have hurt him dreadfully."

Pendleton began to wipe beer bracelets and splats of tabasco sauce from the lacquered plywood counter where the men had been. The restaurant seemed too quiet.

The woman remarked cheerily, "We're from Iowa City."

Pendleton tried to think of something but he had never been to Iowa City or anywhere near it even on a train, so he asked if they would like more coffee.

The husband wondered, "Those two fellows, do they come in here every night?"

Pendleton was seized with contempt and hatred for this domestic little man, though he did not know why, and walked stiffly away from their booth without answering. He stood with both hairy hands on the shining urn while he listened to the sea thrashing and rolling under the night.

"Who?" he said gruffly. "Them two?"

A few minutes later while pouring coffee he said, "Sometimes I feel so miserable I could damn near roll up in a tube."

The couple, overpowered by his manner, looked up uneasily. The woman ventured, "It seems terribly lonely around here."

On the third evening as they seated themselves before the counter Pendleton said to the one who spoke American, "Tell your friend he can't yowl in here anymore."

"He's not my baby," this short fat man replied, not greatly interested. "Six tacos and four beers and a lot of beans."

"What do you think, I'm running a damn concert hall?"

For a moment the little Mexican became eloquent with his eyebrows; then both he and Pendleton turned their attention to the silent one who was staring somberly past the case of pies.

Pendleton leaned on his hands so that his shoulders bulged. "Now looky, Pablo, give him the word and do it quick. Tell him to cut that noise out. You understand me?"

This enraged the small man whose voice rose to a snarl. "Pablo yourself. Don't give me that stuff."

Pendleton was not angry but set about cleaving greens for their tacos as though he were furious. While the blade chunked into the wood again and again beside his thumb he thought about the situation. He did not have anything particular in mind when all at once he banged down the cleaver and with teeth clenched began bending his eyes toward the two.

"*No debe cantar,*" the little one said hurriedly, waggling a negative finger at his companion. No more singing. "*No mas.*"

"That's better, by God," muttered Pendleton as though he understood. He wished to say something in Spanish about the matter but he knew only *mañana, adios,* and *señorita* and none of these seemed to fit. He resumed work, but doubtfully, not certain if the silent one had heard either of them. Over one shoulder he justified himself. "Folks come here to eat their suppers, not to hear any concert."

Abel W. Sharpe, who had once been the sheriff of Coda

City and who now ripped tickets for a movie house on Pacific, came in the door alone but arguing harshly. The Toltec had started playing pinball so Sharpe took the vacant stool, looked up twice at the man beside him, and then dourly ordered waffles and hot milk. It was while he was pouring syrup into the milk that the nickelodeon music died and that the black Mexican did it again.

Pendleton was exasperated with himself for laughing and almost choked by trying to stop.

"Heh?" asked the old man, who at the first note had jumped off his stool and now crouched several feet away from the counter, a knife in one hand and his mug of sweet milk in the other. "I can't hear nothing. The bastard's deefened me."

The Toltec had not stopped playing pinball and paid none of them the least attention because he had lighted four pretty girls which meant he would probably win something. His friend now sat motionless on the stool and looked ahead as though he saw clear into some grief-stricken time.

Not until the eighth or maybe the ninth night did Pendleton realize that the restaurant was drawing more people; there would be six or eight or even as many as a dozen in for dinner.

There came a night when the fat Toltec entered as always but no one followed. That night the restaurant was an uneasy place. Things spilled, and while cleaning up one of the tables Pendleton discovered a menu burned through and through with cigarette holes. By ten-thirty the place was deserted.

Pendleton said, "Hey, Pablo."

The Toltec gave him a furious look.

"All right," Pendleton apologized, "what's your name?"

"What's yours?" he replied. He was deeply insulted.

"Whereabouts is your friend?"

"He's no friend of mine."

Pendleton walked down the counter behind a damp rag,

[447]

wrung it over the sink, then very casually he did something he never did or never even thought of doing: he opened a bottle of beer for the Mexican and indicated without a word that it was free.

Toltec, though still grieved, accepted the gift, saying, "I just met the guy. He asked me where to get some decent cooking."

Pendleton wiped a table and for a time appeared to be idly picking his back teeth. When he judged the interval to be correct he asked, "Got tired of the grub here, I guess."

"No, tonight he's just drunk."

Pendleton allowed several more minutes, then, "He looks like a picture of a bullfighter I saw once in Tijuana called Victoriano Posada."

And this proved to be a shrewd inquiry because after drinking some more of the free beer the fat Mexican remarked, "He calls himself Damaso."

Pendleton, wondering if something else might follow, pretended to stretch and to yawn and smacked his chops mightily. He thought that tomorrow he would say, when the tall one entered, "Howdy, Damaso."

"Know what? He goes and stands by himself on the sea wall a lot of times. Maybe he's going to knock himself off. Wouldn't that be something?"

"Tell him not to do it in front of my place," Pendleton answered.

Through the screen door could be seen a roll of silvery yellow fog and above it the moon, but the water was hidden.

"These Santa Cruz winters," Pendleton said. Opening the icebox he selected a superior beer for himself and moved his high stool far enough away that his guest might not feel their friendship was being forced. Peeling off the wet label he rolled it into a soggy gray ball which he dropped into a bucket under the counter. "Singers make plenty money, I hear."

The Mexican looked at him slyly. "What are you talking about?"

Pendleton, scratching his head, sighed and yawned again. "Huh? Oh. I was just thinking about what's-his-name. That fellow you come in here with once or twice."

"I know it," the Mexican said, laughing.

For a while both of them drank away at their beers and listened to the combers, each of which sounded as if it would smash the door.

"Feels like there's something standing up in the ocean tonight," Pendleton said. "I could use a little summer."

"You want our beach full of tourists? Those sausages? Man, you're crazy. You're off the rocks."

Pendleton judged that the Mexican was about to insult the summer people still more, so he manipulated the conversation once again. "Somebody told me your friend got himself a singing job at that night spot near Capitola."

"Look," said the Toltec, patient, but irritated, "I just met the guy a couple of weeks ago."

"He never said where he's from, I guess."

"Chihuahua, he says. That's one rough town. And full of sand, Jesus Christ."

Breakers continued sounding just beyond the door and the fog now stood against the screen like a person.

"What does he do?"

The Mexican lifted both fat little shoulders.

"Just traveling through?"

The Mexican lifted both hands.

"Where is he going?"

"All I know is he's got a pretty good voice."

"He howls like a god-damn crazy wolf," Pendleton said, "howling for the moon."

"Yah, he's pretty good. Long time ago I saw a murder down south in the mountains and a woman screamed just

[449]

like that."

Both of them thought about things, and Pendleton, having reflected on the brevity of human affairs and the futility of riches, opened his icebox for two more drinks. The Mexican accepted one as though in payment for service. For some seconds they had been able to hear footsteps approaching, audible after every tunnel of water caved in. The footsteps went past the door but no one could be seen.

"Know what? There was an old man washed up on the beach the other day."

"That so?" said Pendleton. "Everything gets to the beach sooner or later."

The Mexican nodded. Somewhere far out on the bay a little boat sounded again and again. "What a night," he said.

Pendleton murmured and scratched.

"Know something, mister?"

Pendleton, now printing wet circles on his side of the counter, asked what that might be.

"Damaso is no Mexicano."

"I didn't think so," Pendleton lied.

"No, because he's got old blood. You know what I mean? I think he's a gypsy from Spain, or wherever those guys come from. He's dark in the wrong way. He just don't *feel* Mexicano to me. There's something about him, and besides he speaks a little Castellano."

Both of them considered all this.

"I suppose he's howling about some girl."

"No, it's bigger than that."

"What's the sound say?"

But here the little Mexican lost interest; he revolved on the stool, from which only his toes could reach to the floor, hopped off, and hurried across to the nickelodeon. Having pushed a nickel through the slit he studied the wonderful colors and followed the bubbles which fluttered up the tubes to vanish; next he dialed *"The Great Speckled Bird"* and began shuffling around the floor, snapping his fingers and undulating so that in certain positions he looked about five months pregnant.

"Who knows?" he asked of no one in particular while he danced.

The next night also he entered alone. When Pendleton mentioned this he replied the dark one was still drunk.

And the next night when asked if the drunk was going into its third day he replied that Damaso was no longer drunk, just sick from being so, that he was at present lying on the wet cement having vomited on his boots, that probably by sunrise he would be all right. This turned out to be correct because both of them came in for supper the following night. Toltec, smiling and tugging at his crotch, was rumpled as usual and smelled human while his tall companion was oiled and groomed and wearing the white silk again. A good many people were loitering about the restaurant—every booth was full—because this thing had come to be expected, and though all of them were eating or drinking or spending money in some way to justify themselves, and although no one looked up at the entrance of the two Mexicans there could be no doubt about the situation. Only these two men seemed not to notice anything; they ate voraciously and drank a lot of beer after which the one went across to his game, which had been deliberately vacated, and Damaso remained on the stool with his long arms crossed on the counter.

Later the nickelodeon lighted up. When at last its music died and the table stopped there was not a sound in all the restaurant. People watched the head of the dark man bow down until it was hidden in his arms. The crucifix disentangled itself and dropped out the top of his gaucho shirt where it began to swing to and fro, glittering as it twisted on the end of its golden chain. He remained like that for almost an hour, finally raised his head to look at the ticket, counted away enough money, and with the sombrero loosely in one hand he stumbled out the door.

The other Mexican paid no attention; he called for more beer, which he drank all at once in an attempt to interest a young girl with silver slippers and breasts like pears who was eating supper with her parents, but, failing to win anything at this or again at the machine, he suddenly grew bored with the evening and walked out.

The next night he entered alone. When asked if his companion had started another drunk he said Damaso was gone.

Pendleton asked late in the evening, "How do you know?"

"I feel it," he said.

Big Pendleton then stood listening to the advancing tide which had begun to pat the pillars like someone gently slapping a dead drum. After taking off his apron he rolled it tight, as he always did, and put it beneath the counter. With slow fingers he untied the sweaty handkerchief from around his neck and folded it over the apron, but there his routine altered; before pulling in shutters he stood a while beside the screen and looked out and listened, but of course received no more than he expected, which was fog, the sound of the sea, and its odor.

Sharply the Toltec said, "I like to dance." And he began to do so. "Next summer I'm really going to cut it up. Nothing's going to catch me." He read Pendleton's face while dancing by himself to the odd and clumsy little step he was inventing, and counseled, "Jesus Christ, he's gone. Forget about it, man."

Eagle Day

By ESTHER R. B. WAGNER

Mrs. Wagner studied in the East and took her doctorate at
Bryn Mawr. She lives in the Arcata-Eureka region of the
extreme North Coast, and was formerly a teacher in the
public schools of that region.

As Marina Sinek sat with her second cup of coffee, staring
out the window in her housing-project dinette, a large eagle
suddenly swooped into her yard and sank his claws into a blue
doll-blanket left there by her neighbor's daughter. He
crouched for a long moment, making a kind of backwater motion with his huge wings. He took off again with the blue nest
ornament hanging limply beneath his body, caught Marina's
eye, and gave her a dirty look as he lurched through the air
past her window. She sat transfixed, cup held motionless below
her lips. It was this sort of thing that obscured for Marina
the fact that she lived in a subdivision full of repulsively
similar little houses, painted in offensive California tones of
cobalt, pistachio, black raspberry. So she did; but three slim
redwoods spired upward from the edge of her yard into the
sky, and far off, the eagle melted into aqueous distance.

A good day on all counts, well begun. She was going to
drive to the Marpessa Union High School, where she taught
the senior classes in College Preparatory English; she had an
extra hour at her disposal because of a Morning Pep Rally
which emptied her classroom; she was going to make known
to the administration that her first year was to be her last, that
she was going back East (and she meant *East*, by God, not
Chicago or Iowa, the ordinary Marpessa meaning of the word)
to take a very satisfactory appointment on the staff of her own
old school, Miss Thurston's august, prestige-enshrouded insti-

tution of which most citizens of Marpessa, California, had never heard.

She had come West after six years of conventional labors in accustomed grooves, lured by high salary, by a picture of black rocks in a blue bay off Marpessa Head, by the fact that nobody in her town, or at great Madson College, or at Miss Thurston's had ever heard of Marpessa, or had the slightest idea of what the West Coast was like north of San Francisco. Further, it was the unlooked-for, exotic chance to experiment with public-school teaching.

Marina's education had nothing to do with anything which the great teachers' certification bodies could recognize as Education. She had a bachelor's degree, with distinction in English, from Madson College, of which even Marpessa had heard. She had taught for six years in a famous private school of the Thurston type. She possessed an M.A. in English from a massive metropolitan university. All this, in the mysterious world of American public-school teaching, entitled her to a Provisional, or Substandard Credential, making it barely legal for her to teach, on the condition that she pursue Education in the form of various courses in classroom management (students get sleepy after lunch unless you open the window), adolescent psychology (adolescents are likely to have problems with their skin and their parents), and testing (California Mental Maturity, True-False, Establishment of Norms and Medians).

But substandard salaries in the Golden State, if you had a little experience, were so far above quite good salaries in the schools where she was prepared to teach in a normal course of events, that she felt she could afford this excursion.

She amused herself in the classes of Dr. George Hoff, Ed.D., State University of Washington, counting his lapses from conventional grammar and justifying them to herself in terms of the new, progressive semantics. She attended a course

in Guidance Techniques and sent the Professor's mimeo-
graphed material back to her friends at home with *sic* written
in her own hand at regular intervals; these materials provided
her and the friends with many moments of harmless pleasure.

But the letter from Thurston's was a recall to her station.
A vision of the little upturned faces in those pleasant classrooms rose before her, with a comparative vision of the im-
probable visages of her senior classes here. The confrontation
confused her for a moment; something rose uneasily in her
throat; her vision blurred. *What*—all right, it had been great,
they were great, there was something . . . it had been *fun*. You
took these trips. Scenery and wild life, the redwoods, the
eagle, the mountain lion she had seen trotting along the Old
Marpessa Road like any Dane or Golden Retriever—that sort
of thing was a part of the soul of this scene, not just of its surface, as was Marina herself. She was a tourist.

At Madson were lawns, little slopes. The rhododendrons
and azaleas were bushes, not trees. Professor Klein sat under
the oak tree in the Common Room garden, looking like an old
frog on a lily-pad and now and then emitting some gentle,
time-honoured croak. My country, my people! she thought
fiercely, all the way to the school, and hung on to the thought
as she darted into the little office where the mailboxes were
stacked in white-bristling tiers.

A curt note summoned her to the presence of the vice-
principal, Joe Ragusa, and she felt a sudden new flood of exultation. With longing she thought of the moment when she
would tell Ragusa she was leaving, and the moment when she
would know at last that never again would she hear his grat-
ing, graceless voice, his unhallowed English, his remarks on
Education for Citizenship ("What we're concerned with here
primar'ly, in my opinion, is what kids kin learn in a larger
context about social relationshups, in terms of getting along

[455]

with other people") and his views on the College Preparatory Program ("I could of wished it was being done a whole lot diffrent than what it is").

"This, here," he said, without rising, thrusting at her, as she came in, a slip she had filed the day before, reporting the fact that she had ejected from a class one Gary Miles for disciplinary reasons. She was required to file a formal report, but with such formalities Marina often failed to concern herself. Her Principal and Division Head, the large-minded people who had hired her, tended to view with tolerance her grave imperfections in the clerical aspect of her job. But this was a very important aspect indeed in the eyes of Joe Ragusa, who considered Marina with a genuine puritan horror as a kind of outrageous luxury, a frill of the laciest nature, a creature who could not possibly make the slightest contribution to the social adjustment of any student. He would, if pressed to articulation, have said that she could be good for nothing but to give them IDEAS. She now took up the slip and waved it airily, assuming her giddiest manner. "Oh, that Gary Miles," she said. "D'you really want to know what he did?"

"It sure would help," he answered heavily, "seeing as I got to make out these reports."

"Well," said Marina chattily, deeply enjoying herself, settling herself uninvited in his other chair, with a flip of silk scarf, a rattle of bracelet, a peeling-off of pale impractical glove, "I was starting an oral quiz—*you* know, when you ask them questions and have them tell you the answers"—her speeches to Ragusa were always full of these offensive parentheses—"and they're all supposed to sit quiet and listen while each individual talks. Well, all of a sudden I hear this snip, snip. Miles is cutting his fingernails with a great big toenail clipper. I told him to cease and desist, I mean stop, and there was a little silence. Then another student started to talk, and sure enough, snip snip, only more like Bang, Bang. So I kicked him out," and she beamed upon Ragusa her most social smile. His face was taking on the congested look it so often wore when he was dealing with Marina, or even with the thought of Marina. Suddenly she spoke in a different tone.

"Mr. Ragusa. Miles shouldn't be in that class. He can't read the texts, he can't write the themes. He can't even listen to the others. He's the only one like that in there. I'll have to flunk him. The Head said you wanted him in there. Do you mind telling me why?" These were the only straightforward words she had ever spoken to Ragusa, and she listened to their urgent sound in faint astonishment. Was she so serious?

"I thought it ud do him some good," said Ragusa. "He needs to associate with that other type of kid, your special ones, Miss Sinek. If I was to ask you what his background was, would you know? You ever look him up?"

Unsmiling, Marina stared at him. He handed her a dirty folder. She opened it and read the first paragraph of the school psychologist's report on Gary Miles. She closed her eyes tight for a moment in deep exasperation over one of his occupational phrases; then she opened them, and her eyes fell on one different sentence: "His father violent; served one term for assault and another for manslaughter." She read no more.

"Miles came back to school of his accord, after his folks ud taken him out," said Ragusa. "He didn't want to hang around those other kids any more, go in the loggers' joints. What harm's it *do* you, having him in there with your college-prep kids? Bright as all *that*, are they?"

"No, Mr. Ragusa, they're not that bright," said Marina with deadly seriousness. "Every day I have a battle, a real battle, trying to make up for things, trying to get them to see what it's all about. They *can* see, that's the difference—they're beginning to—why they have to know Pallas Athena is not a building and why they have to think about plays written 350 years ago, and why when they go to college, they'll be stuck

[457]

into General Courses, even at the State College now, and have to hear about Plato, Socrates, St. Thomas!" An expression of terrible weariness settled on the face of Joseph Ragusa.

"You want to know what harm Miles does in there. Well, he cuts his fingernails when they're taking oral quizzes, and he can't hand in the work. It's not good. It's only a fake good it does him, *pretending* he's in there with them. I'll help him do something, in my free periods. But those classes aren't planned to provide people with the right associations, Mr. Ragusa. Miles can't do the *work*, Mr. Ragusa!"

The lean beautiful face of her student William Gustafson, amateur astronomer, impassioned student of three Huxleys rose before her mind's eye; the thick glasses of Maria Manzoni, bookish, word-loving, avid of discovery, glinted in her thoughts. She caught the eye of Joseph Ragusa as she rose, and a long, powerful gaze passed between them, in which each read the depth and passion of the other's enmity, distilled now, pure, purged of all personality.

As she paused outside the door, looking abstractedly inward at her own seriousness, she realized that she had neglected to deliver her punch line, the announcement of her Eastern appointment.

She ran up the concrete stairs leading to the long outdoor corridor that stretched along the entire front of the New Building. The doors of the empty classrooms stood open to the spring sunlight; in her own room stood two waiting students. She scrabbled among papers on her desk, and spoke to the student standing at her elbow.

"Talk about your Aristotle paper, Sandra? Listen to this, Bart," she addressed the boy, "you'll *like* it, I think," and he smiled gently, his large face lit with pleasure as always when Marina praised any student.

"'The whole long *peripeteia* of the tragic plot in

[458]

Macbeth, from the first minute that Macbeth puts up his hand to speed his fate, proceeds through sub-*agons to katharsis* when . . .' I love *'sub-agons,'* " said Marina.

"I kinda thought you would," said the girl.

" ' . . . perhaps Shakespeare don't (here Marina scowled fiercely) seem too certain at times with respect to (scowl again) the mechanical side of unity of action' "—Marina flashed upon the two of them a wonderful combination of smile and glower—" 'as when he shifts from Scotland to England with a time-shift right in the middle of the space-shift.' " Marina grinned. " 'Shakespeare don't write like Sophocles, but Aristotle would of liked him for the same things he liked Sophocles for, even if they came out so different.' "

Marina explained why she liked the paper in spite of its glaring deficiencies. Bart told her that he would need no extra scholarship for college next year, since he had made an arrangement to live in a professor's home and work for expenses. He could make four hundred in the woods, easy, that summer, he told her. Marina smiled, but her eye caught Sandra's, and to her horror she saw the girl's face suddenly streaked with tears. God! thought Marina, in alarm, but no outbreak occurred. Sandra said in a very soft, thin voice,

"Miss Sinek, I'm gonna have to leave school! I withdrew my scholarship application. I can't come back at all, not even next week."

Marina's mouth dropped open.

"*Why?*"

"Well, it's that I'm gonna have a baby." Bart's forehead creased in gentle concern. Panic stuck in Marina's throat, but she swiftly remembered—the girl *was* married, to the driver of a huge lumbering logging truck. Twenty of her senior girls were married.

She stared helplessly at the girl. The Morning Pep Rally was over and the corridors full of students; exhilarated by their lateness, their escape from earlier classes, they came surging into the room, cavorting, haw-hawing.

Marina shook her mind free of thoughts of Shakespeare-loving Sandra Clary and her truck-driver husband. She stood up to face her class.

Rapidly she ascertained that during the class period the day before, as they sat with a substitute while she judged an inter-class debate, they had twiddled and done nothing. Eyes flashing, voice rising and falling, shrill or sonorous as sense demanded, she castigated her charges. Were they aware of the approaching deadline for this, the new requirements of that? She hissed, grumbled, exhorted. Gradually there begun to come over their upturned and open-mouthed faces that pressurized look Marina felt she should see there upon occasion. She dished out some individual assignments, wrote some depressing instructions on the board, and tore into the day's business.

Their discussion of Conrad's "Outpost of Progress" as a "horror story" was punctuated by the sudden cries of outrage, flights of invective, bursts of laughter, and melting glances of approval which such sessions with her Marpessa students invariably invoked in her. The conversation ended on a comic note, and Marina dismissed her chortling class, to sink down at her desk for a moment. Her eye fell on a sentence from a waiting theme: "My real father was the boss of all the woods around Crescent City." The Head of her division passed briefly by her door, and Marina told her that Bart Connors needed no extra scholarship, that he had it fixed up about next year.

"*Next year,*" she repeated stupidly as the older woman disappeared, for through the brief conversation she had been thinking, "Next year, no one will tell me his real father was the boss of all the woods around Crescent City, and no one will . . ."

Well, face it! The students at Marpessa High had no need of her. She was for them an incident, a trip they took, a scenic railway. Sandra Clary dropped out, Bart Connors went on; under their own steam, because of or in spite of their private pressures, with nothing she could do either hindering or helping much. She had taught Sandra the word for *agon*. But to kid herself that she was some kind of big deal for them was mush. They loved to hear her laugh, to see her lose her temper. She could make them work. She suited them.

But the long sharp claw in the whole thing was that she loved them. She had never laughed so much nor been so angry. Her energies had never been so taxed, nor so inexhaustible. She simply was not tired, she simply was not through.

But was she going to let this fact flap away with her, was she going to hang limply and be used? There was plenty of room in the world for her to live and enjoy herself, to practice her profession in a rational manner. Stay, take the required course in Audio-Visual Aids, fight the weird battle, quiet, patient, submarine, forever waged by her Division Head and her Principal against Ragusa, Dr. Hoff of the State College, all the other strange forms of life fastened by draining suckers, like sea-lampreys, on the gleaming sides of American mental life?

Bitterly she began to scrawl on the board the poem her next class would discuss that day. The title stretched along two squares of the board:

An Irish Airman Forsees His Death

As always, the last lines flowed smoothly from under her chalk, for she knew them well:

A lonely impulse of delight
Drove to this tumult in the clouds.

[461]

> I balanced all, brought all to mind.
> The years to come seemed waste of breath.
> A waste of breath the years behind.
> In balance with this life, this death.

She looked at these lines with sudden alarm. But this was no time for reflection on new meanings. Her class came flooding in, dumping popcorn boxes in her wastebasket, gulping last cookies. Marina knew suddenly that she had had no lunch. They saw the handwriting on the board and knew what was in store.

"Oh-oh! An-AL-a-sis!"

Grinning, they settled into their chairs and began to pop their notebook rings, click down the points of their ballpoint pens, flap their paper. Silence fell while they read, lips moving, and thought. Gravely, sturdily, tentatively they began to discuss the poem with Marina. When she got to the lines:

> My countrymen, Kiltartan's poor,
> No likely end could bring them loss,
> Nor leave them happier than before . . .

she asked what they meant.

"Means they're perfectly okay up in Kiltartan Cross," said Loretta Jaynes in the first row, "no matter what *he* does."

Marina thought this over, chewing her lip and staring out the window. But she did not want to pursue it.

Her student John McClure spoke loudly and suddenly, unable to wait for recognition, sure all year, but especially since his brilliant performance on the national scholarship examinations, of his ability to command her attention.

"Ya know what I think? That guy's got a Tragic Flaw!"

"What?" said Marina weakly.

"A Tragic Flaw! You know like in the other stuff, *Macbeth*. He likes this strong-stuff sort of kick, 'tumult in the clouds.' Wants things to be *live*. Doesn't care what-all. Just doesn't want things to be *dead*, all fixed up beforehand."

"So that's Tragic Flaw?" said Loretta, twisting in her seat with a swish of red curls.

"It's *this* guy's Tragic Flaw, like I said. *As* I said. That kind is trouble. He'll ruin everything for himself, for the crash anna bang. Poem is about Irish guys can stay home, is it any fight of theirs? But no, it is, because he *likes* it. That type. They don't care do they cook their goose. They gotta have that old *red blood.*"

Loud laughs and crude comments put an end to this striking recitation. Marina established order, finished her analysis, got her assignments in before the bell rang. McClure sought her eye as he went out, giving her his Jack Horner, plum-on-thumb look that marked the close of all his insights. Marina made a face at him and told him to go look up "hubris" in the big dictionary.

In her next class Gary Miles, the felon's son, sat sober and motionless while the class sighed and squirmed, writing their theme on Aristotle and *Macbeth*. In the last fifteen minutes he looked up suddenly, flapped paper, wrote spasmodically until the bell rang. Marina collected the papers and looked at his as they filed out. He had written:

I don't dig this Shakesp, this Macb stuff like I tried to tell you but yo wuldnt listen. Well I read this other book, maybe I could tell you about that, anyway it was on that list you gave us. European Short Stories. There was this little boy in one of them stories and he went out to a farm some uncle had, he was a city boy. He was confused when he got there but the green come up in his face and the bees in those old trees, and he knew he liked it. Then one day he saw this pig, this pig that was like him, sort of fat but nice, like him, and it was being killed for the sausage and the bacon. He new it was alright but he also new it was not alright, but terrible. So he poison a lot of the chickens so they wouldnt have to die that terrible way

[463]

with clubs and blood. The chickens werent like him but the pig was, all the more reason for seein they didnt have to have that terrible thing. It didnt say this but I cold see that was what he ment. I thot I was there. You say its so corny to say "he writes so I thot I was there" and I know the kids just say it, but I don't just say it. I thot I was there. The kid in the story, he thot he was the pig when the pig was killed, well I thot I was there in the story. That auther, he has a lot of what you keep saying, scope, the biggest, the biggest look, to see into a small little boys head like that.

Marina read this in a minimum time but with a maximum attention. She felt for another time that peculiar emotion, not unrelated to the stirring of a new love, felt by such teachers as she when they sense suddenly the presence, hitherto unsuspected, of Material. A long preview of the next three months with Miles unreeled itself in her mind: the struggles, the boredom, the excitement; the moments when she would think, Idiot! and he would think, Old Snotbox! He would not learn to write sentences on William Gustafson's and Maria Manzoni's time; but she would get him, by God, she would. The new sort of sentence he would be able to write existed in this preview in form though not in content. She felt its shape.

She hurried down to Ragusa's outer office, filled in a slip, and darted in with it to his inner office.

"Miles do something new? Something tough on the College Prep class?" he inquired, looking savagely at the piece of paper as it lay on his desk.

"Yes, he sat there while they wrote on Aristotle and *Macbeth*," said Marina. "Then he wrote on something else. He was nice and quiet, Mr. Ragusa. But he just doesn't *belong* in there, Mr. Ragusa.

"I'm going to take him in my free period every day. I'm just going in to check it with the Head. I know it's just a bit on the illegal side, with the laws about those periods and all, but

[464]

valuable commodities must be, at certain moments in our history, bootlegged."

"Hear you could get a job at the college," he said suddenly, and on his expressive face there shone a look of hungry longing for what might be.

"Maybe, but I wouldn't take it, Mr. Ragusa. I want to stick around for those sessions after the tests, when you decide about the special-ability classes for next year. The Counselor and the Chief are quite interested in all that. They've been asking me for my ideas," she said, smiling, "and I *have* some ideas, not only about that, but about some of the lower-classmen's programs, too," she added in a soft, vicious tone, smiling sweetly into his upturned face, trading ruthlessly on her popularity with parents, her prestige with School Board and Principal, bending over the serried volumes of the National Education Association journals which edged his desk. He looked at her wordlessly. She gestured with her head toward the report, bared her teeth again, and left him.

But the glow left her as she raced back upstairs. She meandered through her last class in a daze. In the last quarter-hour while they read she pawed listlessly through a pile of themes from the day before, concerning one class's thoughts about their future. As she had known would be the case, they ranged madly from "I have applied for a 'Seven Colleges Scholarship, and will enter Radcliffe or Bryn Mawr if I am lucky, to do my work in chemistry," to "Mom thinks I should be a beautician, I love to fool with hair." But they all *could* do the work she asked of them; what they *did* was their own business. The Thurston's School faces she knew from memory and imagination, quiet attentive faces, giving her what she expected, getting what they expected—she saw them and she knew them in her mind, in a mental convulsion of farewell. Her class left; she sat motionless amid the roars of the

[465]

exhaust pipes of the school buses. She sat for a long time, then got up from her desk and walked to the window. The old-rose light of Marpessa County afternoons suffused the bizarre landscape. At its north edge, the school campus dropped off a cliff; below it, the Marpessa Plywood Company clanged and roared, and the sawdust-burners, grotesque and beautiful in Marina's eyes, belched out their thick saffron smoke. Southward she stared into the old graveyard of the town, which fringed the school property on that side, and where she often walked at noon. A huge myrtle tree spread at its center, exhaling lilac color and soft bitter scent into the air. The forms of the mausoleums belonging to old Marpessa families, the slanting slabs above the graves of long-dead lumbermen and hunters, shone gently against the background of sombre yew and cypress. "Drowned in the Mad River, Nevermore to Roam," remembered Marina, thinking of epitaphs on the stones.

"Drowned in the Mad River, nevermore to roam!" thought Marina, thinking of herself and of American public-school teaching. Between the burners and the graveyard she leaned her hot forehead on cool glass and wept; feeling, deep in the hidden recesses of her body and her spirit, writhing, entangling, the dark irrational coils of ineradicable love.

Member of a distinguished Central Valley family, James
Broughton has produced a series of award-winning film
shorts and three volumes of exquisite short poems.

Don Giovanni to the
Very Nice New Virgin

Is there something dull about the innocent?
That your simple glowing is a glow too pure, and an irritant?

Were I a reforming pagan or Blake's holy child
I might come to you to play at angels incorruptible,
in the childhood of a world set its age aside
and embrace a maid demure with dulcet mood inviolable.

But I am too bedeviled by grand old jigs of Lucifer
to relish minuets Goody-Two-Shoed and petite:
though the world looks dancing candy to the green-armed
    amateur,
I, a Peter Pan unlikely, now prefer more bitter sweets.

So, despite your simply glowing both adorable and innocent,
purity that bores is strictly God's divertissement.

The Clever Troubadour
of Amoret County

Happiest am I when my Ada is most tongue-tied
and her dairydell bushes bulge fat with birds,
for then I can whistle as fine as any Shelley,
be full of fancy talk without spelling out the words.
    I'm a lightfoot buckaroo on a beehop pace
    and Delicate Crazy is my hometown.

Prettiest is Beulah when she is most illerate
and her berries are baked all sweet into pies,
for then I go courting as slick as any Byron.
I rollick foolish talk and feel I'm sitting very wise.
     I'm a tricky toodledoo for a cock and bull race
     and Delicate Crazy is my hometown.

Tempting best is Cleo when awe has struck her dumbest
and her starchy wash hangs a white tent on the lines,
for then I sing niftier than any old Shakespeare,
with a mouth full of kisses I write my valentines.
     I'm a swashbuckle winner of the boy and girl chase
     and Delicate Crazy is my hometown.

The Shepherd's Urban Daughter

Mary has lost her childhood lamb,
she wants the fleece back as pure as it was,
but her pretty bo peep has broken down
and she can't tell a sheep from what a goat does.
     This is the norm, this is the norm,
     this is the way it goes, madam.

She's confused about all the sheep she has known:
if they had tails and where they grew
and whose was whose and how to know
and which was which and what she should do.
     This is the norm, this is the norm,
     this is the way it goes, madam.

She is gathering old wool together now.
With no flock to count, no pastoral crook,
she lies awake nights and knits her brow,
and her doctor is writing it down in a book.
     This is the norm, this is the norm,
     this is the way it goes, madam.

Loony Tom's Song

Give me a tune and I'll slap the bull fife,
I'll spring the hornblower out of his wife.

Any old flutist you care to uncover,
give me his name and I'll be her lover.

La diddle la, the hydrant chatted.
Um titty um, the milkpail said.

For love hid the story under the songbook.
buried the ballad under the hornbook.

Love so they tell me, love so I hear,
love waves the trumpet and butters the tree.

But love will come tooting only if free.
And only to me.

La diddle la, the hydrant chatted.
Um titty um, the milkpail said.

Five Poems

By MURIEL LORAN

Dr. Loran was educated in the East and Middle West, and is now a neurophysical researcher in the University of California Hospital at San Francisco. Her poems have appeared in many journals.

I

The hand and crushed rock
the imperceptible interface
of light and dark
the dimishing gradients drop

a fibril breaks
a lash of sound
and pine careens across a canyon wall

a cacophony of segments bombards
the splintered air
with the conical velocities of denuded space

II

If l come in the darkest night
to be received by enemies and fears
trailing fluids and the comet's blow

to be dissected of my cells
and burnt upon a corner candle
to be digested in the silent word

the fragment of an endless hall remains
the steps and stairs of rattles
the perversion of a bone
a line of lingering frost
the wire of a telephone

never enough is now
for thirds and hexagons of flesh
for testaments to rings and smoke
and I will come

in spite of seminars on pins
even if I cleave alone.

III

The willows and the hungry birds
the creeping glaze of night
upon the tendrils of a dream
the spider's claw incites the moon to sting
the saffron
the roots to empty blood upon the reeds

a stone falls in concavity
and drop develops gradients
into infinite declines

a somnolent artery pulses freeze
into a roaring fall
a rainbow shattered into glass
a spring a lens of ice
relays the impulse of the lost to mass.

IV

In this marooned sky
there are possibly seeds
whose wings have bent a wind
whose armored crusts have scattered suns
and by fortuitous calamities of coincidence
erected pines upon the hills
and place is sigh

[471]

and cycles of the moon and dust
and poisoned pot-holes of the plain
are crossed and bear the fruit of vastness
mass
where chance is only canyon
and the night is only sky

and space
resides in masks and shadow
and time departs with ice
into the frosted mist
of casks and rain.

V

I am leaning with glass and prism
toward points and light
acicular crowns and fire
and searing the night with sound

clear angle of cry
stones of line and running sigh
gleam
the canyons gloss and silent
sun and sign of wind
and arms to crawl
and wall are fissured paths of time

and when all objects empty into shade

I will cover colocynths and you
to smile and sing into the midnight
chalked with bells
the clarinet for two

[472]

BROTHER ANTONINUS, O.P.

Born in Sacramento in 1912 as William Everson, a Valley farmer until World War II, Brother Antoninus then became a conscientious objector and afterward a Dominican tertiary resident in the College of St. Albert the Great (Oakland). Praising his "gnarled honesty," "rugged unliterary diction," and "relentless probing and searching," Kenneth Rexroth has called him "the finest Catholic poet writing today."

Annul in Me My Manhood

"The Lord gives these favors far more to women than to men; I have heard the saintly Fray Peter of Alcantara say that, and I have observed it myself. He would say that women made much more progress on this road than men, and gave excellent reasons for this, which there is no point in my repeating here, all in favor of women."
—St. Teresa of Avila

Annul in me my manhood, Lord, and make
Me woman-sexed and weak
If by that total transformation
I might know Thee more.
What is the worth of my own sex
That the bold possessive instinct
Should but shoulder Thee aside?
What uselessness is housled in my loins,
To drive, drive, the rampant pride of life,
When what is needful is a hushed quiescence?
"The soul is feminine to God,"
And hangs on impregnation,
Fertile influxing Grace. But how achieve
The elemental lapse of that repose,
That watchful, all-abiding silence of the soul,
In which the Lover enters to His own,

[473]

Yielding Himself to her, and her alone?
How may a man assume that hiddenness of heart
Being male, all masculine and male,
Blunt with male hunger? Make me then
Girl-hearted, virgin-souled, woman-docile, maiden-meek;
Cancel in me the rude compulsive tide
That like an angry river surges through,
Flouts off Thy soft lip-touches, froth-blinds
The soul-gaze from its very great delight,
Out-bawls the rare celestial melody.
Restless I churn. The use of sex is union,
Union alone. Here it but cleaves,
Makes man the futile ape of God, all-ape
And no bride, usurps the energizing role, inverts;
And in that wrenched inversion caught
Draws off the needer from his never-ending need, diverts
The seeker from the Sought.

The South Coast

Salt creek mouths unflushed by the sea
And the long day shuts down.
Whose hand stacks rock, cairn-posted,
Churched to the folded sole of this hill,
And Whose mind conceives? Three herons
Gig their necks in the tule brake
And the prying mudhen plies.
Long down, far south to Sur, the wind lags
Slosh-washes his slow heel,
Lays off our coast, rump of the domed
Mountain, woman-backed, bedded
Under his lea. Salt grasses here,
Fringes, twigging the crevice slips,
And the gagging cypress

[474]

Wracked away from the sea.
God *makes*. On earth, in us, most instantly,
On the very now,
His own means conceives.
How many strengths break out unchoked
Where He, Whom all declares,
Delights to make be!

Out of the Ash

Solstice of the dark, the absolute
Zero of the year. Praise God
Who comes for us again, our lives
Pulled to their fisted knot,
Cinched tight with cold, drawn
To the heart's constriction; our faces
Seamed like clinkers in the grate,
Hands like tongs—Praise God
That Christ, phoenix immortal,
Springs up again from solstice ash,
Drives his equatorial ray
Into our cloud, emblazons
Our stiff brow, fries
Our chill tears. Come Christ,
Most gentle and throat-pulsing Bird!
O come, sweet Child! Be gladness
In our church! Waken with anthems
Our bare rafters! O phoenix
Forever! Virgin-wombed
And burning in the dark,
Be born! Be born!

Was Peter Not Brought Up On Kascha?

By IRENA PARKER

An Esthonian by birth, Irena Parker was displaced in the convulsions of World War II. She is now a teacher in the Bay Area.

Should you go apartment hunting in the shady old streets along the panhandle of the Golden Gate Park in the Richmond District of San Francisco, the names of countless Ivanoffs, Petroffs, and Mikhailoffs written on yellowing sheets of paper opposite the door-bells will soon convince you that you are in the middle of one of the city's many White Russian settlements.

Despite the sound of Slavic speech flowing from behind the half-open doors, despite the odor of borsch, kascha, and piroschki escaping from the darkish hall-ways, despite the sight of potted geraniums in the wide open windows, this little colony of White Russians cannot be called typical. There are no sturdy brown-haired children teasing each other in a mixture of Russian and English on the asphalt-covered sidewalks, there are no bosomy matrons leaning out of second story windows and greeting passing-by friends in loud, heavily accented English, and there are no heavyish, strict-looking family men arriving home from work around 5 p.m. and softly swearing in Russian while parking their cars. No, the young and the middle-aged have long ago abandoned the shabby old buildings facing the first trees and bushes of the Golden Gate Park, and now the district belongs entirely to the old, the poor, the non-English speaking Russians, those who live on welfare, on social security, on the meager monthly check sent to them by their grown-up sons and daughters, on occasional jobs as baby-sitters, cleaning-women, janitors.

[476]

Unlike the majority of their fellow countrymen, these elderly men and women boast neither of a distant relationship to the tsars nor of vast baronial estates in the Ukraine. They admit to being what their round, snub-nosed faces and their short, sturdy bodies proclaim them to be—simple Russian peasants. And though often barely literate, all of these wrinkled Ivans and Maryas are childishly, and somewhat touchingly, proud of being members of both the Slavic race and of the soil tilling class.

Strange though it may seem at first, these very poor and uneducated people were not attracted by the promises of the Russian revolution. They preferred, along with their wealthier and more sophisticated compatriots, to leave their native land for a life of uncertainty in foreign countries; the establishment of a closer contact with them soon explains their aversion to Communism. There is not a single one among these toil-worn Ivanoffs and Petroffs who is not deeply, inherently, at times almost fanatically religious. Thus any regime that denies the existence of God and fails to honor the tsar, His Slavic representative on earth, fills their souls with horror and disgust. To them spending even one day without constant contact with their Heavenly Father is unimaginable. Their joys and sorrows are frequently accompanied by short, fervent prayers, the men crossing themselves as eagerly and openly as the women. Their most trivial conversations are filled with continual allusions to God. "The Lord forgive him," the gray-haired Anna Pavlovna will sigh seeing her next-door neighbour helping himself on the sly to her home-made cookies. "The Lord will help us, little mother," the lame Ilya Ilyitch does not hesitate to comfort his wife after the loss of her part-time job. "The Lord have mercy on us," a group of tea drinking gossips cannot help but exclaim upon learning of another atom bomb explosion in the Nevada desert.

On Sunday mornings and on week-day evenings literally

[477]

hundreds of dark, bundled-up figures crowd the small Greek Orthodox church on Fell Street, causing its minister to boast of a nearly perfect attendance record. There, in the sweet smell of incense, the White Russian oldsters pray for a quiet death for themselves, for a long and healthy life for their children, and, above all, for the soul of their departed little father, Tsar Nicholas II. A faded picture of the bearded ruler is considered an absolute necessity for every household, its position under the darkish ikons indicating the close tie these simple peasants believe to be existing between the Russian religion and the Russian monarchy.

Although the men and women of this little White Russian settlement do sincerely want to become American citizens and attend faithfully, if not always too successfully, the available naturalization classes, in everyday life they cling most stubbornly to their native customs and habits. The old women refuse to wear anything but long, dark, sack-like dresses and spend countless hours searching various second-hand stores for black cotton stockings, thick woolen underwear, and dark, heavy bandannas. The old men seldom go out without their ancient, moth-eaten fur hats and equally inappropriate fur-trimmed winter coats. They also insist on wrapping enormous hand-knit scarves around their already well-protected throats. Any use of make-up is completely rejected, because, to use their own phrase, it might spoil the natural beauty of a Russian face.

American food is considered not much better than poison. "No wonder the people in this country are so sickly and skinny," round little Marfa Petrovna likes to repeat to the approving nods of her friends, "no Christian body can be kept together on watery salads and tough raw meats." Instead of the unhealthy lettuce and steaks, the rotund White Russians feed their cast-iron stomachs complicated concoctions of dough and hamburger boiled in fat and called piroschki, or sour cream and butter mixed with cooked cottage cheese and called paska.

American supermarkets are usually ignored. There is, the ladies agree, so much better a selection in the crowded Jewish delicatessen where the owner knows just a little bit of Russian and does not mind bargaining every now and then, or even in the herb-smelling Oriental stores, where the owner with his smooth yellow face brings back memories of good old Harbin days (all of these Russians seem to have come to the United States by the way of China).

Motion pictures, television, and radio have little appeal to the aging sons and daughters of the Volga, and they read little besides the daily Russian newspaper. Their chief form of entertainment consists of visiting each other on their respective birthdays and namedays. At such times they sit comfortably around a piroschki-laden table and drink countless cups of tea, the steaming cup in one hand, a lump of chewed-on sugar in the other. The men talk politics, wonder just when their "Holy Mother Russia" will be free from Communist oppression, and voice their choices for the new tsar. The women remember their youth, boast of the erstwhile thickness of their braids, recount various household remedies for arthritis. On certain festive occasions, such as Christmas or Easter, which this particular group of White Russians conscientiously celebrates according to the Gregorian calendar (that is, two weeks later than everybody else) vodka and marinated herring are produced; and cracking, untrue voices fill the air with boisterous Slavic songs.

During the week the settlement has little contact with the rest of the San Francisco White Russians. On the weekends, however, the oldsters' sons and daughters, nieces and nephews, grandsons and granddaughters invade the panhandle of the Golden Gate Park in order to pay their progenitors an obligatory visit; and the world of the modern, Americanized White

[479]

Russians collides disastrously with that of the true, old-country White Russians. "Babuschka, how many times do I have to remind you to call me Tillie instead of Tanya," wails a brightly rouged teen-age girl, trying to escape her grandmother's long, moist kisses. "Now, Papa, please don't make the sign of a cross over us when we leave," asks a plump, efficient looking business-woman of her gray-haired, gray-bearded father. "Oh, Peter, don't let her give that to the baby," screams a slender American housewife upon discovering her Russian mother-in-law stuffing the two-year old with the fat-oozing piroschki.

For a while the oldsters take it calmly and silently, but sooner or later thèir patience comes to an end amid bitter tears and hoarse accusations. How come Tanya, who is not as yet of a marriageable age, is already painting herself like a Turk's bride? Is Valja no longer a Christian but a miserable Catholic that she is ashamed of the sign of a cross? Was Peter not brought up on kascha and piroschki and did he not grow up to be a fine, husky figure of a man? Young and old voices are raised, young and old faces become flushed, young and old eyes begin to sparkle with anger, young and old feelings get hurt. At long last, the relatives leave, the excitement subsides. "The Lord bless you, the Lord forgive you," mutter the aged mothers and fathers, hurriedly, stealthily, and stubbornly making the sign of a cross over the departed loved ones.

In ten, at the most twenty, years there will be no more White Russians dwelling along the shabby old streets facing the first few bushes and trees of the Golden Gate Park. The oldsters know it and this knowledge makes them doubly anxious to impart all they stand for to their successors and renders their failure to do so doubly pathetic.

Mother Lode, 1960

By JOSEPH McMAHON

> McMahon was born and raised in the gold country. Like
> many of the disappointed young men cited in his essay, he
> left that area in favor of San Francisco.

The visitor to California most often goes directly to the
large metropolitan centers, such as San Francisco, Sacramento,
or Los Angeles. He will take short side trips to such well-known
spots as Redwood country or Yosemite Valley. This is to be
expected since these areas are nationally famous for their
scenic beauty. But there is an area seldom visited now, and
perhaps not so beautiful, but much richer in the history and
folklore of early California. This is the renowned Mother Lode
country, the site of the gold rush of 1849. It is, however, an
area that has become forgotten in our present-day civilization.
The story of the fabulous treasure uncovered in this region has
often been told, and the legends surrounding the gold camps
and their sometimes bizarre citizens are familiar to all Americans. The heterogeneous assortment of humanity that poured
into this area helped develop California into a State in the
short period of three years. The physical marks of their existence still stand in many secluded spots. These ruins and
buildings bear witness to the reasons for their being, the uses
to which they were put, and the materials and workmanship
peculiar to the time and place of their building. In this respect
the Mother Lode area is unique. Nowhere else has the past left
such vivid reminders of a full-blown if short-lived civilization,
and of its rapid decay.

Geologists define the Mother Lode as a narrow strip of
gold-bearing deposits approximately a mile wide and some 150
miles long. However, the Mother Lode, in common usage,

refers to the whole region, from Mariposa to Downieville, wherever gold was panned or mined, and diggings flourished. Throughout this region can be found the towns that have grown up, or gone down, since the days of the gold rush. Some, like Mariposa, Sonora, Angel's Camp, Placerville and Nevada City, remain as fairly good sized towns, living for the most part off lumber mills and occasional tourists. Others have merely become a gas station and grocery store for the ranchers in the area. Little care has been taken to preserve or restore the visible remains of the gold rush. The one outstanding exception is Columbia, which became a State Park recently. The State has undertaken the job of restoring the buildings and restoring the atmosphere of the early days. At first glance, it seems impossible to believe that Columbia once boasted a population of 50,000 people, and missed becoming the State capital by only three votes. Today Columbia has an official population of 700, which includes the neighboring ranchers and farmers as well as the 275 inhabitants of the town itself. Hardly any trace remains of the $17,000,000 of gold that was taken from the surrounding country in one year, except great piles of bleached limestone and quartz.

Sonora, four miles from Columbia, and the county seat of Tuolumne County, claims a population of 2,000 and is the largest town of a county measuring a full 13,000 square miles. Its main street looks much like any other small town in the nation. Yet a ride up any of the streets off the main avenue will reveal the well-hidden secret of the present day gold towns. The old buildings remain, though now partly hidden under false facades and covered with neon lights and bright paint. The backs of the "modern" stores show them to be made of lava blocks and adobe bricks. The doors are guarded by heavy iron sheets and the windows are covered with bars. The most vivid reminder of the past is of a more gruesome nature, however. On one of the side streets stands the old county jail. High

[482]

above the street sways the rope used to hang law-breakers of the past. For seventy-five years this rope has hung there in testimony to the fury of life that has passed. Beneath the rope is the old cell where the condemned prisoner spent his last night. It has only one opening, out onto the street. This gave the townspeople an opportunity to torment the prisoner during his final hours. No one would ever take down this grim reminder, because memory is part of the life these people live today.

It would be hard to describe the inhabitants of this area. They are so tied to the past that it affects not only their daily lives but their way of thinking. Greedily they tear down the few remaining buildings to put up motels and gas stations for the tourists, but they talk about the old days as if they were yesterday, and so tenaciously do they hang on to the legends of that wild period, that anyone who doubts or disbelieves is' completely ignored. They can point out every hideout any bandit ever had and relate with pride how many people were hanged or how often the towns were destroyed by fire. They fight every major change in county policy and will not elect any man who promises improvements other than in school buildings or medical services. The Indians are third class citizens, yet everybody respects their legends and predictions. It is interesting to note that no weather forecasts are published in any newspaper. Instead you will find the latest prediction of the Indian Chief. San Francisco is a great nebulous thing, a threat to their economic safety and their well-being. The counties of Tuolumne and Mariposa distrusted San Francisco ever since Hetch Hetchy Dam was built. They feel that their water is being drained to satiate people who care nothing for them. For this reason, they have gone to court many times to sue the San Francisco Water District, but they always lose. They will never stop trying, though. In fact, six years ago four of the Mother Lode counties threatened to secede from the

State, because they consider themselves independent of California. They consider their interests to be so different from California's that, with a sufficient population, they would overturn the whole political and financial system of state government.

If you should ever have the opportunity to go to this country, go slowly. Look for the old stone fences, the shacks and crumbling adobe buildings. The land is rich in lore as well as gold, yet the natives will not tell you where to look. Too many are fearful that their lives will be changed if visitors come flocking into the area. It is believed that the mountain streams, untouched for a century, are now again filling up with gold; and this too they want for themselves. It is a strange land, living mostly in the past, not much liking the Outside or the present. Many of the young leave and move to the large metropolitan centers, but those that stay behind will carry on the traditions long after the present generation is gone. How could you change what doesn't want to change, if you would want to try?

The Desert

By MICHAEL RUMAKER

Rumaker was born in Philadelphia in 1932. He studied at
Black Mountain College until 1955, afterwards settling
down to write in San Francisco.

Two men sat slumped against the wall of the adobe hut,
their broad-brimmed hats tilted low over their eyes, their
hands resting quietly on their kneecaps. Each pair of eyes,
aslant, watched without expression from their corners a man, a
black speck in the distance, approaching over the desert.

A third man, short and fat, with a bandana, black from
wear, stretched over his skull and knotted at his throat,
squatted before a fire a few paces from the door of the hut.
On a tripod of sticks knotted together at the top with a leather
thong, hung a pot in which bubbled beans and chunks of
bacon. In the pot was a wooden paddle which he now and
then took in his hand and turned idly, stirring the beans. He
was also watching the approach of the stranger.

A blanket hung over the door of the hut and each of the
rough-cut windows was covered with sheets of newspaper,
brown and crumbling from the sun. At one corner of the building was a large cactus plant on the prongs of which hung a
shirt and a pair of dungarees. In the bed of an arroyo, sloping
down a few yards from the hut, sat an old open touring car,
highbacked and rusting. In the shade of the car a dog lay on
its side, as if it were dead. Silt drifted in a fine heap against its
curled spine. Occasionally the dog flicked its rag of a tail,
striking at flies gnawing raw patches in its flanks.

The sun beat down with a dry, white glare over the
desert. Far off, the tablerock pressed hazy and pink against
the horizon. The was no sound, no wind.

[485]

The man in the distance rose and fell from view as he climbed one drift of sand and then plunged down out of sight before ascending the next. The man seated before the fire waited until the man got to a crest, watched him intently, and when he disappeared again between drifts, turned his attention to the small cloud of insects hovering over the cookpot. He brushed them away, lazily, with his plump dark arm.

"Off the track. Lost," he said.

"Thirsty and hungry. Maybe loco from the heat. Maybe an escaped convict," said one of the men crouched against the wall, Hook, a thin, fine-boned man, with a sharp nose and his legs thin as a bird's in his tight levis. On his boots were silver spurs, highly polished, sparkling in the sun.

"Last one was kinda pretty," said Mex, the man at the fire.

"Black suit—that ain't no prison suit." Capon was a thick man, his heavy arms folded across his chest, his hands tucked beneath his armpits.

"Black sucks up the sun," said Mex.

"Never can tell," Capon went on. "Hope not another one of them joyrides in Theodora: 'Turn this way, turn that, who zat following us?' And the desert as flat as your granny's tit and not a human soul for miles and all the while the gun butt in the nape of your neck. I hope he's something different this time."

"It'll break the day," said Hook. "I'm glad for that. And if he's got a gun, I don't care."

"Man wants a little something new to make his heart beat," said Mex.

They watched closely now as the man became more distinct, the two against the wall shifting their bodies slightly to see better. The man wore a dark suit and on his head was a wide-brimmed black hat which he occasionally lifted and fanned his face with. Now and again he cast quick glances

[486]

behind him as he hurried on, in long-legged strides, stumbling and sliding over the sand.

"A loose-tongued preacher," said Hook. "Nits of God in his hair and the lice of the devil crapping over his skull."

"Two-bits he's a undertaker."

"One of them bone-frillers?" said Mex. "Angel smile on his face while one hand or the other gooses your wallet every time you turn to blow your nose for the departed? Well, for myself, I hope he's not."

"Whatever he is, I wish he'd hurry up and get here."

Now the stranger was out of the drifts and was walking over the flat ground surrounding the hut. He had a handkerchief tied around his neck and he kept glancing from side to side and then at the men, walking quickly, his long arms swinging.

Hook pinched between his leathery fingers a twist of paper into which he carefully spilled grains of tobacco from a small cotton sack. Capon rolled his back, scratching it against the adobe wall. Flakes of dried clay fell down in a little heap where his buttocks rested.

"Howdy," said Mex. He got up, rubbing his hands slowly up and down his hips, and smiled at the newcomer. "We been watching you."

The other two rose from their crouched position and eyed him.

The stranger stood near the corner of the hut, his hat in his hands and his fingers snapping and unsnapping the brim. His eyes darted from one to the other while a sly smile contorted his mouth. He stood heels close together, playing with his hat, his throat working. His face was flushed from the heat and there were rings of grime around his neck and in the creases of his brow. Tall, with long bony fingers, and legs that were shaking a little—his hair hanging down over his ears, creased about the skull from his hatband.

[487]

"Where you heading, strange?" said Hook, narrowing his eyes and puffing on the cigaret.

"This looks as good a place as any."

Hook squinted at him.

"You mean you ain't got no destination?"

"No," he stammered, looking and then not looking at them, at their hard-set faces. "Which way is California?"

"Out there," said Mex, pointing toward the horizon.

"I've never seen the Pacific." He put his hat on his head. "Nor orange trees."

The men laughed.

"See one wave you seen 'em all."

"Oranges're behind barbed wire," sneered Hook.

"I wouldn't want to pick them," said the stranger. "I don't believe what you say about the waves."

"Oh, like the sand riffs here, 'cepting out there they're wet."

"I'm William."

"We'll call you Reverend. Rev, for short," said Hook.

Mex went up and walked all around the stranger. The stranger stood still, his eyes following the man as he moved around him. Then Mex reached up and began touching the stranger's hair.

"Don't worry none, strange. He ain't seen clean hair in so long—nor none so soft."

"Say," snapped Capon suddenly, stalking over and pointing his finger in William's face. "You don't know where you're going and you don't know where you're at.—You ain't escaping, are you?"

William thrust his hands in his pockets and looked down at the ground.

"A goddamned convict!" cried Capon, advancing on him. "Where's your gun?" He started to beat the man's coat.

William pushed him away firmly with one hand. Capon

[488]

stood staring at him, his arms swung wide from his sides, his fists doubled.

"You listen.—What I am—" said William, heatedly, smoothing his coat. "I'm a mistaken man.—Yes—I—"

He stared off over the land, his hands trembling.

"What was you saying?" said Hook, scraping his beard with his finger.

"Have you any water, please?"

"Get a dipper of water, Mex."

Mex went behind the hut.

"Queer talk you got in your mouth, strange."

"Sit down a spell, son," said Capon, coming forward and taking him by the elbow. "We got water."

"Thank you, kindly."

"Here, in the doorway," said Capon, leading him over, "where there's shade."

William sat down with a gasp and stretched his legs out before him. There were spots of red amidst spots of white in his face. He snatched his hat off his head and began beating it rapidly in front of him. The two men stood watching, curious and quiet. Mex, waddling, hurried from around the corner of the building, carefully balancing a ladleful of water. He handed it to the man and said, "Guess you're hungry too. We got beans."

William threw the water down in one gulp. "A bit more, please," he said, holding out the empty ladle.

Mex hustled off around to the back of the hut again.

"It's good to be with men," William said, hoarsely, leaning forward and clasping his fingers around his knees.

Hook flipped his cigaret into the fire.

"What you doing off the road, Rev?"

He looked up, thought a moment, and said, "There's something uneasy in me. It's like I'm all known now and nowhere to hide." He blushed and let his head fall.

[489]

Capon coughed and, turning away, spat in the dust. "You'll feel better after sundown," he said.

Mex came back with the water and handed it to William, then went over to the fire. He gave a last stir with the paddle, lifted it out and thumped it on the pot's edge, watching as the thick strings of blackstrap molasses fell back into the beans.

"Slop's done," he said.

" 'Bout time," said Capon, stretching his arms wide. "My belly's got the windjams, it's that empty." He slugged himself in the gut.

"Beans'll push it down a cave or two," said Hook, grinning and loosening his belt.

"I'll play you some after-dinner music," said Capon, slapping him on the back.

"A treat to my ears but it'll take me a clothespin to listen."

"We'll shoot perfume around, comes the bass parts. Jist for you, Hookie, darling."

"And that'll shoot me, that whiff of a woman."

"I guess you gotta strong wind in your belly, aintcha, Reverend?"

"I'm not very hungry."

"Well, a man needs to eat. And when he's et himself full, he starts thinking about a woman, and when he ain't got a woman—"

"He jist conks out to sleep," laughed Hook. "And dreams 'em up. So many quiff he can't handle 'em all. I wisht I had me jist *one* of them babes a' the hunnerds I dreamt. Um-*um!*" He ran his tongue around his mouth and strode over to the pot.

Mex came out of the hut carrying four clay bowls stacked in his hands.

"Hey, Mexicali, can't you stew us up a woman outa this

mess someday?"

"I ain't no frigging witch. If you want a woman take old Theodora into town for a grease job. Now get outa my way while I dish up the beans, nectar a' the gods and sweethard a' the eye o' men for miles around."

He ladled some beans into a bowl and handed them to William. "Guests first. Awful coarse, Reverend. We eat with our hands."

"Then I will." He went over to the hut with his bowl and sat down against the wall.

"Your fingers get callouses after a while," called Capon over his shoulder as he held his bowl out to Mex. "Bean-heels, we call 'em. Careful you don't burn yourself."

The dog came wandering up from the arroyo, paused a moment to sniff the air, then loped straight to the fire.

"The only time Mange wakes up is chow time," said Mex. "Only sharp thing about that dog is his snoot can tell jist about when the beans is done to a turn."

The dog sniffed at the rim of the pot, then groaned pleadingly up into Mex's face, his tail whipping the sand.

"Quit kicking up dust, you'll get yours," he said, kneeing the animal aside. "Humans first."

Hook and Capon sat backs against the wall, blowing on their beans before picking them up to put into their mouths, and then licked the juice off their fingers.

Mex filled his own bowl and then threw a paddleful of beans on the sand. The dog jumped on them and lapped them up in one gulp.

"Mange'll get disaterry, all the time you're throwing his grub on the bare ground," said Hook. "All that dirt he eats stuck with it."

"Ain't killed him yet," said Mex, sending another pile of beans scudding in the sand. He came over and sat down in front of the men, balancing his bowl on one knee, and began

[491]

to eat loudly with his fingers, sucking at the molasses as it ran down his wrists.

"Day's so hot," he said, "my armpits are panting."

"We smell them potent elbows," said Hook, running his tongue meticulously over his knuckles.

"We take sandbaths out here," said Mex to William. "Just like regular chickens. It's kinda undignified for a man, hunched nekkid and scratching and heaving dust on hisself, wouldn't you think? But it keeps the lice low."

"I told you to save up your water," said Capon, smearing his fingers around the bottom of the bowl. "Figure it, a bladderful a day and come Saturday night you'd have a oil barrel full to take a bath in." He got up and went over and helped himself to more beans.

"D'ruther take a sandbath," said Mex. "And you oughtn't to talk that way before the Reverend."

"Don't mind me," said William, wiping his fingers on a crumpled handkerchief.

"You want more beans, Rev?"

"I'm not hungry."

"They're lousy but you get used to them," said Capon, striding back and sitting down with a fresh bowlful.

"I see you never pass them up," said Mex, carefully picking an insect out of his beans. He stared at it clinging to his fingernail, then blew it away.

The dog came up and sniffed at William's hands. He reached out to pet him but the dog backed away, his head to one side, looking at the stranger.

"He thinks you're from Mars," said Hook.

The dog's head swung sharply to its haunches where the gray bubble of a tick poked thru the fur. He rubbed it with his nose and then muzzled into the fur, grasping the thing in his mouth and tore it from his flesh. He cracked the tick between his teeth and swallowed it.

[492]

"Ouch!" cried William.

"Why not?" said Mex, scooping beans into his mouth. "They eat him."

He tilted the bowl to his lips, draining the last of the juice, then set it aside and lay back on the sand, cupping his hands behind his head. Hook rolled and lit a cigaret and tipped his hat down low over his eyes, smoking. William looked from one to the other, then out into the distance and back again. He tied his handkerchief into one knot after another.

The dog trotted back down the arroyo. With one forepaw lifted, he looked from left to right, sniffing, then scuttled under the car. Worming his body around in the sand, hollowing it, he lay still and went to sleep.

"Day like this," said Capon, unbuckling his belt and letting his hands fall loosely at his sides, " 'minds me of the time my granny lit the fire in the oven to get it heated for her to bake a pie. Meantime, she goes out to get more kindling, come back, stacks it, crimples the crust-edge of the pie a little, forks holes in the top, then sticks her nose in the oven to smell how the heat was and, lord! what a stench she gets.—Rears back.—Sticks her finger in her jaw, asking, what can it be? So, pinching her nose, she swings open the door wide and gapes in—and, you'll never guess! You know what it was? Ole Tearose, ancient aunt-gora cat she had all her life, crawled in there to take a nap and got baked instead. Well, Granny has almost a stroke, you know.—She got seven other cats but Tearose her special pet—and the stink! Well, she draw a bucket from the well and splash it on that fire fast as lightning—but ole Tearose a gonner—hair singed to a frazzle and I'd say from Gran's telling it, nearabout medium-sized done—her tail (what was so plumey and fine) coiled up tight as a rattler and her feet poked straight out, no fur on 'em, jist like four burnt matchsticks—and her eyes shot from her head like busted grapes.—Pretty eyes she had too—weird—one green, the other pink.—Well, what was ole Granny gonna do?—The pie set there unbaked and Tearose was, and the stench of her filling the kitchen enough to kill a man with leather lungs.— Well, Gran throw open the windows and then she let Tearose cool a bit 'fore she try to lift her out and, lo, when she try to, that cat is melted to the grill like baked cement.—And Gran, tears running down her cheeks, she fetch Grampa's razor and, you know, poor thing, only thing she could do, she sliced that prize cat of hers off each and every one of them grill bars.— Yessir.—Took a hour or more to do it.—And when she got it done, she put what was left of Tearose in a paper bag and buried her out back of the hollyhocks.—She come back and she was so upset and sad, she hadn't no heart to light that oven again.—So what does she do but put on her hat and trots down to Miz Huffington's to set and have a cup of tea and collect herself.—And she tell Huffie all 'bout it, and then she and Huffie have a big cry together and they both feel better.— But Granny didn't never forget.—And what every time she lit the oven after that, Tearose would come back, like a ghost you might say, every time smelling up the room. But after a couple of months the stink of her got all burnt out of the oven and Gran felt better for that, I can tell you. Why there wasn't a breakfast or a dinner she'd cook and she wouldn't bust into tears or start sniveling in the stew.—And it got Grampa sore. 'A course he was still chewing bile over that razor of his Gran had chipped and wrecked all to hell that day, the one with a motherapearl handle he had sent COD special delivery from New York City."

Capon chuckled and flicked a fly off his nose.

"Being so ancient, she mighta died first.—You know, crawled in there to die stead'a nap," said Mex, "and was off into cat-limbo long before the heat got to her."

"I don't think Granny ever thought of that. Mighta cheered

[494]

her up somewhat."

"More company," said Hook, nodding to the west. They turned and looked.

Across the sand a horse came plodding on which sat an Indian, wearing a 10-gallon hat, an onion sack bulging with cans of beer slung to the saddlehorn. The horse's head slunk almost to the ground, the reins trailing in the dust between its hoofs. The Indian sat swaying in the saddle, a can of beer pressed to his lips, his free hand gesticulating aimlessly to the air.

The horse, without once lifting its head, green saliva foaming at its jaws, padded quietly up to the men and came to a halt.

"Howdy, Morning Light!" exclaimed Mex, going up, hand extended.

The Indian lifted a finger, circled it in the air, smiled foolishly and fell off the horse. He landed in a heap on the other side, still clutching the can from which beer dribbled into the earth.

Mex laid a hand against the horse's ribs, then, bending his knees, he peered under the animal's belly at the collapsed Indian and said, "Why, Morning Light, this a helluva note. You come to pay us a call and here you are drunk enough for ten redskins."

"Glub," said Morning Light, crooking his finger at the sky. "More beer, Chester Axehead. I know you of old."

"He ain't no fun when he's this way," Capon said out of the corner of his mouth to William.

"He ain't killed no white man yet tho when he's been on a toot," said Hook, walking over to the horse. "He's a good Indian." He reached between the horse's front legs and picked up the reins.

"Good innien," muttered Morning Light, trying to pull himself up. "Don't eat jelly on my bread. Hair won't fall out

[495]

—teeth won't fall out—like white man. Mexicali, give a good innien a hand here."

As Hook led the horse to the rear of the hut, Mex grabbed one arm and Capon came over and took the other and together they hauled the Indian to his feet.

"Obliged," he said thickly. "Sick a' looking at the sky."

The two men held him up as the Indian stood unsteadily on his feet, his head wobbling around, his eyes narrowed and blinking.

"Who zat? Unnertaker? Come to get my carcass. Worth a plug quarter."

"Why, that's a guest of ours," said Mex. "Reverend, this is Morning Light, old acquaintance."

"How do you do."

"Reverend, eh? Thought you was taker-under. Ooo, lay me in the shade."

They led him over to the adobe and propped him against the wall. He slid down hard in a sitting position and looked around.

"Hey, where's my horse? Who stole my horse? My beer, where's my beer?" he croaked, struggling to get to his feet. "String the bastard up. There's a law."

"Now that's no way to talk about a white man," said Mex, placing his hands on the Indian's shoulders and pushing him down. "Hook's taking your horse to water him. He'll bring you back your beer."

"Well, he better," grumbled the Indian, letting his head rock loosely against the wall. "There's a free lynch law in this territory 'bout horse-thieving."

"Yeah, fifty years ago," said Capon. "You been reading them Westerns again."

Hook came back carrying the onion sack in his hand.

"I don't know as you need more of this," he said, dropping the sack at the Indian's feet.

"Need beer like I need a bath. Bad." He burrowed his nose in his armpit. "Foo! Can't stand the stink of myself. Get drunk."

"Where'd you get dough for booze?" said Capon. "You ain't never had no cash before."

"Celebrate!" exclaimed the Indian. "Have beer. Star— me, a star."

"Some star," sneered Hook. "Can't even sit his horse right."

"Thinks he's a star," said Mex, rubbing his chin. "You hit your head when you fell?"

"Not star inna sky, idiot. Movie star! They shot pitcher out at Shadow Rock. I was extra brave. Ten clams a day. Et inna commizery. Everybody have beer. Toast. Forget name of pitcher," he said, scratching his head. "Have'a go all cowboy pitchers now to see myself."

"What a dumbbell. He's inna pitcher and he don't even know the name of it."

"Drum-something. Scalped two whitemen. Almost scalped leading lady, but hero—he wore perfume all'a time—he come in last minute and cracks my skull open with a carbine. Gets the prize, Yawww, he can have it," he said, fumbling at the drawstring of the sack. "All she did was yap about the flies in the latrine and how hot it was and when were they gonna go home to Malibu—wherever that is."

"I'm seeing things," said Capon, stepping away from the group and peering out in the distance. The others turned and stared hard in the same direction.

A snow-white Jaguar convertible, the top down, its long low body gleaming, the chrome bubbles of its headlamps glinting in the sun, bounced over the desert, leaving a wide, high wake of yellow dust behind it.

"What inna hell's zat?" said the Indian, bracing himself against the wall and trying to push himself up.

"Ain't you never seen no automobile?"

"Um, not without no highway under it."

"Must be lost."

"May be some of them movie people."

"If it's that friggin' leading lady," grumbled the Indian, falling down again, "I'm gonna hide."

"Coming like a bat outa hell. Hope its brakes are good."

"Looks like everybody's coming to our doorstep today," said Mex, rubbing his hands gleefully. "Think I oughta warm up the beans?"

"See first if it's friend or foe," said Hook.

At the wheel was a young woman wearing sunglasses, her dark hair flying in the wind. Beside her sat an older woman, her features blurred thru the dusty windshield.

The car came straight on, without reducing speed until it got within a few yards of the men when the driver turned the wheel sharply, the car careening in a curve, the rear wheels spinning sand as she put on the brakes. The car rocked to an abrupt halt.

The young woman took off her sunglasses and looked at the men. They stood close in a group and looked back at her.

"Hey there, which way is the highway?" she called.

The men did not answer.

She turned to the woman beside her and shrugged her shoulders.

"Perhaps they don't speak English, dear," said the woman.

The girl's mouth went down at the corners as she surveyed the men again. Then she smoothed her hair, pulled on the emergency brake and stepped out of the car.

As she approached them she ruffled out the folds of her Mexican peasant blouse and the wrinkles in her slacks. On her feet were straw sandals.

"Don't touch them, Claudia!" called the woman from the

car, in a hoarse whisper. "They might be diseased."

"Do you speak English?" said the girl as she came up to the men.

"Sort'a," said Hook.

"Gee, you sure are a far piece from the highway, mam," said Mex.

Hook and Capon laughed.

"What's so funny?" she asked with a perplexed expression. "The point is—how far is it and which way?"

"I'd sure like to know that, mam," said Hook.

"You mean you don't know?"

"Well, not yet, mam."

"That's a snappy looking automobile you got there," said Capon.

Mex, Capon and Hook wandered over to the car and crowded around it, inspecting it closely. Morning Light sat with his head in his hands staring at the scene thru slit eyes. William watched from the doorway, his hands in his pockets.

"Haven't you ever seen a car before? said the older woman, as the men grouped around and looked into the interior. "Don't get too close."

She also wore dark glasses, blue rims festooned with plastic daisies; her thighs stuffed into aquamarine pedalpushers. On her head was a pink straw cap, tilted back, the name SUSIE stitched in letters on the inside of the peak.

"Don't touch anything," warned the girl, nervously.

Mex spelled out MIX with his finger in the dust on the fender.

"How come you're way out here?" said Capon, turning to the girl.

"If you really must know, I came out to sketch desert scenes—and Mother wanted to see the desert . . ."

"Oh, Claudia, you'll be the death of me with your insane notions!—Young man, you're breathing in my face. When was

[499]

the last time you brushed your teeth?—Driving clean off the highway. When I'd only wanted to see the desert, *safely*, from 66. And now we don't know where we are!" she announced to the men. "Haven't seen a square inch of asphalt for miles."

"Hush, mama. This is the Twentieth Century, remember? Women are no longer the frail, helpless non-entities they used to be," she said, turning to the men. "Now, tell us, which way to the highway, if you please?"

"Which highway do you mean, mam?"

"Any one close by. At this point we aren't particular."

"Well, I'm the Nineteenth, dear," interrupted her mother, petulantly, her lips twitching. "And I beg you to remember that. You seem to have no consideration.—And you forget how hard I try to keep up with you."

"All right, mama, that's enough I say!" said Claudia, stamping her foot. "This heat's irritating enough without you feeling sorry for yourself. You wanted to see the desert and you're seeing it."

"Not a clean rest station for miles ...." groaned her mother, fluttering a handkerchief at her throat.

"Well, if you insist upon being in one of your moods," said Claudia. She beckoned to the men. "If you'll just follow me we'll settle this business out of her hearing—as she seems to want to be by herself."

She reached into a leather pocket inside the car door and withdrew a sketch pad and a box of charcoal sticks.

"You always leave me out of everything," said her mother.

The men followed the girl to the hut, casting glances back at the car as they went.

"I might as well sketch the crew of you while I'm here. Except that lout," she said, pointing at the Indian. "You there, get out of the way. I want the rest of you to group yourselves before this enchanting hacienda. Something quaint and.

picturesque—primitive—about it all," she said, then leafed thru the pages of her sketch pad as the men stood around staring dumbly at her.

"Well?" she said, glancing up. "Are you going to stand there like logs? Group yourselves—nothing stiff, a natural pose—to catch the desert-like flavor of you. The day of the daguerreotype still-life is over," she announced. She selected a stick of charcoal from the box and tested it on a corner of the paper.

Mex looked at the others and shrugged his shoulders.

"Hey, lady!" called the Indian, still slumped against the wall, "Where the hell's Malibu?"

"Why aren't you on the reservation, where you belong?"

"I gotta in with the warden. Any time I want a pass I sing 'God Bless America' five times unner his window—and I get out." He winked at her. "You wanta beer?"

"Ugh. And drunk as a fool. Isn't there a law against giving liquor to Indians?" she said, turning to the men.

"We haven't been in town for years, mam," said Hook. "We wouldn't know."

"I'd report it to the authorities, Claudia!" shouted her mother. "Hail the first state trooper we see on the highway. When we *get* to the highway. Hurry those men up with the information, dear."

"Hey there—you—black suit, you look like a cultivated man."

"Not me."

"Don't be modest," said Claudia, smiling. "I see you're not of the same cut as these hombres." She jerked her thumb at the others. "Own up."

"I've given up all that."

"What do you mean?"

"What I say."

"You mean you've thrown away your culture?"

[501]

"Such as it was. That, and other things."

"How queer. The rest of us spend so much money and time getting it and you just up and throw it away. Why?"

"I'd rather not say."

"Why not?" she persisted, advancing upon him, hands clasped loosely about her hips.

"It's so hot to argue. And you would only want to argue."

"You probably hadn't much to begin with, so it wasn't hard for you."

He was silent.

"Aren't you European?"

"No."

"You look European."

She studied his face. "Clean-cut features. Nose a bit too pointed for my taste. And the way that one ear sticks out—spoils the proportion. French, I'd say. Passable eyes, but a bit weak. Hazel?" She leaned into his face. "Yes, *Votre figure* would make a nice portrait. But doing portraits is old hat." She started to walk away and then turned to him again.

"Are you a man of the cloth?"

"Which cloth?"

"The table cloth?" chuckled Mex.

"The loincloth," muttered Hook.

"Out of my dark there sometimes shoots a ray of lucidity." He put his hand to his mouth. "No—that isn't what I want to say."

"What kind of talk is that? Who are you quoting? You look like a castoff parson from Chautauqua," she laughed.

"There's serene music there," said William. "And the old ladies, who won't die, sit on gingerbread porches reading slender volumes of Browning. I'm a stray dog, flirting with everyone—for a bone, a kiss. Right now I'm occupied in translating the Bible into good business English. I must rinse out my rhetoric, hold it up in the sun to dry." He bowed and turned away, biting his lower lip.

"You smell like a dog, that's for certain," sniffed Claudia, crinkling her nose. She brushed her long hair back over her shoulder. "Another of these effeminate Hamlets, always out of joint with the times. Think of nothing but their own selfish broodings. I'll inform you, since you seem so out of it, that this is the Twentieth Century. We care about our fellowman —whether he has enough to eat, whether he has proper living quarters and has decent working conditions. That thru Art we shall lead him to an ennobling and better understanding of himself. You might think of that for a while instead of your sick, egocentric self. Open your eyes to the squalor these men here live in. It would do you some good. We're no longer sel- fish or narrowminded.—We no longer forget or despise our fellowman—black, red, yellow or whatever he be."

"Would you sleep with a black man?" said William, his back still turned.

"Of course not!"

"Then how can you say you love him? Mustn't you then lie down with him, like St. Francis, if you truly believe what you say?"

"I'm speaking the new religion of awareness thru the lib- eral ideal. An awareness of man's suffering and his pitiful ignorance. That beneath the skin we are all alike, struggling toward the ideal. Yes, I take back what I said. I would sleep with a negro—a negress, of course—to prove my point."

"A queer turn. A test-tube marriage with grinding teeth. I smell Plato here. The idea loved more than the man, or your nigger wench, say—"

"Don't use that—!"

"How often we love man from afar when we can't stand the smell of him under our noses."

"All this doubletalk.—What are you, one of those un- frocked jesuits, damned to roam your desert in search of your silly God? One of those hypocritical neo-catholics. The new religion of the Twentieth—"

"Mum, mum, I have a seed in my tooth. Excuse me." William went to the hut and sat down, his head in his hands.

"He's been walking a long while in the heat," explained Mex. "He don't feel so good."

"Talks nonsense. Sounds like the sun fried his brainpan."

"Brains and eggs, that's a good breakfast," smiled Mex, rubbing his belly.

Claudia stared at him a minute and then, with a barely perceptible lift of her eyelids, turned and walked over to Hook.

"Claudia! Whatever's taking you so long?" Her mother, still seated in the car, held up a thermos bottle. "This is bone dry. Ask those men if they have any water."

"Give us some of your water," said Claudia to Hook. "You won't pose for me, you can't tell us the way to the highway, the only intelligent-looking one amongst you talks like an idiot, the least you can do is give us some water."

"Uh, uh."

"What? I ask for a little water and all you do is say 'eh-eh' and scratch your fleas."

"I have as much fleas as you have courtesy, mam."

"That's a pretty turn of speech. Now I'll give you one. I've as much fury as you have rudeness. Don't try me."

"Wanta try *me?*"

"I only want some water. My mother, poor dear, has asthma and her throat must be like sandpaper. Now just give me some safe, reliable H_2O."

"Not till you ask for it courteously, mam."

"I'm speaking to you in a civilized manner—"

"They didn't invite you here," bawled the Indian, lurching between them. "Whyn't you dance a different tune?"

"Your breath is putrid." She shoved him aside. "Look,"

[504]

she said to Hook, "just tell me where that water is and I'll get it myself. I'll show you I'm not helpless."

"It's there in the hut, but I wouldn't go in there alone."

"Why not?"

"Because I'm liable to follow you."

"What cheap nerve!" she cried, slapping his face.

"You get more discourteous by the minute, mam," said Hook, rubbing his cheek.

"Claudia!" called the mother. "What's the trouble? Hurry with the water!"

"These boors expect me to fall down on my knees to them to beg for a drop of their nasty water!" she called over her shoulder. "I won't do it!" she said, facing Hook.

"Drink your gasoline."

"Bet it's good-grade stuff. No rust on the pipes."

"It is, for your information. I buy nothing but the best."

"Claudia! Some water, will you?"

"Listen, at least for her sake. Can't you see she's an old woman?"

"Better not let her hear that," grinned Hook, nodding toward the car. "She seems kinda crabby on that point. You say 'please' for old ladies, too."

Hook turned on his heel and went behind the hut. Claudia, puzzled, watched him go, then ran her fingers thru her hair and rubbed her eyes. She stared around at the other men who stared back at her silently. The Indian was dozing.

Hook came back a moment later, carrying a pint whiskey bottle in his hand.

"Is that water?"

"Smell it."

Claudia winced as he held the bottle out to her. She touched it with the tips of her fingers.

"Is it safe to drink? It's awfully tepid. What do you do, keep it out in the sun?"

[505]

"Mam, Lesson A," said Hook, spitting over his shoulder. "This is the desert. In the desert it's hot. Hot. You feel it? No. I'll go further. In the desert it's not only hot but there ain't no wells, ain't no clear running springs. Lesson B: the water'll cost you ten bucks."

"I won't pay it."

"No water then."

He tilted the bottle and emptied it; a damp mark remained in the sand where it splashed.

"Wait! Listen—I haven't got ten dollars."

"Haven't got? You'd better. Because listen: we got the water, we got the grub, we got the way to the highway. Therefore, we get you. Ten bucks. Cheap."

Claudia glared at him, then spun around and walked quickly to the car. She yanked open the door and jumped in behind the wheel.

"Claudia! Whatever in the world! Did they say vile things to you?"

"Never mind, we're getting out of—. The key! Where's the ignition key?"

She turned to her mother and her mother shook her head, her mouth pursed, her eyes wide and frightened.

"I have it here, mam. In my watchpocket," said Hook, smiling, ambling up. He squatted and leaned his elbows on the sill of the car door. "I lifted it while I was inspecting your lovely dashboard."

"You beast! Two helpless women—!"

"That's right."

"O Claudia! Have we fallen amongst murderers?" cried her mother, grasping her daughter's arm in alarm.

"Not murderers, mam," said Hook, politely tipping his hat to her. "We are all lovers. All us gentlemen here are lovers," he swept his hand towards the group.

Mex came up, looking furtively at the women then at

Hook. "I'd give her the water," he whispered, bending in Hook's ear. "She's kinda upset. And her mother's cheeks look like two red innertubes 'bout to blow out."

"Let 'em rip."

"Will you *please* give me the key."

"Oh good! She said it!" squealed Mex, clapping his hands. "Now you'll get everything."

"But so nasty," said Hook, making a face. "More sweet, huh?"

"Please," said Claudia, her fingers stretched loosely over the wheel.

"Ut, still an edge in it."

"Honestly, please, please, give me the key."

He rose, bowed to the waist and, flourishing the key, placed it in her outstretched palm. She immediately inserted it in the ignition and started the motor.

"Aren't you even gonna thank me?" said Hook, hat in hand.

"The male conceit," snorted Claudia, stepping on the gas pedal and making the motor roar.

"Could, if I wanted to, take that key back," said Hook, wrapping his hand around the wheel. "Your arms are so pretty —so thin and fine. One twist—and—"

"Hurry, Claudia!" cried the mother, hugging the side of the door. "Let's get out of here!"

Claudia released the emergency brake and stamped on the gas, spinning Hook flat on his back, as the car tore off across the desert, moving in the direction it had come.

Hook got up and came back to the hut, jogging his limbs and grinning at the white cloud of dust, all that remained of the car and the two women.

"Makes you feel frisky," he said, slamming himself face down in the earth and rolling his body over and over.

"You let them get away like that?" said Capon, sticking

[507]

his foot out, his heel catching Hook's hip and stopping him in the midst of one of his rolls. Hook sprang up, powdered with dust from head to toe, and throwing his arms around the other man, cried ecstatically, "They'll be back. Oh, they'll be back all right! Think that dame's got nose enough to smell her way to the highway? Think the afternoon's a time to nest her when there's a cool night coming? And she'll want a little heat. She'll want that—bad. Badder'n ever she wanted that water or the key to her car!" And he let the other man go and danced around with great hops, throwing his hat high in the air and catching it. "Man's gonna hafta fight mean'll crack that pearl!" he shouted, slamming his fist in the palm of his hand.

"Too much noise here," growled the Indian, thrusting himself up. He swayed to one side, falling to his knees. Then slowly got himself up again and staggered toward the arroyo. At the edge he collapsed and, crawling on his hands and knees, got down the slope. Rolling over on his back he slid himself beneath the car, elbowing the dog over to make room for his body. The dog whimpered in his sleep and squirmed up beneath the motor. The Indian folded his hands on his chest, his long feet sticking out under the rear bumper. Gurgling noises came from his throat. Soon he began to snore heavily.

The sun sank behind the far mesa. Immediately the air grew cool. The harsh light went out. Dusk filled the desert, deep shadows spread between the drifts of sand. The sky to the east was darkening and already a few stars showed. Mex lugged the cookpot out of the ashes and set it near the hut. The men sat down in a ring around, each taking turns putting in his hand, eating the beans cold. When the pot was empty, Mex brought wood from behind the hut and rebuilt the fire. The men watched as a train, the long length of it seen from engine to caboose, moved slowly across the plain, miles to the north.

The fire blazing, the men drew themselves up to it. Mex pulled out a packet of Jezebel cigarets, opened the lid, scooped out a handful and, thumbing them fanwise in his hand, offered them to the men, the gold tips spread outward.

"Them fairy fags," sneered Hook, turning his face and waving them away.

"You can have them perfume-sticks.—Me, I'll have a squint at Miss J. herself," said Capon, snatching the box out of Mex's hand. Holding it up in the fading light he stared, grinning, at the reclining figure of a buxom woman stamped in gold on the purple lid. Hook leaned over Capon's shoulder, staring at the print of the woman, then traced his finger slowly over the curve of her hip.

William took one of the cigarets, looked at it curiously, then put it between his lips as Mex lit a twig from the fire and, reaching over, lit first William's and then his own. The two men sat puffing quietly, the smoke filling the air with the scent of lavender.

"Makes both of you reek like two-bit whores," said Capon, sliding away from them and rubbing his nose briskly.

"More like some nickel cake of terlet soap," said Hook, tossing the packet back to Mex. "If the two of them was only real whores—now, I wouldn't mind."

"Whyn'a hell don't you smoke an American butt? Least that's a smell a man don't stick his nose up at."

"When the sun goes down," Mex leaned over and said to William, "and everything gets quiet, I like to put on my hat and smoke me a Jezzie. And I like to hear a good story. Hook and Capon here, they tell fine stories, but they're a little on the coarse side.—Now don't rile up you two.

"That's his tale, I'm sitting on mine," said Capon.

"Enough to raise the hackles on your back sometimes," he whispered, putting his hand to the side of his mouth. "But a man once in a while likes to hear a different kind of a story.

[509]

And I was wondering if—" He touched William's knee. "Do you know what I mean?"

"I din't know what story you'd want to hear," said William, glancing at him, then at the cigaret forked between his fingers.

"Aw, gwan, Rev," said Capon. "You can't be no worse'n me and Hook here—or that oily-mouthed spic there—for all he's trying to make hisself out to be a angel."

"I don't know," said William, looking around, embarrassed.

"Hell," said Hook, jumping up. "I'll get you some mescal and maybe that'll warm up your pipes." He went to the door of the hut and, pulling the blanket back, stepped inside. He came out a minute later carrying a tan jug over one shoulder. He squatted down again with the men, and holding the jug steady between the heels of his boots, leaned down and bit the cork out with his teeth.

"Here," he said, spitting the cork to one side and holding the jug out to William, "have a swallow, Rev."

William took the jug, stuck his nose in the opening, then lifting it in both hands, tilted the neck to his mouth, his adam's apple bobbing as he drank. Suddenly he thrust the jug from his lips, and clapping his hand over his mouth, began coughing and sneezing.

"You'll get the hang of it, bye and bye," said Capon, grinning at the others as he took the jug from William. He looped his thumb in the handle and, swinging the jug onto his forearm, tipped his head back and drank long and deep. Then he passed the jug to the others, while he snorted and brushed the palm of his hand back and forth under his nose.

"Burned my throat," said William, his eyes red and running. He blew his nose hard on his handkerchief.

"Good for the night chill," said Hook, swinging the jug to Mex.

Mex drank and then set the mescal in the middle of the circle, saying, "Now you got your vents cleaned out, Rev, you can go on with that story. Anytime you feel yourself running out of words, you're welcome to reach for the jug."

William crunched his cigaret in the sand. Folding his legs under him, he leaned his elbows on his knees and stared down at the ground for a moment. He lifted his head and said, "There was this young man, you see. And he roamed the streets of the city—unbathed for a week, and drunk as long, stubble on his face and nicks and slashes from unremembered falls. His wallet gone, in some alley. In crowds he kept his hands in his pockets. At night, wandering in some deserted side street, he'd come upon a stranger, some derelict; drunk like himself. He'd lean close to the stranger and say, 'You see, I have nothing. I've given it all up. All that.' And he would stumble away, as tho in a hurry to get somewhere, but he had nowhere to go. Finally, exhausted and hungry, his bowels nothing but water, there wasn't anything to do now except to climb the five flights up to her door. He got up there somehow, the eyes of Puerto Rican children watching him curiously through the railings. At the top he almost pitched backward down the stairs but managed to swing himself around to slump against the wall. He waited till he got his breath and his heart stopped hammering and then rang the bell. The door opened and she stood there, dressed in a bathrobe, her hair tied behind. She looked at him, her hand moving up to her mouth. 'I—like—like—how are you, Mary?' he said. She helped him inside and sat him down in a chair. His head swung and his eyes tried to focus on her, his cracked lips moving, fluttering. 'I—I—like—I had meant to come—I—like—like how are you, Mary?' Broken, the words, and his head fell to his breast as she stood watching him, not speaking. He began to cry, dry wrenchings of his shoulders, his hands lying uncoiled on the arms of the chair, not even lifted to shield his face. Silently she stooped, unknotted his tie, unbuttoned his shirt. He began to protest: 'No—Mary—I, no—like—I—I—.' She went into the bathroom, turned on the hot tap in the tub and came back. Kneeling beside him, she removed his shoes and socks, unbuckled his trousers and slid them down. Then she leaned him forward in the chair and pulled off his coat, his shirt, slipped off his underwear. He sat naked in the chair. She folded his clothes neatly in a pile on the table. And all the while he was crying, softly pressing one dirty foot behind the other. She took his arm and helped him from the chair—and he followed her, stumbling, his face pressed in one shoulder, to the bathroom. The tub was full and she turned off the tap, helped him over the side, holding him firmly around the waist as he slid down into the water. He looked at her, trying again to speak, his hands swaying in the water. She placed her hand over his mouth, soaped the cloth and started with the face, gently over the crusts of blood, then his ears, his neck, his arms, the rest of his body, the water turning gray to darker gray. She refilled the tub and dried him with a soft towel. She rubbed oil in his cuts. Taking a robe from behind the door, she placed it over his shoulders and led him out and to a bed, the fresh sheets turned down. He lay down and she pulled the covers over him. He watched her move above him, her palms smoothing the sheet. 'Mary—I —Mary—' His hand moved out from beneath the coverlet, reached to touch her. She leaned over, kissed his lips, his eyes, turned out the light and left, closing the door quietly behind her.''

He stopped speaking and looked around at the faces staring at him, quiet, waiting. He cleared his throat. The light had gone out of the sky.

"Well—go on," urged Mex.

"That's all," he said, shrugging his shoulders. "That's all I have to tell."

[512]

"Well, that was real fine," said Mex, blowing his nose between his fingers.

"Something stuck in his craw, eh?" said Hook.

"Wash it down with another drink," said Capon, giving the jug to William.

William drank. The jug again made the round of the circle.

"That was a woman," said Hook.

"Women," said Capon, "women, women," his arms out before him, his fingers hooked as tho to embrace something in the air. "I like to touch the hollows of their throats."

"Look."

A hush fell over the men. The red moon rose over the desert.

"The itch of the moon."

"Pretty thing tho."

"A torment."

"Rev, you talk like a disappointed man."

"Thump! down the chute."

"Life's a fine thing," said Mex, touching his arm.

"My tongue forgets itself."

"Let's don't make this a wake," said Hook grabbing the jug. They drank again as the moon shed fine red light over the sands.

William's eyes went bright and slight tremors ran over his body. He jumped up and began walking up and down before the men in short quick steps, agitated, rubbing his knuckles in the palm of his other hand.

"You feeling horny, mister?" said Hook, leaning for the mescal.

"The indian, where is he?" cried William, swinging sharply upon the men. "He'll teach us the old dances of the earth. The ancient songs."

"Take it easy, Billy boy."

[513]

"Morning Light?" guffawed Mex. "He's a jazzer. Oughta see him bounding around enough to break a leg outside the dancehall of a Saturday night. Quart of whiskey in him and you can't hold him down."

"Not that," blurted William. The pulse of his heart beat visibly in the tight muscles of his throat. He began pacing again, back and forth, crunching his heels heavily in the sand.

"Mescal's took," chuckled Hook. He took another swig from the jug.

William stepped over the shoulders of Capon and Hook and walked off in the direction of the arroyo. The others looked at each other, questioningly, then back at William who was trotting down into the arroyo, his footsteps sending up puffs of dust.

The men got up and followed him. Mex brought the jug.

When they got down in the bottom of the dry riverbed, they saw William squatting behind the rear of the car, his hands wrapped around the ankles of the indian, tugging to pull him out from beneath.

"Come out! Dance!" he cried, pulling hard on the indian's legs. Sweat ran down his face.

"You men!" he shouted, dropping one leg, "Give me a hand. Drag him out! Make him dance."

The men came over and grouped around him. Hook stooped over and, cupping his hands to his mouth, sang softly, "Arise, O Morning Light!"

The men howled.

The loose foot slid slowly beneath the car and disappeared, then suddenly it shot out, the force of the kick catching William square in the stomach. The other foot flew from his hand and he pitched backward in the sand, groaning and clutching his fingers tight to his belly.

"Leave a man alone," came a muffled voice from beneath the car's body. The legs drew themselves under.

The others went over and picked William up.

"That'll teach you, gringo," laughed Hook, slapping the dust off William's buttocks.

"Don't never fool with a drunk indian," said Mex, trying to unbutton William's shirt. "Did he bust your gut?"

"No!" cried William, thrashing out at them with his arms, his face contorted as tho he were about to cry. He broke away and stood staring down at the motionless feet jutting out. "That's not the white man's music," he gasped.

"That's right," said Capon, walking over and putting his hand about William's neck. "Old proverb 'bout the dead indian's still true. But we can't kill 'em, legal, anymore. And so you let 'em drink themselves to sleep and let them be. 'Cause Morning Light, he's as good as dead that way, or any indian. Right now, that's the only good indian."

"I'll invent the dance," said William. He tossed off Capon's arm and walked away. A few yards from the car he dropped down on his hands and knees and began searching in the dust.

The men laughed, then each took turns tipping the jug to his throat. After they drank they walked over and watched William picking around on the ground.

"What you scratching like a hen for?" laughed Capon.

"Chick, chick, chick," sang Mex, walking around William and swinging his arm as tho he were scattering feed.

Hook let out an earsplitting cockcrow.

William got up, holding a twig of dead brush in his hand. "Sit down, sit down," he said, motioning to the ground.

"Whatcha gonna do, preach us a sermon, Rev?"

The men sat down on the ground, snorting with laughter and elbowing each other in the ribs.

"Hope he don't pass the hat," yelped Capon.

"We're each gentlemen of the flesh," said William, flourishing the twig.

[515]

"Amen," crowed Hook.

"A mouthful, brother, a mouthful."

"This root is my magic stick," said William, holding it up between thumb and forefinger. "I'll conjure it to bud.—From the shriveled pores of it, watch the green shoots pop. Believe, believe, my fingers are suns."

"Looks like a piece a' poor dead drift to me," chuckled Mex, winking at the others.

"Damned stick!" cried William. He flung the twig at the sky and held his hands up before his face. "My fingers are wands."

"Conjure us up a woman, Rev."

"Throw him your Jezzies, Mex. Let him bring that babe to life."

"Rev, you ain't talking sense like a white man. You talking jug-sense."

"Tic of the tongue," said William. He tugged at the cloth of his trousers. "This is heavy." He dropped to the sand, quickly unlaced his shoes and kicked them off, then tore off his socks. "Off with our clothes, gentlemen. We'll make the dance," he said, removing his coat.

"I'm for that," said Hook, unzipping his levis.

"We can take our weekly flea-bath," laughed Mex.

Laughing and jostling each other, the men threw off their clothes and scattered them about the banks of the arroyo.

"Let 'em air out!" shouted Capon, as he heaved his boots in the air. They landed some yards away, plomping in the dust. "Phew! What a smell."

William ripped off his shirt and threw it aside, then dropped his trousers and stepped out of them.

He stood naked facing the other naked men. They were horseplaying, scooping up handfuls of dust and rubbing it in each other's armpits. They pinned Mex to the ground and, while Capon held him, Hook smeared his face with dirt, then

[516]

rolled him over and dusted his buttocks, rubbing it in. Mex pounded the ground with his fists, tears runnning from his eyes with laughter, his fat shoulders quaking. He broke away from the other two and dragging himself off, sat up and began pelting them with handfuls of sand. Hook and Capon advanced on him, throwing sand back at him, until they stood over him. Then each scooped both hands in the dirt and poured handful after handful on top of his head.

"We'll dance!" cried William. "We'll dance now."

"You mean like this?" hooted Hook, and he leaned forward from the waist, and, beating the flat of his hand against his mouth, began whooping, his feet trudging the earth as he stamped around and around in a circle. Capon and Mex filed behind him, naked except for their hats, bending their bodies down and then arching back, a hand beating at their lips, their bodies streaked with dirt, hair hanging in their faces. They raised the dust with their treading feet, the deep howlings in their throats breaking the night silence.

"No, no," said William, waving his hands anxiously. He ran up to them and tried to break up the dance, but they shoved him aside, laughing and yelping, and continued to move around in a swaying, drunken circle. William turned away.

Exhausted, the men fell to the ground, lying flat on their backs, panting with laughter, sweat covering their bodies.

"Just like at the trading post," gasped Capon.

"Hell, better," said Hook, lifting himself and wiping the sweat from his eyes. "We oughta put on a show of our own out there some time for them tourists."

"He slapped Capon's thigh and broke into laughter.

The other two sat up, rubbing their forearms across their brows and breathing heavily.

"Whew!" said Mex, taking a deep breath. "Sure dried up my wind whistle."

He walked over to the jug, his heavy haunches jiggling.
"Walks like a fat whore," snickered Hook.

Mex brought back the jug, took a long drink and gave it
to the others.

"That's the spirit!" shouted Capon. He snatched the jug,
his lips sucking thirstily at the neck.

"Don't drain it," said Hook, tapping him on the shoulder. And as Capon continued to drink, Hook pulled the jug
from his mouth and thrust it to his own.

"Sure fixes me good," grinned Capon, running his tongue
around his lips. "Foo! Damn grit," he said, making a face and
spitting the sand from his mouth.

"We'll need some of this for the ritual," said William,
coming over and laying his hand on the jug.

"Why sure, Reverend, sure," said Hook, handing it to
him. "You gonna baptize us?"

The men laughed. Then they grew quiet, breathing more
easily, and watched as William held the jug close to his ear
and shook it.

"Empty," he said, letting the jug swing loose at his hip.

"Need water for a baptism, do you?" said Hook, hopping
up. "I'll make water." He urinated, the splattering stream
quickly sucked into the dust.

"Blood's thick and will hold," said William. He swung
the jug over his head and the others ducked as he brought it
down upon a rock, shattering it. Picking up a jagged shard of
the splintered jug, he sat down and began slicing crosses in the
soles of his feet.

The men watched him, tensed, their eyes wide.

"Thirsty earth," he said, the palm of his hand carressing
the dust. "My blood, ghost-appeaser." He squeezed blood
from his feet onto his fingertips and sprinkled the dust. "Will
they speak to me now?" He stared down at the drops of blood,
the dust coating and making little balls of it. He clapped his

hands to his head. "My ears smoke awaiting the word. My eyes, for the apparition."

The men sat motionless, their mouths slightly parted, watching his every move.

"She comes," crooned William, rocking back and forth. "Is it you?" he asked suddenly, staring disbelieving at the air. "Queen's robes, gray and root-clotted from the grave. My sight blurs." He gave his head a quick shake. "Are those seed-pearls down the folds?" His hand reached out, the fingers un-coiling slowly, began to brush at the air. "Why don't you speak?" he cried angrily, peering as tho at someone before him. "Dumb mouth a hole of grief. Why do you hold your arms so? To chase crows? How they fill the air, wings beat, black and silken." He flailed his arms about and pressed his chin to his chest, gritting his teeth. He looked up, his hands fluttering over his head, his eyes fearful, as he peered around at the sky. "Gone?" He gradually let his arms fall. His eyes focused again before him. "Listen," he said in harsh voice, crooking his finger, "Close, close—I'm falling asleep, Mother —It's no good." He slumped down in the sand, his lids clos-ing. "The great bird hovers," he murmured. "Alights on my belly, its claws dig into my flesh, its beak sinks straight into my middle!" he shrieked, kicking his legs, his mouth straining, the muscles in his hands taut as they cupped themselves over his stomach. "It's pulling the guts from me, it's lifting me from the bed, the wings shudder over me, drawing me up." He sat erect. His eyes snapped open. "No blood?" he said, huskily, running his fingertips over the skin. He dropped his gaze. "Your arms must be tired," he breathed softly. "A little blood to refresh you." Clutching a foot in his hand, he ran a finger up the sole and whipped blood off at the air. "Let them fall. I'm so tired, Mother," he sighed. His shoulders sagged, his hands twitched on his thighs. "I'm in the bed of the river. Lift me, lift me up. Bring me into the light. Mother, I'm so old, so old and tired. Give me the light. Don't touch me!" He reared back, holding his hands up before him to fend off some invisible thing. "No more of your dry lips. Disintegrate to dust. Don't—yet!" He gesticulated with his hands, desperately motioning something back. "Mother—listen—I'm not anything. Not any of that. I want to be quiet. I'm William-eyes and William-ears. I'm William-mouth and William-heart. Poor dumb cock!" he cried, seizing his groin. "Barbs forged in hell's red belly. There, through smoke, the glamorous jew squints spanishly at me. Lights in his eyes, he says. Brambles, say I."

He pressed his knuckles deep into his sockets.

"Ah ah ah," he whispered. "Ah ah ah."

"Take it easy," croaked a voice from the men.

"To sleep?" he asked, staring out, wild-eyes. "Enough of that." His fingers dumbly stroked the sand. "Only now I see I slept all my years beneath layers of silt." He scooped up some of the blood-moist dust and kneaded it between his fingers. "My soul is blond. Ribs nesting fire. How late it gets. Smash time. Beware those razors in their eyes. They slice you. Hard-won innocence of manhood," he murmured, scattering the dust from his hand. "To bust through—a fist to punch with!" He sprang up and stepped toward the men, his feet tracking prints of themselves, damp in the sand. "I want that," he whispered fierecely, leaning over them. "The sick exhaust me. The body," he said, with awe, running his hands down himself and staring around at the dark. "A man could walk forever out there, his body aching. Christ yap," he said, his fists banging his thighs. "Redskin!" he shouted toward the car. "Dance! Og! He's drunk, the dance sprung from his arches." He walked with measured steps up and down before the men, his heels kicking the dust lightly. "Nevermind nevermind nevermind. Cool gringo—jazz-song—jazz-dance—to it, to it."

He looked around at their faces as tho he did not see

them, then furtively back over either shoulder, his body trembling. "I see I'm on dangerous ground. Fears press in to snap the spine. No turning back. Broken—cold acid leaks in the bones. A corner of cloth to cover—there and there. Wake me before dawn."

Entranced, he rubbed his hands across his chest. staining the skin with blood. He moved toward the men.

"Princes, you are all princes. Above all, don't be afraid. Don't desecrate the wonder. No more nightmares. Walk dreamful in the day. Splendid peoples. Move us as tides, eyes open."

His hand went to his throat and his lids fluttered. "I see I've been dreaming," he said, and fainted, falling face down in the sand.

Mex ran to him and turned him over. He lifted him by the shoulders and propped his head on his knee.

"Mescal finally hit him over the head," said Capon. He got up and walked over. Hook followed him. They stared down at the unconscious man.

From the edge of the arroyo the beams of a car's headlights cut thru the darkness, illuminating the naked bodies in a white glare. The men stared up, blinded, into the lights. The car banked abruptly, the wheels spinning in the earth, sending down a great spray of sand over the men below. It jerked forward, swerving over the sand, then, as the wheels dug in, it shot in a straight line across the desert. Above the roar of the motor on the still night came the sharp screams of women.

"Them?" coughed Capon, beating the dust out of his eyes.

"You shoulda told them, Hook," said Mex, sneezing, his eyes watering.

"They shoulda knowed."

"No water."

"It's cool now."

[521]

The dust settled.

"Come on, Cape! You can have the old lady!" shouted Hook, running for the touring car.

"We'll see about that," said Capon, snatching up his hat and planting it on his head. "You watch out for the invalid," he called over his shoulder. "We'll give you a smell when we get back."

Hook stooped down and cranked the motor, which started with an abrupt explosion, rocking the body on its springs. The dog bolted out from beneath and stood a few yards off, its hair bristled, thin high howls coming out of its throat. The motor hummed down to a steady, quiet knocking, the fenders and headlamps rattling with the vibration. Hook tossed his boots in the back and jumped behind the wheel. Capon sprang up beside him. The car strained up the slope of the arroyo, exposing the prone body of the indian lying between the tire tracks left in the dust, his hands thrashing in his sleep. Once over the edge, it coughed along in the direction the other had gone, the tattered remains of the canvas top fluttering behind. Capon, naked, except for his hat, clutched the top of the windshield with both hands and leaned far out over the hood, straining to see thru the thick dust the other car had made.

"The turtle and the rabbit," sighed Mex, letting his arms fall from his hips. He watched the car, the sound of the motor growing faint as it moved away, then he turned as it disappeared in the dust. He reached down and lifted William in his arms and carried him up out of the arroyo and back to the fire which was now a heap of smoldering coals. He lay William down close to it, then kicked up the coals with his heels and threw on more wood. He went into the hut and came back with a blanket, spread it on the sand and rolled William into it, then wrapped the blanket about him. The dog trotted up to the fire and lay down, shivering, and curled himself near the flames. Mex went behind the hut and brought back a clay bowlful of water. He paused and peered out to where the car had gone, then set the water down at the foot of the blanket and, kneeling, uncovered William's feet. Whipping a large rag from his pocket, he dipped it in the water, wrung it out, and began carefully wiping at the crusts of blood and dirt on the soles of the feet. William cried out in his sleep and tried to draw his legs up into the blanket, but Mex held them firmly by the ankles and kept dabbing gently until he had scraped the crud away. Then he rinsed out the rag and wiped the soles of the feet clean. He leaned back on his heels and surveyed the feet, clucking his tongue and shaking his head. He looked around, then seeing the cactus, went over and stood running his fingers down the sleeve of the shirt hanging there.

"Hook'll have my ass," he said and whisked the shirt down. Bringing it back to the fire, he began tearing it into long strips. These he bound around William's feet. The dog came over and began lapping the dirty water. Mex put his hand over the dog's face and shoved him away.

"Git disaterry," he said and, lifting the bowl, heaved the water away into the darkness. He tucked William's feet into the blanket and then sat down before the fire, close to the dog, and began stroking the animal's throat.

The moon, now high in the sky, poured white light over the desert.

Soon he heard a motor and, looking, saw the touring car returning, the far, dim headlamps throwing a faint light before it. Capon stood on the runningboard, kicking one leg out and waving his hat. Suddenly the car swerved to the left and started going around and around in wide circles, Hook turning the wheel sharp first one way and then the other, making the car zigzag and kick up mounds of dust.

"Yip! Yip!" came the voice of Hook, clear and far away over the quiet night.

[523]

"Yip!"

"Spur 'er, Hook—gash blood from 'er!" came Capon's voice, deep and distant.

Hook swung the car thru a series of crude figure eights, the car careening over the sand, the dust rising white and powdery as smoke, in the moonlight.

"Yip!" came, like shrieks. "Yip! Yip!"

Hook cut the wheel hard and the car tipped to one side on two wheels, balanced there an instant, then thudded down with a loud groan on its springs. He put it in reverse and it shot backward. Then, the gears grinding, he steered the car toward the hut, the engine sputtering and missing.

Mex stepped from the fire to meet them but the car kept on coming and he jumped out of its path as it bore down on him.

"Hey! Where you going?" he shouted as it roared past him. Capon leaped, startled, from the runningboard and fell to his knees on the ground, as Hook, hunched over the wheel, his teeth clenched, his eyes narrowed, headed straight for the hut. The car rammed the wall and shuddered to a halt. There was a trickle of spilling liquid somewhere beneath the car, then silence.

Mex came running over, and Capon, pulling himself up, followed, rubbing his shins.

Hook squeezed himself out from behind the wheel and stepped nimbly to the ground, a bruise swelling to a lump on his forehead, his lower lip split and bleeding.

"Old whore!" he shouted, booting a mangled fender. "Won't do no more'n thirty-five per hour."

"You hurt bad?" said Mex, peering at him.

"The-oh-whore!" shouted Hook, spitting on the motor standing upright out of the hood. "That's your name!" He smashed the crumpled hood down with his fists. "We'll straighten you out in the morning," he said, turning on his heel. "I'm gonna crap out."

He snatched his boots from the rear seat and stalked over to the doorway, whipped the blanket aside and went in. Mex and Capon stood listening to him stamp around, muttering curses, then the heavy thump of the boots heaved against the wall, the last jingle of the spurs ringing tinnily. Then all was quiet.

"Guess it's okay to go in," said Capon. He walked around the wreck, inspecting it. "To treat her like that just 'cause she ain't got no more pep. And, hell, it ain't like he rolled her off the floor yesterday.—To be so mad 'cause she busts a gasket doing thirty.—And who wouldn't, taken the beating she's took all her life."

"Hook'll like fixing her up," said Mex.

"I'm gonna turn in," said Capon. "Prob'ly woulda got the ole lady anyhow," he mumbled, disappearing into the hut.

When Mex returned to the fire, he saw the indian squatting over the flames, his hands thrust to the warmth.

"Whata commotion out here," he yawned, as Mex came up. He shook his head, his eyes puffy with sleep. "Coo-coo fades," he muttered. "I'm gone back to town."

"How you feel, Morning?" said Mex, tossing a stick on the fire.

"Head like thirteen heads," he said, scratching his scalp. "All concrete."

William sat bolt upright, the blanket falling away from his shoulders. "Still night?" he said, staring up at the sky.

"Them the best stockings he got?" said the indian.

"He stepped on a mesquite bush," grinned Mex.

William looked around him with strained eyes. He saw the indian and then Mex, and drew the blanket up about him.

"Shut your eyes before you bleed to death," said the indian.

"I've got to go," William said. He struggled to get up.

"I've got to get out of here." He got to his feet and immediately fell down, wincing and clutching his ankles.

"I scraped off the mess," said Mex. "You oughta rest up here a while."

"Where're my clothes?" he asked.

"Clothes are still down there," said Mex.

"You gone to town? I'm gone to town," said the indian. "You come with me." He shuffled off behind the hut.

"You oughta stay here," said Mex. "Let your feet heal."

"I've got to push on."

Mex shrugged his shoulders. "It's your skin." He went down into the arroyo and picked up William's clothes and his own and came back just as the indian was leading his horse out from behind the hut.

William put on his shirt. Then Mex helped him slide into his trousers as he lay on the blanket.

"Better carry your shoes and socks. Won't do to put them on yet."

Mex started putting on his own clothes.

"What you guys nekkid for?" said the indian, adjusting the saddle strap," on the horse. "Think night's hot as day?"

"Little party," said Mex, stepping into his dungarees.

"Party and no women," said the indian, slapping the horse's belly. "I don't know what to think of that."

Mex laughed.

The indian climbed onto the horse. "You get on behind me," he said to William.

William walked on his heels to the horse. "Put these here," said the indian, reaching down and taking his shoes and socks from him. He lifted the flap of the saddlebag and dropped them inside. Mex boosted William and William swung onto the back of the horse. He placed his arms around the indian's waist.

"Ready?"

"All set," said Mex. "Good luck there, Reverend," he said, touching tl e calf of William's leg.

William's head had fallen against the indian's neck and he was asleep.

"I'll talk to myself," said the indian. "Gee-up," he clucked, tugging at the reins. The horse started off at a slow walk.

"And you, Morning, you come again," said Mex, walking alongside.

The indian grunted and Mex stood still, hands on hips, and watched as they went off, William's head bobbing on the other's shoulder. He watched until they had gotten quite a distance away and then turned and walked back to the fire. He stood a moment gazing around at the horizon. To the east was a faint flush of light. He threw more wood on the fire. He looked around once more, then dropped down on the blanket and, tipping his hat over his eyes, rolled himself up for sleep.

Quite the Largest Thing
the World Has Seen

By BRUCE DEXTER

From the first chapter of Dexter's novel in progress, entitled *With Multitudes Bent*. Dexter makes his home in
Los Angeles, having come there from Massachusetts.

There is no getting around the fact that Los Angeles is a
very big city and the first thing to remember about it is that it
is much, much bigger than anyone says it is, so much bigger
that if the rest of the country really knew how big it is they
would do something about it. True enough, Texas is very large
but Texas is a state and then too so much of Texas is vacant
that no one thinks it worthwhile doing anything about it such
as giving it back to Mexico or letting the Gulf of Mexico in on
it so that Arkansas could have a seaport.

But practically none of Los Angeles is vacant. It is full to
the throat with people, and things that people own like houses,
cars, businesses. So full that it spills out of its surveyed boundaries. And this is why it is much bigger than anyone says it is.
The legal limits make it the largest city by area in the United
States, but the cultural and psychological limits make it quite
the largest thing the world has ever seen, for these limits
include surrounding towns and small cities which on the ordinary misleading maps are considered separate entities.

Looking at it this way, Los Angeles sprawls across the
southern part of California so that it is impossible, for example,
to go from San Francisco to San Diego without going through
Los Angeles, unless you go many miles inland and totally out
of your way. This spreading seems self-conscious for in some
cases Los Angeles extends itself by long thin tentacles such as
that one which reaches from downtown to the harbor at Wil-

mington or that even more fantastic one, owned by the Metropolitan Water District, which in one long aqueductial thread curls from the thirsty San Fernando Valley over three hundred miles to the Owens Valley at the base of the High Sierras.

Legitimately the city could be said to extend in an unbroken psychological and housing swath to the east and southeast as far as Covina, Whittier and Buena Park; to the south as far as, perhaps including most of, Long Beach; to the north as far as San Fernando, Glendale and Pasadena; and to the west as far as Santa Catalina Island. This is roughly twenty-five hundred square miles, not including the channel waters between Point Fermin and Santa Catalina, on which Los Angeles hasn't managed to put housing yet, and is enough to make the rest of the country take pause and think a bit. Needless to say there are many million people living in those twenty-five hundred miles, and that many million anything, Angelenos, mosquitoes or carp, is enough for the sober citizen to ponder: this is a sizeable piece of the U. S. A.

Citizens of Los Angeles have many ways of coping with the magnitude of their garden—they must, for if the rest of the country is awed by, and suspicious of, the sprawl, the residents might well be terrified.

The first thing attempted was to cover with buildings as much of the area as possible, thus giving at least the illusion of a community. This might have succeeded in the pre-automobile days, but once a man could spend half a day driving in a straight line within the city limits he was not to be comforted by having the landscape composed of stucco, concrete and boards.

Next, worried but enterprising citizens withdrew to try and establish self-contained suburban communities within the city. But not only did most of the residents refuse to confine their work and play to these enclaves, the city itself crowded around them, breathing with a heavy and smoggy breath.

[529]

So, most recently but most importantly, the mind of Los Angeles man caught up with the mind of science and applied the principle that when imagination fails, only speed shrinks space. Thus the freeways were built, predicated on the supposition that if a citizen could rush quickly enough from his place of eating, sleeping and breeding to his place of work or play, then he need not be terrorized by his own insignificance as measured against the unreasonable distances of his home town. Also, the freeways were supposed to convey a feeling of unity by analogy with the human organism: these bands of concrete being the arteries that made sense out of the multitudinous jumble of veins of streets and the incredible corpulence of the body itself. Now at last all was connected, all was one.

But at least three generations of pre-freeway Angelenos were not so easily deluded. Speed might diminish space but not memory, and millions of men and women still knew what an immensity they inhabited and still had their daydreams and nightdreams troubled by it.

The Slide Area

By GAVIN LAMBERT

> Gavin Lambert was born and raised in Great Britain,
> where he wrote film criticism and was for several years
> editor of *Sight and Sound*. At present he is living in
> Hollywood and writing screen plays. This selection is
> from *The Slide Area* (1959), a volume of connected short
> stories.

About this hour and season, four o'clock in the afternoon
and early summer, I find myself looking out of the window and
wondering why the world seems bright yet melancholy.

I am sitting in office 298 of a Hollywood film studio,
working on a script and thinking that the film Cliff Harriston
is going to make of it won't do either of us much good. This
morning I noticed a truck parked outside one of the shooting
stages. Scenery was being unloaded, the walls and furniture of
a living-room carried into the empty stage where camera,
lights and the high crane are already waiting. There is no stopping it now, I thought. Later, imagining the reality being hammered and painted and wheeled into shape over there, I
looked at the pages on my desk and found them more unreal,
more impossible than ever. Tomorrow there will be more argu-
ments with executives. We shall plead our cause and discuss
what is truth. I would like to start work on the novel I am
hoping to write and pretend is already under way.

Office 298 is small and square and rather dim, because
there are venetian blinds across the windows and heavy faded
curtains that cannot be pulled back far enough. I have tried
letting up the blinds, but the heat is unendurable. Better to be
cool and slightly depressed. There is a desk with a telephone
and typewriter and stack of paper, a tray full of finely-
sharpened pencils and a calendar with leaves you are supposed

to tear off each day. It doesn't seem worthwhile to tear off the leaves. Let time stand still or move back, it doesn't matter.

There used to be pictures hanging on the walls, coloured sketches for the sets of a recent production laid in ancient Rome. Another sketch was labelled *Costume for Mr. Victor Mature*. The designer had autographed them all with a grave flourish in the lower right-hand corner. I took them down my first day here and hid them behind the filing cabinet. No one will take them away, although I have asked the office cop several times and once in desperation left a note for the cleaners.

I glance at the cabinet and know they are *there*. About twice a week this obliges me to leave the office early. It always happens at the same time. From my swivel chair at the desk I face this cabinet and the door leading into the corridor; the dim light is strange and enervating, it reminds me of an unoccupied house swathed in blinds and dust-sheets. Swivelling, I look out of the window across the parking lot with its rows of shining two-toned saloons and convertibles, and the neat flower-beds dustily brilliant in puce and yellow. The sun is climbing down the sky. In another hour it will be cooler.

As I leave the building, the cop silently notes my early departure in his little book. He has already noted my late arrival this morning. A friendly ritual that we do not even bother to talk about.

Two men are staring at the newspaper rack near his desk. Both are plump and clean and perspiring, and wear white nylon shirts with sleeves rolled up. They have familiar anonymous executive faces.

For once a political event, though it was later found not to have taken place, occupies the front page headlines. With no kidnappings, aeroplane crashes or sex crimes blocked out in huge letters anywhere, I feel for a moment that something has gone wrong. So do the executives, as they gaze at each paper in turn and find no escape from REDS INVADE BURMA!

Their faces are solemn, sweat pours down. They scan the pages like people trying to find their bearings. Then, his eyes narrowing, one turns to the other. 'It says Bobo Rockefeller's got herself arrested.'

With sighs of relief they move on.

A white Lincoln shoots past, I glimpse a woman in a white sleeveless dress at the wheel, green silk scarf fluttering out of the window. She pulls up with a squall of brakes at a STOP sign, two feet from a weakly handsome young man in a beige tussore suit.

'Hi, Julie! Trying to kill me?'

She laughs loudly. 'Yeah, but I changed my mind.'

This is Julie Forbes, a famous star. She has been in pictures for thirty years and everyone is always saying how good she looks. The young man is an actor recently arrived from Broadway and placed under contract to the studio.

He leans charmingly on the window of the car. 'How about dinner this week?'

She shakes her head. 'I'm busy every night.'

'Next week?'

'Call me over the week-end and see how I'm fixed.'

He looks disappointed. She pats his hand. 'And pine for me, loved one.'

She drives away, scarf fluttering.

The studio is like a large country estate. Haphazardly ranged buildings are white and clean and look entirely uninhabited. What to do? I put a coin in the automatic Coca-Cola machine, the bottle slides out on a tray and I place it under the automatic opener. I don't like Coca-Cola much, but drink a little and pass the smiling Negro shoeblack at his stand.

'Hi, how are *you*?'

'I'm fine. How are *You*?'

[533]

Back lots with permanent exterior sets occupy most of the grounds. The residential street of white frame-houses with sprinklers on the front lawn, a nice replica of anywhere in the more modest stretches of Beverly Hills, has as much and perhaps more reality than the real thing. So has the small town square: well stocked drugstore, a bank and a school, a church and an empty green. The windows of the bank are still shattered from a robbery scene staged there last month.

In the western town, the St. Louis Midland Express is always standing at the railway station. The Last Chance Saloon is empty except for silence and a few chairs broken and overturned from the last brawl. The main street turns a corner and is suddenly a footbridge across a dried-up stream. Beyond it lies something that began as a medieval French village and has been altered here and there to suit the centuries as a corner of Italy or Corsica. A rotted pulpit leans across the entrance to Our Lady of the Fields.

Further away the ground slopes up, then down again to an abandoned harbour town, slightly Dutch with its moored barges and rosebrick warehouses along the quayside. It is watched by an artificial canvas sky, shaped like an immense blue panoramic screen, bluer than the thing above my head. Spotlights are standing by, ready to reinforce the sun.

Then comes the point of no return. The great open air scene dock is like landscaped bric-à-brac. Derelict pioneer wagons left to flake and lurch in the dry grasses; a huddle of chipped classical pillars; an early ranch house with no glass in the windows and one wall missing and the stains of fire; an old stockade, a Chinese palace arch, a tall unhinged door fallen across a wheel, a rowing boat propped up against a castle watchtower, and a staircase winding to the sky.

Here it sleeps in the sun, this neglected litter of the past. Time and heat make their inroads a little more each day. A ruined secret world more real than practical avenues and bouievards, the only place you can be certain that ghosts walk.

What to do? In the parking lot, hidden among princely roadsters, stands my fog-grey seventy dollar 1947 Chevrolet with the battered front I refuse to have mended. As I drive out, the cop at the gate looks glad to see it go. Then he waves as a young actress and her massive grim-faced aunt edge quickly past me in a damask Cadillac embroidered from radiator cap to rear mudguard with mother-of-pearl.

It becomes a day for interesting cars. Stopping at a drugstore for cigarettes, I park behind a twenty-five-year-old Rolls-Royce that I know very well. A landaulette, painted silver and white, and the royal crest of the old Austro-Hungarian empire engraved on the doors. A young chauffeur sits at the wheel, chewing gum.

The drugstroe is fairly empty, at the soda fountain a group of girls sip chocolate malts and a Filipino workman eats a hamburger. Everyone else is watching the Countess Osterberg-Steblechi, who pays no attention but very slowly revolves the paperbacked crime novels on their stands. It is the fate of the Countess to be stared at, and one cannot be surprised. She is like a balloon blown up into roughly human shape and ready to burst. All swollen and sagging contours except for her face; her beaky nose and sharp hooded eyes remind you of a falcon. She has hair that looks like a wig but is really her own dyed .red, and wears a piece of garish linen printed all over with flowers and cornucopias like old-fashioned wallpaper.

Each time I see this great aristocratic wreck, I have the impression she has *got inside* her shoes, her dress, her hat if she wears one, by mistake. And she cannot get out. She is trapped, any movement could be fatal. She waddles dangerously up to me now, a paperbacked novel in one hand, a crocodile leather bag in the other.

'Dear child, have you read *The Case of the Black-Eyed*

Blonde?' I shake my head as she holds up the book in front of me. 'How strange, nobody has. I looked at the first page and nearly fainted with excitement. Are you coming to tea with me Sunday?'

'I'd love to.'

She wheezes with pleasure, but the strain contracts her face. Now it looks like the moon after an explosion, the features are blasted fragments. 'There may be a kind of jumble sale, I hope to raise a few hundred dollars.'

'For what?' I ask, though I know the answer.

'For myself, of course, dear child. I wish I were not so heartrendingly poor.' She scratches her nose with a jewelled and freckled finger. 'Are you sure you haven't read *The Case of the Black-Eyed Blond?*'

'Absolutely.'

'Then I shall have to take it on trust. With an opening paragraph like that I think . . .' She breaks off vaguely, fumbling in her crocodile bag and giving the assistant a quarter.

The assistant says: 'Thirty-five cents, please.'

She takes an alarmed step backwards. 'You mean it's one of the expensive ones?'

'It's thirty-five cents.'

The Countess replaces the book in the Westerns rack. 'Much too expensive,' she says firmly, 'when no one knows if it's really good. I adore pulp literature but one must retain one's sense of values. Where is your selection of twenty-five cent crime novels, please?'

She is the widow of a distinguished European banker.

It is only a few miles' drive to the ocean, but before reaching it I shall be nowhere. Hard to describe the impression of unreality, because it is intangible; almost supernatural; something in the air. (The air . . . Last night on the weather telecast the commentator, mentioning electric storms near Palm Springs and heavy smog in Los Angeles, described the behaviour of the air as 'neurotic'. Of course. Like everything else the air must be imported and displaced, like the water driven along huge aqueducts from distant reservoirs, like the palm trees tilting above mortuary signs and laundromats along Sunset Boulevard.) Nothing belongs. Nothing belongs except the desert soil and the gruff eroded-looking mountains to the north. Because the earth is desert, its surface always has that terrible dusty brilliance. Sometimes it looks like the Riviera with a film of neglect over villas and gardens, a veil of fine invisible sand drawn across tropical colours. It is hard to be reminded of any single thing for long. The houses are real because they exist and people use them for eating and sleeping and making love, but they have no style of their own and look as if they've been imported from half a dozen different countries. They are imitation 'French Provincial' or 'new' Regency or Tudor or Spanish hacienda or Cape Cod, and except for a few crazy mansions seem to have sprung up overnight. The first settlers will be arriving tomorrow from parts unknown.

Los Angeles is not a city, but a series of suburban approaches to a city that never materializes. The noisy populous down-town section with its mixture of Americans and Mexicans, Negroes and Orientals, its glass and concrete new structures jostling fragile wooden slums, its heavy police force and ugly untidy look of sudden industrial growth, is a little like Casablanca. The older parts are exotic but tired, collapsing under the sleek thrust of commerce. There is a modest little Japanese quarter with movie houses, gift shops, *sukiyaki* signs, a steam bath and massage parlour and the Bank of Tokyo; a Chinatown pretty and synthetic as a planner's lifesize model; a Mexican quarter with a gaudy street market, sombreros and bullfighters' capes and scented candles always on display. There are oil derricks and power plants massed like geometrical forests, and a thin bitter smoke hangs in the air on a windless day.

[537]

No settlement can ever have grown more wastefully and swiftly. A century and a half ago pirates still raided this coast, were captured and hung in the village square, Indian slaves were dragging timber from the mountains to build first a jail and then a church. Invasion began with the Gold Rush, fishermen from the East and Scandinavia and Italy found the Pacific rich in salmon and tuna, even convicts arrived from Australia in stolen ships. Now Los Angeles is a welter of nearly five hundred square miles and four million people making aeroplanes and pumping oil, assembling automobiles and movies, processing food and petroleum, building quick frame-houses that you can see being drawn along the streets at night by a truck and placed on a vacant lot like scenery for a movie set.

Along the main boulevards, between the office blocks, plots of untouched land are still for sale. On one of the plots, not long ago, the skeleton of a prehistoric animal was excavated. In the paleozoic past, before the land dried and crusted into desert, this was a quagmire under a hot sun, sloths and mastodons were trapped and dying there. Now the last victim has gone, the grave is cleared and the offices of a great insurance company can go up.

How to grasp something unfinished yet always remodelling itself, changing without a basis for change? So much visible impatience to be born, to grow, such wild tracts of space to be filled: difficult to settle in a comfortable unfinished desert. Because of the long confusing distances, the streets are empty of walking people, full of moving cars. Between where you are and where you are going to be is a no-man's-land. At night the neon signs glitter and the shop windows are lighted stages, but hardly anyone stops to look. A few people huddle at coffee stalls and hamburger bars. Those dark flat areas are parking lots, crammed solid.

I suppose that Europeans, accustomed to a world that changes more calmly and slowly, are not much interested any more in imitating its surface. It becomes more exciting to see appearances as a mask, a disguise or illusion that conceals an unexpected meaning. The theme of illusion and reality is very common in Europe. In America, illusion and reality are still often the same thing. The dream is the achievement, the achievement is the dream.

The ocean appears suddenly. You turn another hairpin bend and the land falls away and there is a long high view down Santa Monica Canyon to the pale Pacific waters. A clear day is not often. Sky and air are hazed now, diffusing the sun and dredging the ocean of its rightful blue. The Pacific is a sad blue-grey, and nearly always looks cold.

Each time I drive down here it feels like the end of the world. The geographical end. Shabby and uncared for, buildings lie around like nomads' tents in the desert. There is nowhere further to go, those pale waters stretch away to the blurred horizon and stretch away beyond it. There is no more land ever.

High lurching cliffs confront the ocean, and are just beginning to fall apart. Signs have been posted along the highway, DRIVE CAREFULLY and SLIDE AREA. Lumps of earth and stone fall down. The land is restless here, restless and sliding. Driving inland towards the mountains, it is the same: BEWARE OF ROCKS. The land is falling. Rocks fall down all over and the cliffs called Pacific Palisades are crumbling slowly down to the ocean. Who called them Palisades, I wonder? They cannot keep out the Pacific. There are mad eccentric houses above the Palisades, with turrets and castellations and tall Gothic windows, but no one wants to live in them any more in case the ground slides away.

It has slid again this afternoon. On one section of the highway a crowd has gathered. An ambulance stands by, winking red lights. A sheriff directs operations. From a great pile of mud and stones and sandy earth, the legs of old ladies are sticking out. Men with shovels are working to free the rest of their bodies. Objects are rescued first, a soiled table-cloth and a thermos flask and what looks like a jumbo sandwich, long as a baby eel. Then an air cushion and more long sandwiches, and a picnic basket, and at last the three old ladies themselves. They are all right. They look shaken and angry, which is to be expected. A few minutes ago they had been sitting on the Palisades, in a pleasant little hollow free from the wind. The cloth was spread for a picnic. Miss Natalie O'Gorman laid out sandwiches on a plastic dish, her sister Clara unscrewed the thermos flask to pour out coffee, and their friend Willa North decided to blow up her air cushion.

Absolutely silent at first, the ground beneath them disappeared. The slide meant for a moment that there was no ground at all, it ceased to exist, and then as it gained momentum and scudded away like clouds breaking up in a gale, there was a light rumbling sound. The three ladies, Natalie O'Gorman with a sandwich in her hand, her sister with the flask and Willa North with her mouth pressed to the air cushion, went with the land and were practically submerged by it at the side of the highway below.

Now they are brushing their dresses with distracted motions and shaking little stones out of their bosoms and little clods out of their hair. Everyone is saying it is a miracle. Natalie O'Gorman would like to find her hat. Bones are felt and nothing is broken; they are scratched and bruised, that is all. 'We are all right,' they tell the crowd. 'Yes, we are quite all right.' Willa North says: 'I was taken completely by surprise!"

I drive on, past another SLIDE AREA sign. The beaches are still quite full. A group of tanned young men are wrestling and playing ball. Two girls watch them, eating hot dogs. An old Negro in a tattered blue suit walks by the edge of the ocean, a mongrel dog following him. Out to sea, someone is surfing. Stretching his arms, the muscular young lifeguard watches from his tower.

The southern end of Santa Monica, the ocean suburb, is not impeccable. Unlike the correct mechanized residential areas, Beverly Hills, Westwood, Glendale, it is rather slatternly and interesting. Little wooden houses, their green and blue and yellow paint fading, slant above narrow streets. There are bins overflowing with garbage and trash. People walk in the streets, hang about on corners or outside bars where a juke-box is always playing. There is a pier, due to be condemned soon, with all the usual sideshows: hot dog, hamburger and ice-cream stands, and a submarine contraption that takes you under water and shows you an old disgruntled whale. The beach has fine dull sand and the water smells faintly rancid.

It is only five o'clock but the bar called The Place is quite full. *Mackie Messer* comes from the juke-box. An old man in a panama hat and dark glasses dances slowly with his cane. At the bar a tall drunk woman finishes her whisky and lights a cigarette from the stub of the one she has just finished. She has once been beautiful, but now her face has something ruined about it, as if she's been waiting too long, in vain, for the telephone to ring. She sees me, waves, runs unsteadily over, pulls at my arm and speaks in a fierce urgent whisper.

'She's dying!'

'Who?'

'Hank, my sister Hank.'

'What happened?'

She makes vague distracted movements with her hands. 'He shot her, darling, that's all I know. It doesn't matter. It's too late!' She pulls at my arm again. 'I call and call the hospital and they won't let me speak to her, and the nurse says not to worry in a way that means it's no use.' Tears are streaming down her face now. 'Hank's dying, darling, dying!'

I offer to phone the hospital.

'No use! They'll lie, it's a conspiracy of lies.'

'Let me try, Zeena.' I go to the telephone and put in a coin. She follows, muttering, 'hopeless . . .'

'St. Judith's.'

'I want some information about Miss Henrietta Nelson, please.'

A pause, a whispering, a clicking, and presently a new voice with a German accent comes on the line:

'St. Judith's.'

'I want some information about Miss Henrietta Nelson.'

'Who are you?'

'A friend of Miss Nelson.'

Another pause. Zeena clutches my elbow. 'You know they're all nuns? *Nuns!*'

I can hear footsteps approaching, then going away. The line crackles for a moment.

'Are you still there?'

'Yes.'

'Miss Henrietta Nelson is dead.'

'What?'

'Miss Nelson died shortly after four o'clock this afternoon.' The voice is merciless, pedantic, never shifting its level. 'We did not inform her sister as we did not care to break such news on the telephone. We asked her to arrive here and see us immediately, but her reply was not comprehensible. We received the impression she was not . . . sober. Last night we were obliged not to admit her to visit her sister as she arrived not . . . sober. Excuse me, but are you a responsible person?'

I hang up. Zeena is no longer there. The old man still dances with his cane.

[542]

The barman says: 'She just wandered out the way she does.'

She is not in the street outside. I get in my car, drive along side the beach, which is almost deserted now. The sand looks grey, a fine white mist is dredging colour out of everything as the hazy sun slips down.

A figure walks uncertainly by the water's edge.

'Zeena,' I say as I come up to her, 'I'm afraid it's bad news.'

She has a weary look, throws her cigarette into the sea. 'Was it the German, darling? She's the worst.'

'They say Hank is dead.'

Zeena is very pale. A wave breaks, runs along the sand and wets her feet, she doesn't mind.

When the sun cools and everyone leaves the beach, only messages remain. Often there are dozens of them, traced with a stick or a finger in the sand. Zeena is looking at one now. JIMMY LOVES ELLA. And a little further away, MY NAME IS GRIFFIN.

She smiles, mutters 'I'll see you later,' and walks away.

She walks past I'M MAD ABOUT BOB, JOHNNY WAITED HERE and OH BILL I WANT TO MAKE YOU and a dead gull.

All this will be washed away tomorrow.

Dusk falls as I drive home. The mountains look black and farther away. The road winds uphill and there is a point where you can see Los Angeles sprawling away in the distance. Lights are coming on there now. Looking down on the straight intersecting lines of pink and yellow and green is like finding a vast abstract painting laid out on the earth. It has nothing at all to do with living. It is a bright winking mirage in the desert; you are afraid to look away in case it has vanished when you look back.

[543]

A mauve searchlight sweeps monotonously across the sky like a great silent pendulum.

When I get back to my apartment the telephone is ringing.

'Will you come immediately please?' The German nun from the hospital sounds a little breathless, but dry as ever. 'Miss Zeena Nelson refuses to go home. The police have asked all their questions and we give her a sedative, but she lies down in the waiting-room and refuses to go home. Come please.'

Unlike her voice, Sister Hertha seems plump and friendly. She wears a capacious white robe and a silver crucifix on a chain round her waist. When I ask her to tell me what happened, she looks surprised and straightens her rimless glasses, which have been a little askew. 'You know nothing?'

'Nothing. Except, something about a shooting.'

'That is so.' Sister Hertha lowers her voice. 'Last night a young man . . .' A nun passes with a tray of tea, Sister Hertha smiles and gives a little bow. 'Good evening, Sister!' She turns back to me. 'A young man in a red jacket came home with Miss Henrietta Nelson last night. He . . . eventually shot her through the head.' She fingers the crucifix at her stomach. 'A neighbour saw him leave, she saw his jacket but not his face. It appears Miss Nelson had many young friends. The police try to find if any of them wore a red jacket. Naturally.'

She leads me to the waiting-room, where Zeena lies back on a couch with her eyes closed. Sister Hertha coughs, and she looks up.

'Hello darling.'

'You still have no recollection of a young man in a red jacket?' asks the nun.

Zeena shakes her head. 'If he's been in The Place or any of the places, I must have seen him. But what does a person look like when he's crazy?'

Sister Hertha makes a sympathetic little noise with her teeth.

'Zeena, you mustn't stay here,' I tell her.

She gets up obediently. Sister Herta gives an encouraging smile. 'I advise rest. A great deal of rest. Such situations are . . .' She wrinkles her nose, partly because she is searching for a word, partly because she has just noticed a pile of cigarette stubs on the floor near Zeena's feet. 'They are most disturbing,' she says, rattling her crucifix a little.

Zeena decides she wants to go home. We drive in silence, towards a full moon low in the sky. I feel that Sister Hertha has found the right word. There is a case like this quite often in the newspapers: SEX FIEND SLAYS GIRL. Tomorrow it will make a row of headlines on the studio rack.

'Turn the radio on, darling.' A moment later we are listening to Brahms. Zeena twists the knob, then drowses as somebody sings *Your Cheatin' Heart*.

Two months ago I passed a second-hand furniture store on the street along which we are now driving. There was an elegant little coffee table in the window. I went inside, found Zeena and Hank sitting on a broken-down antique couch with the stuffing split out, drinking canned beer. Probably I was the first customer they'd had for hours. The place was vague and untidy, like somewhere after an earthquake. 'This is really catching on,' Zeena said, trying to interest me in a heavy Victorian commode they'd sponged over with gold and white paint. I bought the coffee table. After that, I saw Zeena and Hank occasionally: in bars or on the beach. Once, coming out of an all-night movie theatre. This is how everybody met them. This is how I am with Zeena today, by accident.

She lives in Venice, near the furniture store. A mouldering unfinished little town along the coast beyond Santa Monica, it began fifty years ago as an imitation of the Italian

[545]

city. Moonstruck, an industrialist from the Middle West decided to create a romantic resort on the dreary tidal flats. He built some florid villas, a copy of St. Mark's Square, a network of bridges, canals, lagoons, colonnades. The aged Sarah Bernhardt was imported to play *La Dame aux Camélias* on what is now a tawdry, neglected amusement pier. Hardly anyone went to see her. Hardly anyone hired a gondola for a trip along the mosquito-ridden flats. Then oil was struck, machinery converged upon the lagoons. A few bridges still remain, spanning dried up canals, with pumps and derricks stretching away beyond them. Drugstores, banks, service stations have settled in the empty spaces between colonnades, and the villas are apartment houses with rooms always vacant.

As we pass St. Mark's Square, I notice a group of young motor cyclists dressed in black, with tight belts and slanted caps, leaning against the colonnades. Pigeons cluster nearby, then disperse as the cyclists set off with a roar, speeding along the empty boulevard, past a neon sign announcing BEER, past the Bridge of Sighs and the derricks in silhouette.

The noise rouses Zeena. She blinks, looks out of the window and recognizes landmarks: a closed-up hotel with broken windows, a plot of waste land with an abandoned moonlit sign, BOATS FOR SALE. She murmurs: 'Why, I'm almost home!'

JACK SPICER

Southern Californian by origin (b. 1925), Jack Spicer roamed widely before settling in San Francisco's North Beach, where he now writes and lives.

The Dancing Ape

The dancing ape is whirling round the beds
Of all the coupled animals; they, sleeping there
In warmth of sex, ignore his fur and fuss
And feel no terror in his gait of loneliness.
Quaint though the dancer is, his furry fists
Are locked like lightning over all their heads.
His legs are thrashing out in discontent
As if they were the lightning's strict embodiment.
But let the dancing stop, the apish face go shut in sleep,
The hands unclench, the trembling legs go loose—
And let some curious animal bend and touch that face
With nuzzling mouth, would not the storm break—
And that ape kiss?

Berkeley in Time of Plague

Plague took us and the land from under us,
Rose like a boil, enclosing us within.
We waited and the blue skies writhed a while
Becoming black with death.

Plague took us and the chairs from under us,
Stepped cautiously while entering the room
(We were discussing Yeats); it paused a while
Then smiled and made us die.

Plague took us, laughed and reproportioned us,
Swelled us to dizzy, unaccustomed size.
We died prodigiously; it hurt a while
But left a certain quiet in our eyes.

Psychoanalysis: An Elegy

What are you thinking about?

I am thinking of an early summer.
I am thinking of wet hills in the rain
Pouring water. Shedding it
Down empty acres of oak and manzanita
Down to the old green brush tangled in the sun,
Greasewood, sage, and spring mustard.
Or the hot wind coming down from Santa Ana
Driving the hills crazy,
A fast wind with a bit of dust in it
Bruising everything and making the seed sweet.
Or down in the city where the peach trees
Are awkward as young horses,
And there are kites caught on the wires
Up above the street lamps,
And the storm drains are all choked with dead branches.

What are you thinking?

I think that I would like to write a poem that is slow as a
    summer
As slow getting started
As 4th of July somewhere around the middle of the second
    stanza
After a lot of unusual rain
California seems long in the summer.

[548]

I would like to write a poem as long as California
And as slow as a summer.
Do you get me, Doctor? It would have to be as slow
As the very tip of summer.
As slow as the summer seems
On a hot day drinking beer outside Riverside
Or standing in the middle of a white-hot road
Between Bakersfield and Hell
Waiting for Santa Claus.

What are you thinking now?

I'm thinking that she is very much like California.
When she is still her dress is like a roadmap. Highways
Traveling up and down her skin
Long empty highways
With the moon chasing jackrabbits across them
On hot summer nights.
I am thinking that her body could be California
And I a rich Eastern tourist
Lost somewhere between Hell and Texas
Looking at a map of a long, wet, dancing California
That I have never seen.
Send me some penny picture-postcards, lady,
Send them.
One of each breast photographed looking
Like curious national monuments,
One of your body sweeping like a three-lane highway
Twenty-seven miles from a night's lodging
In the world's oldest hotel.

What are you thinking?

I am thinking of how many times this poem

[549]

Will be repeated. How many summers
Will torture California
Until the damned maps burn
Until the mad cartographer
Falls to the ground and possesses
The sweet thick earth from which he has been hiding.

What are you thinking now?

I am thinking that a poem could go on forever.

LAWRENCE FERLINGHETTI

Born in New York in 1919, Lawrence Ferlinghetti served in the Navy during World War II and afterwards studied at the Sorbonne. He is now proprietor of the City Lights Bookshop in San Francisco and is publisher for many other poets—including Allen Ginsberg, whose *Howl* (1957) made Ferlinghetti the central figure in a famous obscenity trial. Ferlinghetti's own books include *Pictures of the Gone World* (1955) and *A Coney Island of the Mind* (1958).

Dog

The dog trots freely in the street
and sees reality
and the things he sees
are bigger than himself
and the things he sees
are his reality
Drunks in doorways
Moons on trees
The dog trots freely thru the street
and the things he sees
are smaller than himself
Fish on newsprint
Ants in holes
Chickens in Chinatown windows
their heads a block away
The dog trots freely in the street
and the things he smells
smell something like himself
The dog trots freely in the street
past puddles and babies
cats and cigars

poolrooms and policemen
He doesn't hate cops
He merely has no use for them
and he goes past them
and past the dead cows hung up whole
in front of the San Francisco Meat Market
He would rather eat a tender cow
than a tough policeman
though either might do
And he goes past the Romeo Ravioli Factory
and past Coit's Tower
and past Congressman Doyle
He's afraid of Coit's Tower
but he's not afraid of Congressman Doyle
although what he hears is very discouraging
very depressing
very absurd
to a sad young dog like himself
to a serious dog like himself
But he has his own free world to live in
His own fleas to eat
He will not be muzzled
Congressman Doyle is just another
fire hydrant
to him
The dog trots freely in the street
and has his own dog's life to live
and to think about
and to reflect upon
touching and tasting and testing everything
investigating everthing
without benefit of perjury
a real realist
with a real tale to tell

and a real tail to tell it with
a real live
        barking
              democratic dog
engaged in real
            free enterprise
with something to say
               about ontology
something to say
            about reality
                  and how to see it
                     and how to hear it
with his head cocked sideways
               at streetcorners
as if he is just about to have
              his picture taken
                   for Victor Records
            listening for
               His Master's Voice
        and looking
              like a living questionmark
                into the
                 great gramaphone
                 of puzzling existence
        with its wondrous hollow horn
           which always seems
         just about to spout forth
              some Victorious answer
               to everything

They Were Putting Up the Statue

They were putting up the statue
     of Saint Francis
   in front of the church
     of Saint Francis
       in the city of San Francisco
in a little side street
     just off the Avenue
            where no birds sang
  and the sun was coming up on time
              in its usual fashion
     and just beginning to shine
          on the statue of Saint Francis
     where no birds sang
And a lot of old Italians
          were standing all around
     in the little side street
        just off the Avenue
    watching the wily workers
         who were hoisting up the statue
  with a chain and a crane
        and other implements
And a lot of young reporters
       in button-down clothes
   were taking down the words
        of one young priest
    who was propping up the statue
       with all his arguments
     And all the while
       while no birds sang
         any Saint Francis Passion
and while the lookers kept looking

up at Saint Francis
with his arms outstretched
to the birds which weren't there
a very tall and very purely naked
young virgin
with very long and very straight
straw hair
and wearing only a very small bird's nest
in a very existential place
kept passing thru the crowd
all the while
and up and down the steps
in front of Saint Francis
her eyes downcast all the while
and singing to herself

Index